Topics in Applied Physics   Volume 5

Topics in Applied Physics Founded by Helmut K. V. Lotsch

Mössbauer Spectroscopy

Edited by U. Gonser

With Contributions by
F. E. Fujita   U. Gonser   R. W. Grant   P. Gütlich
S. S. Hafner   C. E. Johnson

With 96 Figures

Springer-Verlag New York Heidelberg Berlin 1975

Professor Dr. Uli Gonser

Fachbereich Angewandte Physik, Universität des Saarlandes,
D-6600 Saarbrücken, Fed. Rep. of Germany

ISBN 0-387-07120-2 Springer-Verlag New York Heidelberg Berlin
ISBN 3-540-07120-2 Springer-Verlag Berlin Heidelberg New York

Library of Congress Cataloging in Publication Data. Main entry under title: Mössbauer spectroscopy. (Topics in applied physics; v.5). Bibliography: p. Includes index. 1. Mössbauer spectroscopy. I. Gonser, U. QC491.M6. 537.5'352. 75-4664.

Printed in Germany

Monophoto typesetting, offset printing and bookbinding: Brühlsche Universitätsdruckerei, Gießen

Foreword

Eighteen years have passed since the discovery of the Mössbauer effect—certainly one of the most brilliant findings in modern physics. This strange, at first almost unbelievable, effect straddled the border between nuclear and solid-state physics and soon formed the basis for a new technique, that of Mössbauer or gamma-resonance spectroscopy. It went on to prove itself to be a powerful tool in almost all disciplines of the natural sciences and technology.

Mössbauer spectroscopy has been used as a key to unlock some basic physical, chemical, and biological phenomena, as a guide for finding new ways of solving applied scientific and technical problems of mechanics, metallurgy, geology, and mineralogy, and even in archaeology and the fine arts.

The continuing rapid growth in the number of publications on Mössbauer spectroscopy and its various applications can be illustrated by simply comparing the sizes of the annual Mössbauer Effect Data Indices published over the last few years in the USA by Plenum Publishing Corp. 1969: 292 pages, 1970: 382 pages, 1971: 430 pages, 1972: 489 pages, 1973: 495 pages (Fe^{57} references after the pages for the specific isotopes have been dropped to cut down on the number of pages), 1974—let us see.

Under such circumstances it becomes increasingly difficult to present a comparatively short but well selected and oriented survey of the most important and impressive problems connected with the use of Mössbauer spectroscopy. However, as the reader acquaints himself with the collection of papers offered here, I am sure he will conclude that this work fulfills the above standards and is presented in a clear, lucid manner.

Mössbauer spectroscopy is utilized in a wide diversity of fields. Each contributor to the volume, being an expert in a different area, not only summarizes the applications in his field but also relates the basic principles to the general introduction prepared by the editor himself. Readers are therefore sure to find this book informative and stimulating.

Moscow, March 1975   VITALII I. GOLDANSKII

Preface

Mössbauer's discovery that γ-ray emission and absorption can occur in a recoil-free fashion might have seemed at first glance to be no more than just an interesting new phenomenon. However, as soon as it became generally realized that the Mössbauer resonance line is extremely narrow and allows hyperfine interactions to be resolved and evaluated in a rather straightforward way, this handy new method created an avalanche of research activity. Within a few years nearly all disciplines in the natural sciences enjoyed a boom in the application of Mössbauer spectroscopy. Some journals were swamped to such an extent that editorials were written to limit the publication of Mössbauer results.

This book is addressed to persons interested in learning about what has been done and what can be done with this tool. In an introduction the basic principle is explained and the general parameters governing Mössbauer spectroscopy are tabulated. For the following five chapters various disciplines are chosen and the wide applicability of this measuring technique is demonstrated. The authors of all the articles are leaders in their respective fields and have been closely associated with Mössbauer spectroscopy for at least ten years. Typical cases are carefully selected. Among more than 100 excited nuclear states available to demonstrate the resonance effect, the 14.4 keV state of Fe^{57}—which is, of course, the most significant one—serves throughout the book as the prime example. It is not, however, intended to give a comprehensive treatment. There are already a number of excellent books on the market for experts, in particular, the Mössbauer Effect Data Index.

Rudolf Mössbauer's concluding remark concerning the effect that bears his name in his Nobel Laureate speech of December 1961 has proved to be correct and has retained its significance to the present day; it can also be regarded as a prognosis for the future. "We may therefore hope that this young branch of physics stands only at its threshold, and that it will be developed in the future, not only to extend the application of existing knowledge but to make possible new advances in the exciting world of unknown phenomena and effects".

Saarbrücken, March 1975   ULI GONSER

Contents

4. Mössbauer Spectroscopy in Biology. By C. E. JOHNSON (With 16 Figures)

5. Mössbauer Spectroscopy in Lunar Geology and Mineralogy. By S. S. HAFNER (With 11 Figures)

6. Mössbauer Spectroscopy in Physical Metallurgy. By F. E. FUJITA (With 19 Figures)

Contributors

FUJITA, FRANCIS EIICHI

Department of Material Physics, Faculty of Engineering Science, Osaka University, Toyonaka, Osaka, Japan

GONSER, ULI

Fachbereich Angewandte Physik, Universität des Saarlandes, D-6600 Saarbrücken, Fed. Rep. of Germany

GRANT, RONALD W.

Science Center, Rockwell International, Thousand Oaks, CA 91360, USA

GÜTLICH, PHILIPP

Institut für Anorganische und Analytische Chemie, Fachbereich Chemie, Johannes-Gutenberg-Universität, D-6500 Mainz, Fed. Rep. of Germany

HAFNER, STEPHAN S.

Fachbereich Geowissenschaften, Philipps Universität Marburg, D-3550 Marburg, Fed. Rep. of Germany

JOHNSON, CHARLES E.

Oliver Lodge Laboratory, University of Liverpool, Liverpool, England

List of Frequently Used Symbols

a	Clebsch-Gordan coefficient
a_a	Isotopic abundance
A	Hyperfine coupling
α^2	Covalency factor
α_s	s-Electron conversion coefficient
α_t	Total internal conversion coefficient
β	Bohr magneton
β_N	Nuclear Bohr magneton
c	Velocity of light
d	Distance or thickness
D	Zero field splitting parameter
D_d	Diffusion coefficient
D_T	Doppler broadening
δ	Isomer shift
δ_F	Faraday rotation
δ_g	Gravitational red shift
δ_R	Relativistic shifts, second-order Doppler effect
Δ	Quadrupole splitting ($\equiv \Delta E_Q$)
Δ_o	Crystal field splitting parameter in octahedral complexes
Δ_t	Crystal field splitting parameter in tetrahedral complexes
e	Charge of the proton
eQ	Nuclear electric quadrupole moment
eV	Electron Volt
$e0$	Electric monopole interaction
$e2$	Electric quadrupole interaction
E_D	Doppler energy
E_k	Kinetic energy
E_m	Eigenvalues of magnetic dipole interaction
E_Q	Eigenvalues of electric quadrupole interaction
E_R	Recoil energy
E_t	Total energy of harmonic oscillator
$E_{S,A}$	Nuclear transition energies in source (S) or absorber (A), respectively

E_0	Nuclear transition energy in the absence of hyperfine interaction
E_γ	Energy of γ-radiation
EFG	Electric field gradient
ε	Crystal field distortion parameter
ε_a	Vibrational anisotropy
η	Asymmetry parameter
f	Recoil-free fraction
f_c	Diffusion correlation factor
g	Electronic g-factor
g_N	Nuclear Landé splitting factor (nuclear g-factor)
g_g	Acceleration in gravitational field
g_r	Gyromagnetic ratio
Γ	Natural line width, theoretical full width at half maximum
γ_∞	Sternheimer antishielding factor
h	$(= 2\pi\hbar)$ Planck's constant
h_p	Number of electron holes in p-shell
H	Magnitude of magnetic field vector, $\boldsymbol{H}$
H_{int}	Internal magnetic field
H_{ext}	External magnetic field
H_c	Core polarization (Fermi contact term) magnetic field
H_{dip}	Dipolar magnetic field
H_{orb}	Orbital magnetic field
$\mathscr{H}$	Hamiltonian
$I_{e,g}$	Nuclear spin quantum number, excited (e) or ground (g) state, respectively
$\hat{I}$	Nuclear spin operator
$\hat{I}_\pm$	Nuclear spin shift operator
$\hat{I}_x, \hat{I}_y, \hat{I}_z$	Nuclear spin component operator
$I_{2,3,4,5}$	Line intensities in the nuclear Zeeman pattern
k	Magnitude of wave vector of γ-ray, $\boldsymbol{k}$
k_B	Boltzmann constant
K_a	Magnetocrystalline anisotropy
χ	Susceptibility
χ_P	Pauling electronegativity
λ	$(= 2\pi\lambdabar)$ wave length of γ-radiation
λ_0	Spin-orbit coupling constant of free ions
$m1$	Magnetic dipole interaction
m_I	Magnetic nuclear spin quantum number
M	Nuclear mass
M_{sat}	Saturation magnetization
μ	Nuclear magnetic dipole moment
n	Quantum number

n_a	Number of atoms per cm^3
N_{nlm}	Electron population in orbital state $\lvert nlm \rangle$
NMR	Nuclear magnetic resonance
$\nu_{E,D}$	Vibrational frequency (Einstein or Debye oscillators, respectively)
p_n	Magnitude of momentum of nucleus, $\boldsymbol{p}_n$
p_γ	Magnitude of momentum of γ-quantum, $\boldsymbol{p}_\gamma$
p.i.s.	Partial isomer shift
p.f.g.	Partial field gradient
p.q.s.	Partial quadrupole splitting
P	Configurational probability
P_i	Fractional electron population of i-th level due to thermal energy
Π	Mean spin pairing energy
$\langle r^{-3} \rangle$	Expectation value of $1/r^3$
R	Nuclear radius
$R_{e,g}$	Nuclear radius of excited (e) and ground state (g)
$\delta R/R$	Relative change of nuclear radius between excited state and ground state
$R_{ns}(r)$	radial part of s-wave function of main quantum number n
$\mathscr{R}$	Sternheimer shielding factor
R_m, R_q	Ratio of line intensities in magnetic or quadrupole hyperfine spectra
$R(\omega), R_0, R_1$	Count rate parameters determining the Malus curve
ϱ	Birefringence rotation
ϱ_n	Nuclear charge
ϱ_{el}	$= -e\lvert\psi(0)\rvert^2$ electron density at the nucleus
Ψ	Many-electron wave function
S	Electron spin
$S(Z)$	Relativistic correction factor
SNP	Sodium nitroprusside dihydrate, $Na_2[Fe(CN)_5NO] \cdot 2H_2O$
σ	Total resonance cross section
σ_0	Maximum resonance cross section in barn
T	Absolute temperature
t	Time
$t_{1/2}$	Half lifetime
$t_{S,A,T}$	Effective Mössbauer thickness of source, absorber or transmitter, respectively
τ	Mean lifetime
τ_L	Nuclear Larmor precession time
τ_s	Electron spin relaxation time
τ_0	Mean time an atom stays at a lattice site

τ_r	Reorientation rate
θ_D	Debye temperature
θ_E	Einstein temperature
θ_q	Angle between γ-ray propagation direction and principal axis of the EFG
θ_m	Angle between γ-ray propagation direction and orientation of magnetic spin
u	$\cos\theta_m$ or $\cos\theta_q$
v	Magnitude of velocity, v
v_R	Velocity gained by recoil
V_{ij}	Components of EFG tensor, $i, j = x, y, z$
V_{zz}	$(= eq)$ total effective EFG in principal axis system
$(V_{zz})_{val}$	Contribution to EFG from valence electrons, in general
$(V_{zz})_{CF}$	Contribution to EFG from valence electron imbalance in crystal field split atomic orbitals of the Mössbauer atom
$(V_{zz})_{MO}$	Contribution to EFG from valence electron imbalance in molecular orbitals
$(V_{zz})_L$	Contribution to EFG from distant charges in the ligand sphere and/or lattice surroundings (the index L stands for "ligand/lattice")
$W_{x,z}$	Ratio of mean square vibrational amplitudes
$\langle x^2 \rangle$	Mean square vibrational amplitude in the x-direction
$\omega_{E,D}$	Vibrational angular frequency (Einstein or Debye oscillators, respectively)
ω	Angle determining Malus curve
Z	Proton number

Additional symbols (α, β, γ, x, y, z, m, n, etc.) have been used and defined in various chapters.

1. From a Strange Effect to Mössbauer Spectroscopy

U. GONSER

With 17 Figures

1.1. Introduction

The rapid development of all scientific disciplines and the growing sophistication of our tools has resulted in the experimentalist having to choose between two alternatives: either he uses a method and applies it to various fields or he investigates a field by various methods. These alternatives are shown in Fig. 1.1. The choice between these two operational modes is necessary because nowadays it is impossible to be an expert in many fields and many methods simultaneously. One might draw the Atlantic between the two circles indicating that in America the scientist usually works with one method at a time, applying it in team operation to various fields, while in Europe there is a tendency for the scientist, by his affiliation to the institutions, to be more oriented toward a field.

In the last two decades a large number of new methods in physics have been developed which have become of great significance in many fields of natural sciences, e.g.

NMR	(nuclear magnetic resonance),
PAC	(perturbed angular correlation),
IMPACT	(implantation perturbed angular correlation technique),
EPR	(electron paramagnetic resonance),
NQR	(nuclear quadrupole resonance),
ENDOR	(electron nuclear double resonance),
LEED	(low energy electron diffraction),
SHEED	(scanning high energy electron diffraction),
ESCA	(electron spectroscopy for chemical analysis),
FIM	(field ion microscopy), and
Mössbauer spectroscopy	(recoil-free nuclear resonance absorption).

At least in one respect, Mössbauer spectroscopy is an exception in this family of methods: it has been given a proper and unabbreviated name. Of course, this does not mean that this method is more significant than the others; the name indicates the special kind of the discovery.

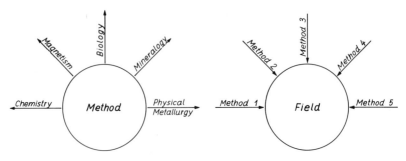

Fig. 1.1. The two alternatives for an experimentalist

Usually a new method is created by advancing, refining, and combining certain aspects in theory, experimental sophistication and engineering skill. In most cases a large number of scientists at different laboratories are engaged in the progress and final applicability of the tool. Often it is difficult to trace all the individual contributions which led to the final success of the method. Sometimes theoreticians have made predictions and have announced their priority by a so-called "Gedankenexperiment", while it took the effort of many years to overcome the experimental difficulties. In contrast to the usual development of new methods Mössbauer spectroscopy has all the attributes of a wonderful—one might even say romantic—discovery by a young experimentalist. Whilst working on his thesis RUDOLF MÖSSBAUER stumbled on a strange phenomenon. His greatness can be shown by the fact that he did not ignore this small peculiar irregularity in his γ-ray counting system, instead he made an effort to understand this unknown effect fully from an experimental as well as from a theoretical point of view. In his first papers published in 1958 the important features were clearly described [1.1, 2]. However, it took nearly one year until the effect was really accepted and appreciated. Then, suddenly the scientific community became excited about the handy new tool so useful in nearly all fields of natural science. Recognition in the form of the Nobel prize was awarded to RUDOLF MÖSSBAUER a few years later in 1961 [1.3]. The circumstances and details of his early experiments leading to the Mössbauer effect are like a fairy tale in science. Retrospectively, one might be surprised that this effect was not discovered earlier. The application of elementary quantum mechanics both to nuclear and to solid state physics has been understood for many years. It seems that the failure to realize the basic principle of this effect earlier was the lack of interaction between the nuclear physics and solid state physics communities. The Mössbauer effect might be an incentive for young scientists who should realize that their own research work may also suddenly become a "gold mine".

The wide and diversified applicability of the Mössbauer effect, commonly known as Mössbauer spectroscopy, makes it a powerful tool in most disciplines of natural science ranging from nuclear physics to biology. A number of excellent articles and books describe the basic aspects and sophisticated applications of this spectroscopy in detail [1.4–16]. The existence of the Mössbauer Effect Data Index which contains a compilation of all references and from which significant data [1.17] can be extracted is of great importance to the scientist working in the field of Mössbauer spectroscopy. It is advisable to consult this Data Index before using a Mössbauer spectrometer.

The various aspects aiding in the understanding of this type of nuclear resonance phenomena are well-suited for teaching the important principles of physics and related fields. However, most of the existing literature is written for experts or scientists actively engaged in applying this tool. This book is primarily aimed at the non-expert, i.e. those interested in obtaining general information on the principles of the phenomena with typical examples of its use in various fields of natural science. Chemists, biologists, mineralogists, metallurgists, physicists, and engineers might refer to certain chapters which are related to their own field of interest. To make this introduction easy to read the selected cases are demonstrated mostly with one isotope—Fe^{57}— which, of course, is also the most important one in Mössbauer spectroscopy.

1.2. The pre-Mössbauer Time

Our understanding in natural science is usually based on models. These models range in their dimension from the micro-scale of the nucleus to the macro-cosmos of the universe. Also, for the emission and absorption of γ-rays leading to γ-ray nuclear resonance fluorescence, various models have been used to demonstrate the recoil processes involved or—as we will see later—the absence of recoil. The realization that the latter exists and that there are processes in γ-ray emission and absorption with a certain probability of being recoil-free is the basic principle of the Mössbauer effect.

In our daily life we take into account the recoil in the motion of bodies and as physicists in our equation of motion. Figure 1.2a illustrates the general concepts of recoil. "Gamma" jumps from a boat with an effort of energy E_0. It experiences that such a jump causes a recoil E_R,

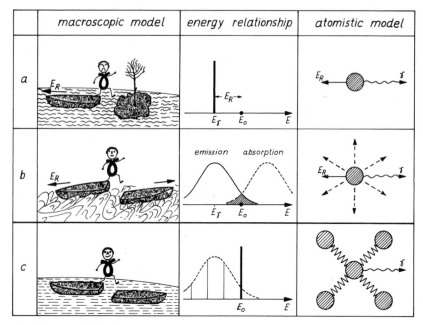

	macroscopic model	energy relationship	atomistic model
a			
b		emission absorption	
c			

Fig. 1.2a-c. Models and energy relationship relevant to Mössbauer spectroscopy

and only the energy E_γ is available to it. Conservation of energy

$$E_0 = E_\gamma + E_R .\qquad(1.1)$$

This energy relationship is schematically shown in the figure. Assuming the boat representing the nucleus which has a mass M is originally at rest, it will gain a velocity v_R, by the emission process of the γ-ray, leading to

$$E_R = \frac{M}{2}\,v_R^2 = \frac{(Mv_R)^2}{2M} = \frac{p_n^2}{2M} .\qquad(1.2)$$

The magnitude of the momentum of the γ-ray is given by

$$p_\gamma = \frac{E_\gamma}{c} = \hbar k ,\qquad(1.3)$$

where c is the velocity of light, k the magnitude of the wave vector of the γ-ray, and $\hbar$ Planck's constant divided by 2π.

Momentum conservation requires that the momentum of the γ-ray, p_γ, and the momentum gained by the nucleus of the system recoiling, p_n, are equal in magnitude and opposite in sign. Because the recoils considered here are rather small ($E_R \ll Mc^2$) the problem can be treated in a non-relativistic manner.

Conservation of momentum yields

$$E_R = \frac{p_\gamma^2}{2M} = \frac{E_\gamma^2}{2Mc^2} \approx \frac{E_0^2}{2Mc^2}. \tag{1.4}$$

In the latter equation E_γ may be replaced by E_0 without changing the value of E_R significantly. For atoms with $M = 50$, 100, and 200 the recoil energy loss versus emitted photon energy is plotted in Fig. 1.3. For $E_0 \approx E_\gamma \approx 10^4$ eV and $M = 100$ a typical value of $E_R \approx 5 \cdot 10^{-4}$ eV is obtained. Typical energy ranges for available resonance isotopes are shown in Fig. 1.4. The special case of the isotope Fe^{57} and α-Fe is marked by arrows. In Table 1.1 the values of E_R and E_0 are given for the Mössbauer isotopes [1.17].

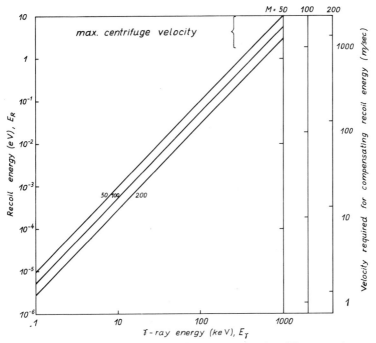

Fig. 1.3. Recoil energy loss E_R versus γ-ray energy E_γ for different nuclear mass ($M = 50$, 100, and 200). The velocity required for compensating the recoil energy loss is shown on the right ordinate

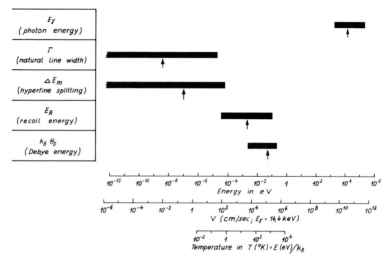

Fig. 1.4. Ranges of energies relevant to Mössbauer spectroscopy. The arrows indicate the values for the isotope Fe⁵⁷ and α-Fe

When a γ-ray is emitted from a nucleus moving with a velocity v along the γ-ray propagation the energy of the γ-ray is shifted by a first-order linear Doppler effect

$$E_D = \frac{v}{c} E_\gamma .$$ (1.5)

The velocity required to compensate for the recoil energy loss of nuclei with $M \doteq 50$, 100, and 200 is shown on the right-hand side of Fig. 1.3. Thermal motions of the nucleus, indicated by waves in the model of Fig. 1.2b, are of particular interest with regard to the Doppler shift. If atoms move with a velocity v during the γ-ray emitting process, the resulting linear Doppler effect is

$$E_D = \frac{p_n \cdot p_\gamma}{M} = \frac{v}{c} E_\gamma \cos\alpha ,$$ (1.6)

where α is the angle between the momentum vectors of the moving atom and the photon, p_n and p_γ. Taking into account the motion of the atom we add the Doppler effect to (1.1)

$$E_\gamma = E_0 - E_R + E_D .$$ (1.7)

Table 1.1. Mössbauer isotopes and relevant properties of the resonance transitions [1.17]

Isotope	a_a [%]	E_0 [keV]	$t_{1/2}$ [ns]	I_e	I_g	σ_0 [10^{-20} cm^2]	2Γ [mm/sec]	E_R [10^{-3} eV]
^{40}K	0.0118	29.4	4.26	3	4	28.97	2.184	11.60
^{57}Fe	2.19	14.4125	97.81	$\frac{3}{2}$	$\frac{1}{2}$	256.6	0.1940	1.957
^{57}Fe	2.19	136.46	8.7	$\frac{5}{2}$	$\frac{1}{2}$	4.300	0.2304	175.4
^{61}Ni	1.25	67.40	5.06	$\frac{5}{2}$	$\frac{3}{2}$	72.12	0.8021	39.99
^{67}Zn	4.11	93.31	9150	$\frac{3}{2}$	$\frac{5}{2}$	10.12	0.000320	69.78
^{73}Ge	7.76	13.263	4000	$\frac{5}{2}$	$\frac{9}{2}$	361.2	0.005156	1.294
^{73}Ge	7.76	68.752	1.86	$\frac{7}{2}$	$\frac{9}{2}$	22.88	2.139	34.77
^{83}Kr	11.55	9.40	147	$\frac{7}{2}$	$\frac{9}{2}$	107.5	0.1980	0.5716
^{99}Tc	(radioactive)	140.511	0.192	$\frac{7}{2}$	$\frac{9}{2}$	8.772	10.14	107.1
^{99}Ru	12.72	89.36	20.5	$\frac{3}{2}$	$\frac{5}{2}$	14.28	0.1493	43.31
^{101}Ru	17.07	127.22	0.585	$\frac{3}{2}$	$\frac{5}{2}$	8.687	3.676	86.04
^{119}Sn	8.58	23.871	17.75	$\frac{3}{2}$	$\frac{1}{2}$	140.3	0.6456	2.571
^{121}Sb	57.25	37.15	3.5	$\frac{7}{2}$	$\frac{5}{2}$	19.70	2.104	6.124
^{125}Te	6.99	35.46	1.48	$\frac{3}{2}$	$\frac{1}{2}$	26.56	5.212	5.401
^{127}I	100	57.60	1.9	$\frac{7}{2}$	$\frac{5}{2}$	21.37	2.500	14.03
^{129}I	(radioactive)	27.77	16.8	$\frac{5}{2}$	$\frac{7}{2}$	40.32	0.5863	3.210
^{129}Xe	26.44	39.58	1.01	$\frac{3}{2}$	$\frac{1}{2}$	23.31	6.843	6.521
^{131}Xe	21.18	80.16	0.50	$\frac{1}{2}$	$\frac{3}{2}$	7.183	6.825	26.34
^{133}Cs	100	89.997	6.30	$\frac{5}{2}$	$\frac{7}{2}$	10.21	0.5361	26.49
^{133}Ba	(radioactive)	12.29	8.1	$\frac{3}{2}$	$\frac{1}{2}$	29.18	2.748	0.6098
^{141}Pr	100	145.2	1.85	$\frac{7}{2}$	$\frac{5}{2}$	10.67	1.018	80.29
^{145}Nd	8.30	67.25	29.4	$\frac{3}{2}$	$\frac{7}{2}$	3.809	0.1384	16.75
^{145}Nd	8.30	72.50	0.72	$\frac{5}{2}$	$\frac{7}{2}$	5.916	5.240	19.46
^{147}Pm	(radioactive)	91.03	2.57	$\frac{5}{2}$	$\frac{7}{2}$	6.919	1.169	30.27
^{147}Sm	14.97	122.1	0.80	$\frac{5}{2}$	$\frac{7}{2}$	6.153	2.800	54.46
^{149}Sm	13.83	22.5	7.12	$\frac{5}{2}$	$\frac{7}{2}$	7.106	1.708	1.824
^{151}Sm	(radioactive)	65.83	20	–	–	28.23	0.2078	15.41
^{152}Sm	26.73	121.78	1.42	2	0	35.86	1.582	52.39
^{153}Sm	(radioactive)	35.842	2	$\frac{3}{2}$	$\frac{3}{2}$	146.5	3.816	4.508
^{154}Sm	22.71	81.99	3.00	2	0	30.08	1.112	23.44
^{151}Eu	47.82	21.64	9.7	$\frac{7}{2}$	$\frac{5}{2}$	11.42	1.303	1.665
^{153}Eu	52.18	83.3652	0.82	$\frac{7}{2}$	$\frac{5}{2}$	6.705	4.002	24.39
^{153}Eu	52.18	97.4283	0.21	$\frac{5}{2}$	$\frac{5}{2}$	17.97	13.37	33.31
^{153}Eu	52.18	103.1774	3.9	$\frac{3}{2}$	$\frac{5}{2}$	5.417	0.6798	37.36
^{154}Gd	2.15	123.14	1.17	2	0	36.67	1.899	52.87
^{155}Gd	14.73	60.012	0.155	$\frac{5}{2}$	$\frac{3}{2}$	9.989	29.41	12.48
^{155}Gd	14.73	86.54	6.32	$\frac{5}{2}$	$\frac{3}{2}$	34.40	0.5002	25.94
^{155}Gd	14.73	105.308	1.16	$\frac{5}{2}$	$\frac{3}{2}$	24.88	2.239	38.42
^{156}Gd	20.47	88.967	2.22	2	0	30.42	1.385	27.24
^{157}Gd	15.68	54.54	0.187	$\frac{5}{2}$	$\frac{3}{2}$	9.071	26.82	10.17
^{157}Gd	15.68	64.0	460	$\frac{5}{2}$	$\frac{3}{2}$	44.79	0.009292	14.01
^{158}Gd	24.87	79.51	2.46	2	0	27.88	1.399	21.48
^{160}Gd	21.90	75.3	2.63	2	0	21.15	1.381	19.03
^{159}Tb	100	58.0	13	$\frac{5}{2}$	$\frac{3}{2}$	9.827	0.3628	11.36
^{160}Dy	2.29	86.788	1.98	2	0	29.42	1.592	25.28
^{161}Dy	18.88	25.65	28.1	$\frac{5}{2}$	$\frac{5}{2}$	95.34	0.3795	2.194
^{161}Dy	18.88	43.84	920	$\frac{7}{2}$	$\frac{5}{2}$	28.29	0.006782	6.410

Table 1.1 (continued)

Isotope	a_a [%]	E_0 [keV]	$t_{1/2}$ [ns]	I_e	I_g	σ_0 [10^{-20} cm²]	2Γ [mm/sec]	E_R [10^{-3} eV]
^{161}Dy	18.88	74.57	3.35	$\frac{3}{2}$	$\frac{5}{2}$	6.755	1.095	18.55
^{162}Dy	25.53	80.7	2.25	2	0	26.09	1.507	21.59
^{164}Dy	28.18	73.39	2.4	2	0	20.86	1.553	17.63
^{165}Ho	100	94.70	0.0222	$\frac{9}{2}$	$\frac{7}{2}$	3.552	130.12	29.18
^{164}Er	1.56	91.5	1.73	2	0	28.10	1.728	27.41
^{166}Er	33.41	80.56	1.82	2	0	23.56	1.866	20.99
^{167}Er	22.94	79.321	0.103	$\frac{9}{2}$	$\frac{7}{2}$	7.715	33.48	20.23
^{168}Er	27.07	79.80	1.91	2	0	12.80	1.795	20.35
^{170}Er	14.88	79.3	1.92	2	0	24.31	1.797	18.97
^{169}Tm	100	8.42	3.9	$\frac{3}{2}$	$\frac{1}{2}$	21.17	8.330	0.2253
^{170}Yb	3.03	84.262	1.60	2	0	23.93	2.029	22.43
^{171}Yb	14.31	66.74	0.87	$\frac{3}{2}$	$\frac{1}{2}$	9.004	4.711	13.99
^{171}Yb	14.31	75.89	1.7	$\frac{5}{2}$	$\frac{1}{2}$	13.14	2.120	18.08
^{172}Yb	21.82	78.67	1.8	2	0	20.80	1.932	19.32
^{174}Yb	31.84	76.5	1.76	2	0	20.69	2.032	18.06
^{176}Yb	12.73	82.1	2.0	2	0	20.16	1.666	20.56
^{175}Lu	97.41	113.81	0.10	$\frac{9}{2}$	$\frac{7}{2}$	7.154	24.04	39.74
^{176}Hf	5.20	88.36	1.39	2	0	25.27	2.227	23.82
^{177}Hf	18.50	112.97	0.5	$\frac{9}{2}$	$\frac{7}{2}$	5.990	4.843	38.72
^{178}Hf	27.14	93.17	1.50	2	0	25.16	1.957	26.19
^{180}Hf	35.24	93.33	1.50	2	0	25.53	1.954	25.98
^{181}Ta	99.99	6.23	6800	$\frac{8}{2}$	$\frac{7}{2}$	167.6	0.006457	0.1151
^{181}Ta	99.99	136.25	0.0406	$\frac{9}{2}$	$\frac{9}{2}$	5.968	49.45	55.07
^{180}W	0.135	103.65	1.47	2	0	25.88	1.795	32.05
^{182}W	26.41	100.102	1.37	2	0	25.17	1.995	29.56
^{183}W	14.40	46.4837	0.183	$\frac{3}{2}$	$\frac{1}{2}$	5.523	32.16	6.640
^{183}W	14.40	99.0788	0.692	$\frac{5}{2}$	$\frac{1}{2}$	14.95	3.990	28.80
^{184}W	30.64	111.192	1.26	2	0	26.04	1.953	36.08
^{186}W	28.41	122.5	1.01	2	0	31.35	2.211	43.32
^{187}Re	62.93	134.24	0.01	$\frac{7}{2}$	$\frac{5}{2}$	5.371	203.8	51.74
^{186}Os	1.64	137.157	0.84	2	0	28.39	2.374	54.31
^{188}Os	13.3	155.03	0.695	2	0	27.96	2.539	68.65
^{189}Os	16.1	36.22	0.50	$\frac{1}{2}$	$\frac{3}{2}$	1.151	15.10	3.727
^{189}Os	16.1	69.59	1.64	$\frac{5}{2}$	$\frac{3}{2}$	8.419	2.397	13.76
^{189}Os	16.1	95.23	0.3	$\frac{3}{2}$	$\frac{3}{2}$	3.503	9.575	25.76
^{190}Os	26.4	186.9	0.47	2	0	33.61	3.114	98.72
^{191}Ir	37.3	82.398	4.02	$\frac{1}{2}$	$\frac{3}{2}$	1.540	0.8258	19.09
^{191}Ir	37.3	129.400	0.089	$\frac{5}{2}$	$\frac{3}{2}$	5.692	23.75	47.07
^{193}Ir	62.7	73.028	6.3	$\frac{1}{2}$	$\frac{3}{2}$	3.058	0.5946	14.84
^{193}Ir	62.7	138.92	0.080	$\frac{5}{2}$	$\frac{3}{2}$	5.833	24.61	53.69
^{195}Pt	33.8	98.857	0.170	$\frac{3}{2}$	$\frac{1}{2}$	6.106	16.28	26.91
^{195}Pt	33.8	129.735	0.620	$\frac{5}{2}$	$\frac{1}{2}$	7.425	3.401	46.35
^{197}Au	100	77.35	1.90	$\frac{1}{2}$	$\frac{3}{2}$	3.857	1.861	16.31
^{201}Hg	13.22	32.19	< 0.2	$\frac{1}{2}$	$\frac{3}{2}$	1.935	42.49	2.768
^{232}Th	100	49.369	0.345	2	0	1.667	16.06	5.641
^{231}Pa	(radioactive)	84.20	39.	$\frac{5}{2}$	$\frac{3}{2}$	25.88	0.08330	16.48
^{234}U	(radioactive)	43.491	0.252	2	0	0.862	24.96	4.340

Table 1.1 (continued)

Isotope	a_a [%]	E_0 [keV]	$t_{1/2}$ [ns]	I_e	I_g	σ_0 [10^{-20} cm^2]	2Γ [mm/sec]	E_R [10^{-3} eV]
^{236}U	(radioactive)	45.242	0.235	2	0	0.983	25.73	4.657
^{238}U	99.27	44.915	245	2	0	0.917	0.2486	4.551
^{237}Np	(radioactive)	59.537	68.3	$\frac{5}{2}$	$\frac{5}{2}$	32.55	0.06727	8.031
^{239}Pu	(radioactive)	57.26	0.101	$\frac{5}{2}$	$\frac{1}{2}$	0.999	47.30	7.366
^{243}Am	(radioactive)	84.00	2.34	$\frac{5}{2}$	$\frac{5}{2}$	26.67	1.392	15.59

a_a isotopic abundance, E_0 nuclear transition energy, $t_{1/2}$ half lifetime, I_e and I_g nuclear spin quantum number, excited (e) or ground (g) state, respectively, σ_0 maximum resonance cross section in barn, Γ natural line width, theoretical full width at half maximum, E_R recoil energy.

If the atoms move isotropically the energy distribution due to the linear Doppler effect centered at E_γ will reflect the Maxwell velocity distribution (see Fig. 1.2b).

The Doppler width of this distribution is of interest and can be estimated from the theory of ideal gases. The mean kinetic translational energy per degree of freedom of an atom is

$$E_k = (1/2)k_B T = M/2\overline{v^2} , \qquad (1.8)$$

where k_B is the Boltzmann constant, T the absolute temperature, and $\overline{v^2}$ the mean square velocity in the direction of observation. By taking the mean of the Doppler effect of the randomly moving atoms we can obtain an estimate of the Doppler broadening of the energy distribution, i.e.

$$D_T \approx \sqrt{\frac{\overline{v^2}}{c^2} E_\gamma^2} \qquad (1.9)$$

and with (1.4) and (1.8)

$$D_T \approx 2\sqrt{E_k E_R} . \qquad (1.10)$$

Thus, the Doppler broadening is proportional to the square root of the thermal energy E_k and the recoil energy E_R. The thermal Doppler width for a gas consisting of atoms with $M = 100$ at room temperature is about 10^{-3} eV for 1 keV γ-ray transitions and about 1 eV for 1 MeV transitions.

So far we have only considered emission processes. In absorption processes the sign of E_R and E_D in (1.7) is reversed. Thus, the distribution in energy is mirrored at E_0, as indicated in Fig. 1.2b.

Up to now the situation in the pre-Mössbauer time has been discussed. However, during this time γ-ray resonance fluorescence experiments had already been performed. It was realized that the existing small overlap between the emission and absorption energy distributions (shaded area in Fig. 1.2b) made nuclear resonance fluorescence experiments possible. Note that in ultraviolet and optical spectroscopy the emission and absorption areas overlap to a great extent due to the small recoil E_R involved.

The phenomena of resonance may occur between two bodies, in our case in the two nuclei shown schematically in their excited and ground states in Fig. 1.5. The separation represents the nuclear transition energy E_0. A nucleus of a source emits a γ-ray by transition from the excited state to the ground state. This γ-ray might be absorbed in another nucleus of the same kind by the reverse process. The two arrows connecting the excited and ground nuclear states represent the actual resonance effect. Resonance effects of two bodies with inherent equal resonance frequencies are quite familiar to us from acoustics, e.g. two tuning-forks with the same frequency. Also, the hearing process is based on small resonators in our ears which are sensitive to specific frequencies.

Various methods have been used to improve the situation in γ-ray resonance fluorescence by making the overlap between the emission and absorption curves larger and therefore increasing the yield of fluorescence. All methods are based on the idea of compensating for the recoil loss E_R by motion of the emitting or absorbing nuclei (linear Doppler effect). Such motion can be achieved either mechanically, thermally, or by using the recoil of a preceding radioactive decay or nuclear reaction. In the first method, the source fixed to a high speed rotor (centrifuge) moves during a small duty cycle toward the absorber. According to our model (Fig. 1.2a) the boat speeds toward the island

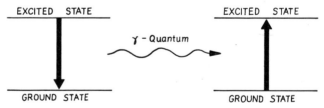

Fig. 1.5. Schematic representation of the nuclear resonance transitions between excited and ground states in two nuclei

and consequently the energy of the emission line E_γ (left of E_0) is shifted by the linear Doppler effect toward the right. The velocities required to compensate for the recoil in the emission process are indicated in Fig. 1.3 on the right-hand ordinate. The upper region of the figure roughly represents the maximum centrifugal velocity which can be achieved in an experiment. The second method is based on the broadening of source and absorber lines with increasing temperature, Eqs. (1.8)–(1.10), making the overlap of emission and absorption line larger. The third method makes use of the recoil with sufficient energy obtained from the preceding decay or a nuclear reaction (dashed arrows in Fig. 1.2b). Various environmental materials in the solid, liquid, or gaseous state can be selected with an appropriate slowing-down time. The last two methods can be represented in our model (Fig. 1.2b) by jumping from one boat to another making use of the waves. The jump has to occur at the right time, i.e. when the recoil energy E_R is just compensated by the motion of the boats (nuclei), as indicated by the dashed arrows.

The starting point of MÖSSBAUER'S work in his thesis and dissertation was along the line described here. To his surprise γ-ray fluorescence became stronger at lower temperatures instead of at higher temperatures, as was expected at that time. One might simply express his finding that jumps from one boat to the other occured without recoil when the boats were frozen in ice or the nuclei are solidly fixed as indicated by the springs (Fig. 1.2c). Thus, Fig. 1.2a and b characterize the pre-Mössbauer time with its difficult experimental arrangements and Fig. 1.2c represents MÖSSBAUER'S discovery, i.e. the realization that a recoil-free line exists at E_0. This line is called the Mössbauer line.

1.3. Existence and Intensity of the Mössbauer Line

The failure to observe recoil-free nuclear resonance absorption some decades earlier is reminiscent of the difficulties of applying the Dulong-Petit law to low temperature heat capacity data. In both cases the departure from classical theory becomes significant and an explanation can only be given on the basis of quantum mechanics.

As we have already noticed, the mean kinetic energy per degree of freedom for an ideal gas is $E_k = (1/2) k_B T$. In extending this result to the solid state we are reminded that the position of the atoms are determined by the balance between attractive and repulsive forces. In the equilibrium position the potential energy is at a minimum and no net force is expected on an atom by its neighbors. The interaction between atoms can be represented by springs connecting the nearest neighboring atoms in their respective crystallographic symmetry shown in Fig. 1.2c. In the simple Einstein model the thermal properties of a lattice are described by the vibrational oscillations of the atoms with frequency v_E or angular frequency ω_E. Assuming harmonic interaction forces the mean kinetic energy per degree of freedom is the same as for an ideal gas and is also equal to the mean potential energy, for the total energy E_t we can write

$$E_t = k_B T = \frac{M\overline{v^2}}{2} + \frac{M\omega_E^2 \langle x^2 \rangle}{2} = M\overline{v^2} = M\omega_E^2 \langle x^2 \rangle, \qquad (1.11)$$

where $\langle x^2 \rangle$ is the mean square vibrational amplitude in the x direction. Planck's original work led to the postulation that the energy of the oscillators is quantized in discrete units of hv_E or $\hbar\omega_E$, $h(=2\pi\hbar)$ being Planck's constant. Thus, the average energy in the classical theory has to be replaced by the quantum theory where the energy of an oscillator is described by phonons with energy E_t

$$E_t = hv_E\left(n + \frac{1}{2}\right) = \hbar\omega_E\left(n + \frac{1}{2}\right), \qquad (1.12)$$

where n is the quantum number, i.e. any positive integer or zero.

For the lowest Einstein oscillator level, $n = 0$, we can write

$$\langle x^2 \rangle = \frac{\hbar}{2M\omega_E}. \qquad (1.13)$$

In quantum mechanics the energy distribution is defined by the population of the levels spaced by hv_E or $\hbar\omega_E$. This is shown schematically in Fig. 1.6 for an Einstein solid. The lowest level corresponds to the absolute zero temperature state. At elevated temperatures higher levels will be occupied. A somewhat more realistic representation of a solid, particularly at low temperatures, is the Debye model. The vibrational states are given by a certain distribution of frequencies with a characteristic maximum vibrational frequency v_D and ω_D, respectively. It is convenient to define an Einstein temperature θ_E and a Debye temperature θ_D for the description of the vibrational states of the solid

$$hv_E = k_B\theta_E, \qquad (1.14a)$$
$$hv_D = k_B\theta_D. \qquad (1.14b)$$

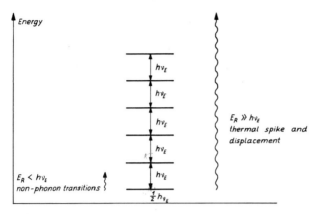

Fig. 1.6. Energy levels separated by $h\nu_E$ of an Einstein solid. Schematically two cases of high and low recoil energies E_R are considered. On the right: $E_R \gg h\nu_E$ where displacements of atoms and thermal spikes are created and on the left: $E_R < h\nu_E$ where non-phonon transitions occur

The Debye (or Einstein) temperature can be visualized as an approximate limit which separates the high temperature region where the oscillators or the solid can be treated in a classical fashion, from the low temperature region where quantum mechanical effects are significant. Characteristic energy ranges $k_B\theta_D$ for typical elements are shown in Fig. 1.4. The corresponding Debye temperature θ_D can be read from the lower scale. Typical frequencies of vibration, ν, for atoms are in the order of $10^{12}-10^{13}$ Hz.

The γ-emission process of a bound atom in a solid will now be considered. If the emission occurs with an energy well above 1 MeV the recoil energy (1.4) might be above the threshold displacement energy, i.e. the atom knocks itself from a lattice site leaving a vacancy and it comes to rest elsewhere in the lattice. For a typical solid the threshold displacement energy is in the order of 10–50 eV depending mainly on mass, crystal structure, and direction. If the emitted γ-ray has an energy of several hundred keV the recoil energy will be in the order of several eV which is insufficient to displace the atom. A "thermal spike" is created and many high levels in the oscillator scheme will be populated by thermal excitation. This hot spot very rapidly reaches a thermal equilibrium with the surrounding lattice. The condition of $E_R \gg h\nu_E$ which causes displacement of atoms and thermal spikes is shown on the right-hand side of the Einstein solid scheme in Fig. 1.6. Low energy γ-rays with an energy of about 5–150 keV are important for our considerations. Then the recoil energy is in the order of the phonon energies $h\nu_E$. The left-hand side of Fig. 1.6 shows the case where the recoil energy is less than the separation of the vibrational levels of an Einstein solid; specifically, we selected a recoil energy $E_R = (2/3) h\nu_E$. Such a figure suggests that there must be zero-phonon transitions, i.e. emission processes without excitation of phonons in the lattice. The probability f of such processes is of interest. By quantum mechanics it can be shown that the mean energy transferred to the lattice per emission of a γ-quantum is equal to the free energy E_R (Lipkin's sum rule) [1.16]. Neglecting the infrequent occurrence of multiphonon processes the mean recoil energy of single-phonon processes becomes

$$E_R = (1 - f) \hbar\omega_E , \tag{1.15}$$

where f is the recoil-free fraction. With (1.3) and (1.4) we obtain

$$f = 1 - \frac{E_R}{\hbar\omega_E} = 1 - \frac{\hbar^2 k^2}{\hbar\omega_E \, 2M} \tag{1.16}$$

and with (1.13) and taking x as the propagation direction of the γ-ray

$$f = 1 - k^2 \langle x^2 \rangle . \tag{1.17}$$

An exact treatment of this problem leads to the equation

$$f = \exp(-k^2 \langle x^2 \rangle) . \tag{1.18}$$

Equation (1.17) can be regarded as an approximation if $k^2 \langle x^2 \rangle \ll 1$. With this equation we have obtained an important result for the Mössbauer effect:

1) the recoil-free fraction f decreases with increasing k, i.e. higher energy γ-rays and

2) the recoil-free fraction f is a measure of the mean square vibrational amplitude of the resonating atom in the direction of observation $\langle x^2 \rangle$. A decrease in $\langle x^2 \rangle$ is accomplished by high Einstein or Debye oscillator frequencies (ω_E, ω_D) and temperatures (θ_E, θ_D), respectively. At higher temperatures higher oscillator levels with increasing quantum number n are excited whereby the energy of the harmonic oscillator system becomes proportional to $\langle x^2 \rangle$, see (1.11) and (1.12). The recoil-free fraction becomes large at low temperatures. This important observation in MÖSSBAUER'S early experiments is represented in Fig. 1.2c by the boat frozen in the solid ice. For the bound nucleus the quantum mechanical description allows

only discrete levels separated by the oscillator quanta (phonons). The emission spectrum of such an oscillator consists of discrete narrow "spectral lines", as indicated. The significant feature is the zero-phonon transition, i.e. the existence of emission processes without loss of energy to the lattice and of course, conversely, the existence of similar absorption processes. The line appearing at E_0 is the Mössbauer line. And for this case the nuclear transition energy E_0 is equal to the energy of the γ-radiation E_γ. Quantitatively, the intensity of the Mössbauer line represents the probability of the occurrence of recoil-free events according to (1.18). Higher states separated by $h\nu_D$ are also excited because the mean energy transferred to the lattice must be E_R (Lipkin's sum rule).

When a Debye model is used instead of an Einstein model we have to consider the large number of oscillator levels in the solid and their frequency distribution. Each of the levels available has a certain probability to be excited by the recoil. The mean energy transferred to the lattice is again E_R and a recoil-free line appears at E_0 — the Mössbauer line. Quantitatively the Debye model gives the following expression for the recoil-free fraction

$$f = \exp \left\{ - \frac{3E_R}{2k_B \theta_D} \left[1 + 4 \left(\frac{T}{\theta_D} \right)^2 \int_0^{\theta_D/T} \frac{x}{e^x - 1} \, dx \right] \right\} . \tag{1.19}$$

In the limit of low or high temperatures (above θ_D) we obtain approximately

$$f = \exp \left(- \frac{3E_R}{2k_B \theta_D} \right) ; \quad T \ll \theta_D , \tag{1.20}$$

$$f = \exp \left(- \frac{6E_R T}{k_B \theta_D^2} \right) ; \quad T > \theta_D . \tag{1.21}$$

Actually, the recoil-free fraction f was known as the Debye-Waller factor in the analysis of X-rays scattered from a crystal resulting in an X-ray diffraction pattern long before the discovery of the Mössbauer effect. Low energy γ-rays and X-rays are basically of the same electromagnetic nature in the same energy region. Only the origin of the radiation—nuclear or electronic shell transition—enables the two to be distinguished. The scattering process of X-rays from a solid can be treated in its momentum and energy transfer to available phonon states in a similar fashion as the description of emission and absorption of γ-rays. X-ray diffraction is always seen in the wave picture while

Table 1.2. Mössbauer parameters and effects

Symbol	Definition and units used	Corresponds in wave or particle picture, respectively	Physical parameter	Cause of the effects	Observed or predicted effe
f	Number of recoil free γ-ray events (emission or absorption) divided by total number of γ-ray events, dimensionless (Debye-Waller factor)	Relative intensity of resonance line Probability of recoil-free events	Probability of phonon creation or annihilation by the emitting or absorbing atom or mean square of vibrational amplitude	Vibrational modes of the resonating atom (as function of direction, temperature and pressure, in different lattices, phases, near critical temperatures, at surfaces and close to other lattice defects)	Intensity of Mössbauer li Intensity dependence
				Vibrational modes of the resonating atom in non-cubic symmetry of single crystals, and polycrystalline materials	Change in the relative line intensities of hyperfine sp spectra (Goldanskii-Karyagin effect)
Γ	Full width at half maximum in energy units	Line width or spread in wave length	Mean lifetime of the excited state	Saturation effects Diffusion and Brownian motion of the atoms or molecules, Relaxation processes, Spin-flip processes, Superparamagnetism, Fluctuations near critical temperatures (magnetic, ferroelectric and other phase transitions)	Natural line width ⎫ ⎬ Line broadening ⎭
		Uncertainty or spread in energy	Apparent mean lifetime of the excited state		
			Atomic, magnetic electric relaxation processes	Delay coincidence measurements Thermal spike	⎫ Line narrowing ⎬
				Change in the mean lifetime of the excited state	Line narrowing or line broadening
E_γ	Mean energy of radiation in energy units	Mean wavelength of γ-radiation Mean energy of γ-radiation	Energy difference between excited and ground state	Interaction of the nuclear charge distribution with the electron density at the nuclei in source and absorber (electric monopole interaction)	Isomer shift
				Interaction of the nuclear magnetic dipole moment with a magnetic field at the nucleus (magnetic dipole interaction); Angular dependence of the nuclear Zeeman effect in single crystals, preferred oriented materials (texture) and polycrystalline materials; Symmetry tests in γ-decay (time reversal invariance, parity conservation); Boltzmann population of the hyperfine sublevels at low temperature ($\ll 1$ K)	Nuclear Zeeman effect Change in the relative line intensities, polarizati of the γ-radiation (linear, elliptical, circular) Change in relative line intensities Change in relative line intensities
				Interaction of the nuclear quadrupole moment with EFG at the nucleus (electric quadrupole interaction) Angular dependence of the quadrupole interaction in single crystals, preferrentially oriented materials (texture) and polycrystalline materials	Quadrupole splitting Change in the relative line intensities, polarization of the γ-radiation
				Change in temperature Change in pressure Acceleration and gravitational fields	Temperature shift Pressure shift Acceleration and gravi tational red shift

(Hyperfine interaction applies to the nuclear Zeeman and quadrupole interaction rows; Relativistic effects applies to the temperature/pressure/acceleration rows)

Formulation	Fe^{57} energy level diagram with allowed transitions — Source (S) / Absorber (A)	Schematic representation of observation (resonance absorption vs. velocity)
$= \exp - k^2 \langle x^2 \rangle$		
$\Gamma_{ff} = \dfrac{h}{\tau_{eff}}$		
$= C \dfrac{\delta R}{R} [\,|\psi_A(0)|^2 - |\psi_S(0)|^2\,]$		
$= -g_N \beta_N H m_I$		
$= \pm \tfrac{1}{4} e Q V_{zz} \; (1+\tfrac{1}{3}\eta^2)^{\frac{1}{2}}$		
$= \dfrac{v^2}{2c^2} E_\gamma$		

in nuclear fluorescene and Mössbauer spectroscopy, where quanta are counted statistically, the particle picture is in the foreground. It seems that in the past the duality of wave and particle made it difficult to recognize the same phenomena.

It should be pointed out that the bound state required to obtain recoil-free processes is solely determined by $\langle x^2 \rangle$, see (1.18). No further specification regarding the solid state is necessary, i.e. the crystalline state is not required. Therefore, the Mössbauer effect is not limited to the crystalline state but has also been observed in liquid and amorphous or glaseous materials. The f-factor in Mössbauer spectroscopy and the Debye-Waller factor in X-ray diffraction—even though they have basically the same physical origin—are somewhat different. The Mössbauer effect offers the possibility to single out one atom and determine by the f-factor the mean-square vibrational amplitude of this resonance atom which might be in very specific environments, e.g. on a surface or associated with defects.

Information regarding the f-factor is summarized in Table 1.2.

1.4. Line Width

Uncertainty is a daily experience. In physics the uncertainty can be formulated precisely by Heisenberg's uncertainty principle

$$(\Delta E) \cdot (\Delta t) \geq \hbar . \tag{1.22}$$

The product of conjugate variables is given here in terms of energy and time. It can also be expressed for momentum and position or other conjugate variables. Δ indicates the uncertainties in the properties (E and t). The product is related to Planck's constant. The consequence of this principle is the fact that no measurement or observation of the two conjugate variables can be made simultaneously with higher accuracy than stated here. This inherent error cannot be overcome by any improvement of the instrument. Physics has to live with this lower limit of accuracy.

Applying this principle to Mössbauer transitions we recall that in a recoil-free transition from an excited nuclear state to the ground state (Fig. 1.5) no energy is lost to the system, and the γ-ray carries the total energy of this transition. The excited state has a mean lifetime τ or half lifetime $t_{1/2} = \tau \ln 2$. The ground state is stable, or has a long lifetime, and its energy level is well defined. Therefore, the uncertainty relation for this case is given from resonance theory as

$$\Delta E = \Gamma = \frac{\hbar}{\tau} = \frac{0.693\,\hbar}{t_{1/2}}, \qquad (1.23)$$

where Γ is called the natural line width of the source emission or the absorption line. The line width is defined as the full width at half maximum. The first excited state of Fe^{57} (14.4 keV) has a value of $t_{1/2} \approx 10^{-7}$ sec. Thus, the natural line width is $\Gamma \approx 5 \cdot 10^{-9}$ eV. Table 1.1 is taken from the Mössbauer Effect Data Index [1.17] and contains, as well as other relevant properties, 2Γ and $t_{1/2}$ values of the isotopes where resonance transitions have been reported. The spike drawn in Fig. 1.2c as the Mössbauer line indicates the extremely narrow width. This line width is many orders of magnitude smaller than typical phonon energies $h\nu_E$ or $h\nu_D$. The ratio of the natural line width and the photon energy, Γ/E_γ, is a measure of the accuracy in the determination of relative energy or frequency changes. For Fe^{57} this ratio is about $3 \cdot 10^{-13}$. Returning to the energy ranges relevant to Mössbauer spectroscopy in Fig. 1.4 the resolution of this method for Fe^{57} can also be visualized by the distance between the two arrows of E_γ and Γ of more than 12 orders of magnitude. It should be pointed out that only relative energy or frequency changes between two resonating nuclei can be measured with such an accuracy. A determination on an absolute scale is not possible by this method. Small line shifts can be measured to a fraction of 1% of the line width, thus, the method allows information to be obtained in the relative line position on the Fe^{57} line to one part in 10^{15}. With other isotopes even a higher accuracy can be achieved. The ability to detect such extremely small changes in relative energy makes the Mössbauer effect very attractive. It might be of interest just to consider the length scale which would have to be used to measure the relative changes in distance to the center of the moon with the same accuracy: the measurement would have to be made on the micron scale (10^{-3} mm).

To understand the Mössbauer effect one has to anticipate that the magnitude of characteristic phonon energies, $h\nu_D = k_B\theta_D$, of typical solids and the recoil energies E_R in low energy γ-emission or absorption are of the same order of magnitude (lower two ranges in Fig. 1.4) while for the significance and relative accuracy of the effect the large distance between γ-ray energy E_γ and line width Γ is decisive (upper two ranges in Fig. 1.4).

A method usually involves a characteristic or inherent time. This is the time taken for the information to be collected and transmitted to an instrument for measuring experimental data. The lifetime of the excited state or the natural line width defined by (1.23) is the characteristic time in Mössbauer spectroscopy. In his early papers MÖSSBAUER [1.1] suggested the use of his newly discovered line as a direct method for determination of the level width or lifetime of low lying excited nuclear states.

The energy distribution of the emission and the absorption process is given by the Breit-Wigner formula which can be derived classically by considering the exponentially decaying wave train with a certain amplitude [1.18]. The shape of the resulting line is Lorentzian. If in a resonance experiment an emission line of natural line width Γ is moved over an absorption line of natural line width Γ the sum of both resonance line widths, 2Γ, will be observed. The Lorentzian line of such an absorption experiment is represented by the total cross section

$$\sigma = \sigma_0 \frac{\Gamma^2}{\Gamma^2 + 4(E - E_0)^2} \tag{1.24}$$

with the maximum cross section

$$\sigma_0 = 2\pi \lambda^2 \frac{2I_e + 1}{2I_g + 1} \frac{1}{\alpha_t + 1}, \tag{1.25}$$

where I_e and I_g are the nuclear spins of the excited and ground state, respectively, and $\lambda (= 2\pi \lambda)$ is the wavelength of the γ-ray. α_t is the total internal conversion coefficient and takes into account the competing mode of the transition. For Fe^{57}, α_t is in the order of 10. In some cases the high value of the internal conversion coefficient α_t makes it difficult to observe the resonance line.

The reason why the observation of deviations from the natural line width might be trivial could be due to Doppler broadening of an improper functioning Mössbauer apparatus (vibration) or saturation effects in the absorber or in the source (self absorption) [1.19]. However, there are also a number of inherent physical processes causing line broadening. In 1960 it was predicted that the diffusive motion of atoms can have an effect on the line width [1.20]. The resonance line will be broadened when the jump frequency of the resonance atom in the lattice, caused by a vacancy, interstitial, or other mechanism, approaches the reciprocal of the mean lifetime of the excited state, $1/\tau$. Line broadening attributed to this condition has been observed and the diffusion coefficient was derived [1.21, 22]. Under appropriate circumstances information can be obtained from diffusion of large organic molecules in liquids [1.23].

It is possible to observe resonance lines narrower than the natural line width. For instance, the foregoing decay to the nuclear excited state can be used as a signal in a delay coincidence experiment. In the following transition to the ground state only γ-rays emerging from long-lived excited states are selected. The effective mean lifetime τ_{eff} has been artificially increased and therefore—with the uncertainty principle [1.23]—decreased Γ_{eff} [1.24]. The following possibility may also be considered. The foregoing decay is usually associated with the creation of a thermal spike where according to the scheme in Fig. 1.6 high oscillator levels will be occupied. In the case of the transition $Co^{57} \rightarrow Fe^{57}$ more than 3 eV are dissipated. The probability of the following recoil-free emission processes can become an increasing function of the time the nuclear excited state has existed during the thermalization process with a decrease of $\langle x^2 \rangle$. Therefore, the γ-rays which contribute to the resonance line come from excited states with apparently longer mean lifetimes [1.25]. Of course, the narrow line width described here does not violate the uncertainty principle. Line broadening due to relaxation processes will be discussed in conjunction with the nuclear Zeeman effect. The parameters governing the line width are summarized in Table 1.2.

1.5. Hyperfine Interaction

The sharpness of the Mössbauer line in conjunction with the possibility to determine the energy positions of the emitted γ-ray from a source relative to an absorber with a high degree of accuracy is the most important feature of this spectroscopy. With respect to the line positions there are two main contributions of great significance: the hyperfine interaction and relativistic effects.

Before the Mössbauer effect was discovered experiments were performed from which the hyperfine interaction parameter could be deduced, although in a rather indirect way. The Mössbauer effect made it possible to resolve the hyperfine interactions [1.26] and provided a wealth of new information. The resolution of this method can be visualized by the splitting of the energy-level diagram described in Table 1.2. Considering the scale of a typical splitting, the broken lines between ground state and excited state roughly represent the distance between the earth and moon.

The hyperfine interaction consists of interactions between a nuclear (moment) property and an appropriate electronic or atomic property. The hyperfine coupling mechanisms are of great significance yielding information regarding electron- and spin-density distributions. There arc three main hyperfine interactions corresponding to the nuclear moments determining the nuclear levels:

1) Electric monopole interaction $(e0)$ — isomer shift.
2) Magnetic dipole interaction $(m1)$ — nuclear Zeeman effect.
3) Electric quadrupole interaction $(e2)$ — quadrupole splitting.

In the following, some general aspects of hyperfine interaction are presented and summarized in Table 1.2. Details and various applications will be discussed later, particularly in Chapter 2 by P. GÜTLICH, and Chapter 3 by R. W. GRANT.

1.5.1. Isomer Shift

The origin of the isomer shift δ is the result of the Coulomb interaction of the nuclear-charge distribution over a finite nuclear radius R in the excited and ground states and the electron-charge density at the nucleus (s electrons) [1.26–29]. The s electron density of the resonating nuclei in the source and in the absorber can be varied by the chemical environment. By Coulomb interaction the levels of the ground and of the excited state are changed, as indicated in the energy level diagram of Table 1.2, and also the transition energies E_S and E_A. E_0 can be considered as the hypothetical case of a point nucleus with the same charge. In the resonance experiment the difference between E_S and E_A is shown by a shift, which is called the isomer shift.

This shift can be expressed (in the non-relativistic approximation) as

$$\delta = C \, \frac{\delta R}{R} \, (|\psi_A(0)|^2 - |\psi_S(0)|^2), \qquad (1.26)$$

where C is a constant for a given isotope containing nuclear parameters, $\delta R/R$ is the relative change of nuclear radius between excited state and ground state, and the term in parenthesis represents the difference in the total electron density evaluated at the nucleus $|\psi(0)|^2$, between absorber and source isotopes. Because the electron density at the nucleus is a function of the valence state and chemical bonding, the isomer shift is also sometimes called "chemical shift" or "differential chemical shift".

From the directions of the resonance line shift with increasing s electron density one can deduce that δR has a negative sign for Fe^{57}, i.e. the nuclear radius of the excited state is smaller than the radius of the ground state. With the isotope Sn^{119} the opposite—and common —result is found. It has also been recognized that the isomer shift— particularly of the transition metals—is strongly influenced by the screening effects of the d electrons. The isomer shifts of Fe^{57} corresponding to the various charge states of iron provide evidence for this screening, and the interpretation is mostly made in terms of the main contributions: $4s$ and $3d$ electrons with their appropriate configurations [1.27]. A general systematic study of isomer shifts in transition metals has been recently reported [1.30]. A correlation between the isomer shift and the electronegativity of the surrounding matrix [1.31] and a correlation to the quadrupole splittings [1.32] has been established with various isotopes. Experiments with different isotopes of the same element are interesting. In these cases one can keep the chemical environment the same and only change the nuclear parameters.

Mössbauer spectroscopy is a relative method: the source spectrum is related to the absorber spectrum by Doppler motion. Therefore, one of the two has to be known or fixed in order to determine the other. In many cases the source-line position is taken as a reference position. This is often unsatisfactory, especially when various spectra are taken with different sources—and thus different isomer shifts—are compared. It is desirable to establish a unique reference standard matrix for each resonance isotope so that various measurements can be easily compared with the standard $|\psi(0)|^2$ value [1.33]. An ad hoc panel on Mössbauer data of the Numerical Data Advisory Board, Division of Chemistry and Chemical Technology of the National Research Council (USA) proposed and recommended the isomer shift standards given in Table 1.3.

Table 1.3. Reference standard materials

Element	Material	Element	Material
K	KCl	Eu	EuS
Fe	α-Fe	Gd	$GdAl_2$
	Sodium nitroprusside	Dy	Dy
Zn	ZnS	Er	Er
Ge	Ge	Yb	$YbAl_2$
Kr	Kr (solid)	W	W
Ru	$K_4(Ru(CN)_6) \cdot 3H_2O$	Os	$K_4(Os(CN)_6)$
Sn	SnTe	Ir	Ir
	$BaSnO_3$	Pt	Pt
Sb	InSb	Au	Au
Te	SnTe	Np	$NpAl_2$
I	CsI		
Xe	Xe (solid)		
Sm	SmF_2		

Recently a correlation between isomer shift and effective lifetime of the resonance isotope [1.34] has been found. The internal conversion coefficients α_s are proportional to the s electron densities of the various corresponding shells. The difference in the electron density at the nucleus in different chemical environments influences the mean lifetime of the radioactive decay by the relation

$$\frac{\Delta 1/\tau}{1/\tau} = \frac{\alpha_s}{\alpha_t + 1} \frac{\Delta |\psi_s(0)|^2}{|\psi_s(0)|^2} . \tag{1.27}$$

The chemically induced change in the mean nuclear lifetime can be used as a tool for calibrating Fe^{57}, and other isomer shifts, and in principle, the Mössbauer line width should indicate this effect according to (1.23).

1.5.2. Nuclear Zeeman Effect

The interaction of the nuclear magnetic dipole moment μ with a magnetic field H at the site of the nucleus, splits the nuclear state with spin $I(I > 0)$ into $(2I + 1)$ sublevels with the eigenvalues

$$E_m = -\frac{\mu H m_I}{I} = -g_N \beta_N H m_I , \tag{1.28}$$

where m_I is the magnetic quantum number with the values $m_I = I$, $I - 1$, ... $- I$. The nuclear magnetic moment is related to the nuclear Bohr magneton β_N by the nuclear Landé splitting factor g_N

$$\mu = g_N \beta_N I . \tag{1.29}$$

The isotope Fe^{57} has $I = 1/2$ for the ground state and $I = 3/2$ for the 14.4 keV first excited state. A magnetic field at the site of the nucleus (no quadrupole interaction) causes a splitting of the nuclear states, as shown in the energy-level diagram of Table 1.2. The ordering of the sublevels m_I indicates the fact that the ground state magnetic moment is positive, while the excited state has a negative magnetic moment. The multipolarity of the 14.4 keV γ-ray transition is almost exclusively a magnetic dipole ($M1$) in nature, thus, for the nuclear Zeeman effect we have the selection rule $\Delta m = 0, \pm 1$. The allowed transitions leading to the six-line pattern are shown in the diagram. A Mössbauer spectrum of an α-Fe foil with a hyperfine magnetic field of $H_{int} = 330\,kOe$ is shown in Fig. 1.7a.

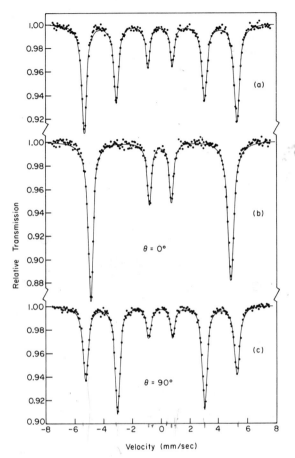

Fig. 1.7a-c. Mössbauer transmission spectra of α-Fe at room temperature: a) $H_{ext} = 0$, b) $H_{ext} = 50\,kOe$, $\theta_m = 0°$, c) $H_{ext} = 3.5\,kOe$, $\theta_m = 90°$

The angular dependence of the allowed transitions in the nuclear Zeeman pattern is given in Table 1.4. Here θ_m represents the angle between the direction of the magnetic field at the nucleus and the propagation direction of the γ-ray. From this table one can find the relative line intensities of a Zeeman hyperfine pattern in the thin absorber approximation, assuming isotropy of the lattice vibrations. The relative line intensities for $\theta_m = 0°$ are 3:0:1:1:0:3 and for $\theta_m = 90°$, 3:4:1:1:4:3. Because the total radiation pattern is isotropic it follows by integration over all directions that the relative line intensities for a randomly oriented magnetic material is 3:2:1:1:2:3. The angular

Table 1.4. Angular dependence of the allowed transitions in a pure nuclear Zeeman pattern of Fe^{57}. θ_m represents the angle between the direction of the magnetic field at the nucleus and the propagation direction of the γ-radiation

Transition	Δm	Angular dependence
$\pm 3/2 \rightarrow \pm 1/2$	± 1	$3/4\,(1 + \cos^2 \theta_m)$
$\pm 1/2 \rightarrow \pm 1/2$	0	$\sin^2 \theta_m$
$\mp 1/2 \rightarrow \pm 1/2$	∓ 1	$1/4\,(1 + \cos^2 \theta_m)$

dependence of the hyperfine interaction can be seen from the Mössbauer pattern of an α-Fe foil in Fig. 1.7. The spectra were obtained by: a) no external magnetic field H_{ext}; b) applied field $H_{ext} = 50\,kOe$, $\theta_m = 0°$; c) $H_{ext} = 3.5\,kOe$, $\theta_m = 90°$. For the case b) $\theta_m = 0°$ a large magnetic field was applied perpendicular to the foil plane well in excess of the demagnetizing field of about 21 kOe. In this spectrum it should be noted that the splitting is reduced by the external field. This indicates that the hyperfine interaction has a negative sign: atomic moment and the magnetic field at the nucleus are oppositely oriented, as is also the case for Fe^{57} in most alloys and ferrites [1.35].

The magnetic hyperfine interaction (nuclear Zeeman effect) observed by Mössbauer spectroscopy has contributed significantly to the understanding of the magnetic properties of materials. It is of particular interest that in ferrites, compounds, and alloys each lattice site exhibits its own hyperfine pattern, thus sublattice behavior or the influence of impurities in specific environments to the resonating atom can be studied. Information regarding the origin and various contributions of the magnetic field and, in particular, the characterization of magnetically ordered compounds are given in Chapter 3 by R. W. GRANT.

1.5.3. Quadrupole Splitting

The interaction of the nuclear electric quadrupole moment eQ with the principal component of the diagonalized electric field gradient (EFG) tensor $V_{zz} = \partial^2 V / \partial z^2$ at the site of the nucleus splits the nuclear state into sublevels with the eigenvalues

$$E_Q = \frac{eQ\,V_{zz}}{4I(2I-1)}\,[3m_I^2 - I(I+1)]\left(1 + \frac{\eta^2}{3}\right)^{1/2}. \qquad (1.30)$$

The asymmetry parameter η is given by

$$\eta = \frac{V_{xx} - V_{yy}}{V_{zz}} \qquad (1.31)$$

with $|V_{zz}| \geq |V_{yy}| \geq |V_{xx}|$; $V_{zz} + V_{yy} + V_{xx} = 0$ thus, $0 \leq \eta \leq 1$.

The electric quadrupole interaction splits the first nuclear excited state of Fe^{57} and Sn^{119}, $(I = 3/2)$ into sublevels, as indicated in the energy-level diagram of Table 1.2, with the eigenvalues

$$E_Q = \pm \frac{1}{4} eQ \, V_{zz} \left(1 + \frac{1}{3} \eta^2\right)^{1/2}. \qquad (1.32)$$

It should be noted that a considerable amount of uncertainty exists about the absolute value of the nuclear quadrupole moment eQ of the first excited state of Fe^{57}, thus the inaccuracy of the absolute value of the derived EFG is rather high. The reverse situation applies to the magnetic hyperfine interaction where the excited and ground state magnetic nuclear moment of Fe^{57} are known very presicely [1.17].

The angular dependence of the radiation pattern produced at the Fe^{57} nucleus by an EFG with axial symmetry ($\eta = 0$) is given in Table 1.5. In this case θ_q represents the angle between the principal axis of the EFG and the propagation direction of the γ-ray. The relative line intensities of the two quadrupole split lines (in the thin absorber approximation and assuming isotropy in the lattice vibration) are for $\theta_q = 0°$, 3:1 and for $\theta_q = 90°$, 3:5. The relative line intensity will deviate from these values whenever $\eta \neq 0$, because the nuclear wave functions are no longer pure $|m\rangle$ states. For a randomly oriented polycrystalline material, the relative line intensities are 1:1. The quadrupole interaction deduced from Mössbauer spectra is of great significance, particularly in chemistry and solid state physics. The problem concerning the origin of the electric field gradient and examples of quadrupole split spectra with the appropriate interpretation can be found in the following chapters.

Table 1.5. Angular dependence of the electric quadrupole interaction of Fe^{57} ($\eta = 0$). θ_q represents the angle between the direction of the principal axis of the electric field gradient and the propagation direction of the γ-radiation

Transition	Angular dependence
$\pm 3/2 \rightarrow \pm 1/2$	$1 + \cos^2 \theta_q$
$\pm 1/2 \rightarrow \pm 1/2$	$2/3 + \sin^2 \theta_q$

1.6. Perturbation or Combined Effects in the Hyperfine Interaction

Perturbation or combined effects might cause a change in the line positions and/or in the relative line intensities or width in the hyperfine pattern. The shifts are rather simple cases. An isomer shift or a relativistic shift (see below) will move the spectrum as a whole in one direction, corresponding to the net interaction in source and absorber. Four examples concerning the more complex perturbation in the hyperfine interaction are presented and references are given for further information.

1.6.1. Magnetic Dipole and Electric Quadrupole Interaction

The interpretation of spectra becomes more complicated if the splitting of a nuclear state reveals simultaneous magnetic dipole and electric quadrupole interaction. Only in simple cases, for instance, if the principal axis of the electric field gradient and the internal magnetic field are colinear eigenvalues of the excited state can be written in a closed form [1.36]; in other words, only for the cases where $|m\rangle$ is a good quantum number. In general, additional "forbidden" transitions occur. For the cases of Fe^{57} two additional "forbidden" lines appear in the six-line spectrum. Normally one interaction is small compared to the other, thus, either the magnetic hyperfine interaction is perturbed by an electric quadrupole interaction (in this way the quadrupole hyperfine interaction was discovered [1.26]) or the quadrupole interaction is perturbed by a magnetic dipole interaction, for instance, by an applied external magnetic field [1.37]. A number of computer programs which synthesize spectra from assumed interaction parameters are available and helpful in analyzing the spectra in terms of line positions and relative line intensities [1.38, 39]. The programs involve the following interaction parameters: the isomer shift δ, the hyperfine magnetic field H_{int}, the principal component of the EFG V_{zz}, the polar and azimuthal angles relating the direction of H_{int}, and the γ-ray propagation direction to the principal axes (x, y, z) of the EFG tensor, and the asymmetry parameter η.

1.6.2. Lattice Vibrational Anisotropy (Goldanskii-Karyagin Effect)

The angular dependence of the magnetic dipole and of the electric quadrupole interaction is reflected in the relative line intensities (see Tables 1.4 and 1.5 for Fe^{57}). In the case of the magnetic hyperfine inter-

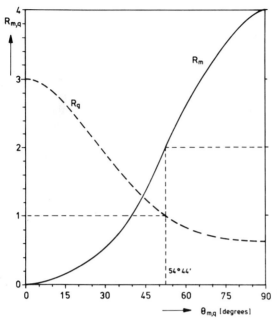

Fig. 1.8. Ratio of the line intensities $R_{m,q}$ vs. the angle $\theta_{m,q}$ between the propagation direction of the γ-ray and the orientation of the magnetic field at the nucleus or the principal axis of the EFG, respectively

action (subindex m) the intensities of the $\Delta m = 0$ lines (I_2, I_5) and the inner lines $\Delta m = \pm 1$ lines (I_3, I_4) are defined by the ratio

$$R_m = \frac{I_{2,5}}{I_{3,4}} = \frac{\sin^2 \theta_m}{\frac{1}{4}(1 + \cos^2 \theta_m)} \tag{1.33a}$$

and correspondingly, in the case of the quadrupole hyperfine inter-action (subindex q) the intensities $(I_{\pm 3/2}; I_{\pm 1/2})$ of the γ-transitions to the $\pm 3/2$ or $\pm 1/2$ excited nuclear states, respectively, are defined by the ratio

$$R_q = \frac{I_{\pm 3/2}}{I_{\pm 1/2}} = \frac{1 + \cos^2 \theta_q}{\frac{2}{3} + \sin^2 \theta_q}. \tag{1.33b}$$

θ_m and θ_q are the angles between the propagation direction of the γ-rays and the orientation of the magnetic field or the principal axis of the EFG, respectively. The ratio $R_{m,q}$ vs. $\theta_{m,q}$ is plotted in Fig. 1.8. R_m ranges from zero $(\theta_m = 0°)$ to 4 $(\theta_m = 90°)$ and R_q ranges from 3

($\theta_q = 0°$) to 0.6 ($\theta_q = 90°$). The values $R_m = 2$ and $R_q = 1$ are obtained for $\theta_{m,q} = 54°44'$ and for an assembly randomly oriented crystallites. If the recoil-free fraction f depends on the crystallographic orientation it will also depend on the orientation of the EFG axes system or the spin in a magnetic material. In this case the relative line intensities R_m or R_q of the magnetic and/or quadrupole hyperfine pattern will reflect the vibrational anisotropy. This dependence is called the Goldanskii-Karyagin effect (GKE) [1.40–42]. The anisotropy can be expressed in terms of mean square vibrational amplitudes parallel $\langle z^2 \rangle$, and perpendicular $\langle x^2 \rangle$, to the direction of the spin and the principal axis of the EFG respectively,

$$\varepsilon_a = k^2 \{ \langle z^2 \rangle - \langle x^2 \rangle \}, \tag{1.34}$$

where k is the magnitude of the wave vector for the γ-radiation. The assumption of axial asymmetry is made: $\langle x^2 \rangle = \langle y^2 \rangle$. For randomly oriented polycrystalline materials, and substituting $\cos\theta_{m,q} = u$ one obtains in the harmonic approximation

$$R_m = \frac{\int_0^1 (1 - u^2) \exp(-\varepsilon_a u^2) \, du}{\int_0^1 \frac{1}{4} (1 + u^2) \exp(-\varepsilon_a u^2) \, du} \tag{1.35a}$$

$$R_q = \frac{\int_0^1 (1 + u^2) \exp(-\varepsilon_a u^2) \, du}{\int_0^1 \left(\frac{5}{3} - u^2 \right) \exp(-\varepsilon_a u^2) \, du}. \tag{1.35b}$$

In Fig. 1.9, R_q and R_m are plotted as functions of the vibrational anisotropy ε_a. However, for a physical interpretation of the curve it seems more appropriate to obtain the ratios of the mean square displacements [1.43]

$$W_x(\theta_D(x) = 300 \text{ K}) \equiv \frac{\langle z^2 \rangle}{\langle x^2 \rangle} = 1 + \frac{\varepsilon_a}{k^2 \langle x^2 \rangle}, \tag{1.36a}$$

$$W_z(\theta_D(z) = 300 \text{ K}) \equiv \frac{\langle x^2 \rangle}{\langle z^2 \rangle} = 1 - \frac{\varepsilon_a}{k^2 \langle z^2 \rangle}. \tag{1.36b}$$

Using the Debye model and a Debye temperature of $\theta_D = 300$ K a value of $\langle x^2 \rangle = 8.76 \cdot 10^{-3}$ Å^2 is calculated. In Fig. 1.9 the R_m values versus

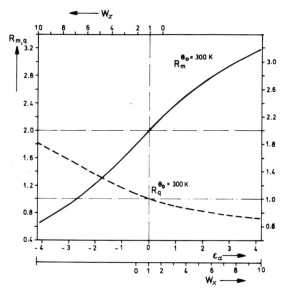

Fig. 1.9. Ratio of the line intensities $R_{m,q}$ vs. the lattice anisotropy parameter ε_a and the anisotropy ratio W_x and W_z for various Debye temperatures (magnetic and quadrupole GKE)

W_x (lower abscissa) and W_z (upper abscissa) are shown for 14.4 keV γ-rays of Fe^{57} ($k = 7.28$ A^{-1}) where the denominator $\langle x^2 \rangle$ or $\langle z^2 \rangle$ was fixed to a mean-square displacement corresponding to $\theta_D = 300$ K for a solid at room temperature. It should be emphasized that these equations only apply to a truly randomly oriented polycrystalline material. In addition to this atomistic or intrinsic effect there exists a competing extrinsic effect of a macroscopic nature which is due to any deviation from randomness, i.e. by a preferred orientation of crystallites, molecules, or spins (texture). Texture has a rather sensitive effect on the relative line intensities of a magnetic or quadrupole hyperfine pattern [1.43, 44]. From an experimental point of view, it is difficult to differentiate between the two effects: Goldanskii-Karyagin effect and texture.

1.6.3. Relaxation Effects

In a hyperfine interaction pattern, time dependent features are often observed. The fluctuating fields causing broadening can be described by a correlation time characterizing various relaxation processes. In the case of superparamagnetism the net magnetization of single domain particles fluctuates thermally between different easy directions for sufficiently small particles [1.45–47]. In the presence of a paramagnetic hyperfine interaction, the following two characteristic times have to be considered: the relaxation time of the electron spin (spin-spin and spin-lattice) τ_s and the nuclear Larmor precession time τ_L. If $\tau_s \gg \tau_L$, a "static" nonvanishing hyperfine interaction is present at the nucleus and a hyperfine spectrum with sharp lines is expected. If $\tau_s \ll \tau_L$ the hyperfine interaction produces an average value as a result of the rapidly fluctuating electron spins and the splitting collapses. Under the condition $\tau_s \approx \tau_L$ complicated spectra with broad lines are found which allow an estimate of the electron relaxation time to be made. The line broadening in the Mössbauer Zeeman pattern is closely connected to the motional narrowing in NMR. Relaxation effects are reported in a number of excellent articles [1.48–53].

1.6.4. Low Temperature Boltzmann Distribution of Nuclear Levels

At very low temperatures $T \ll 1$ K the hyperfine splitting ΔE_m and thermal energy $k_B T$ are of the same order of magnitude (see Fig. 1.4). Under such conditions a Boltzmann distribution governs the population of the nuclear levels. The higher levels are less occupied and the transitions corresponding to these levels are less frequent. Consequently, the spectra become asymmetric with respect to relative line intensities. This effect was observed [1.54, 55] for the parent isotope Co^{57} ($I = 7/2$) which has a large magnetic moment and the polarization is maintained through the decay to Fe^{57}.

1.7. Relativistic Effects

In general the vibrating atoms in a solid make many oscillations ($\approx 10^{13}$/sec) during the lifetime of the excited nuclear states (10^{-5}–10^{-10} sec), thus the average velocity is zero and a first-order Doppler effect cannot be expected. However, the average squared velocity of the oscillating atoms, $\overline{v^2}$, causes a shift of the resonance line by a second-order Doppler effect [1.56, 57]; i.e.

$$\delta_R = \frac{\overline{v^2}}{2c^2} E_\gamma . \tag{1.37}$$

$\overline{v^2}$ is dependent on temperature, pressure, Debye temperature of the surrounding matrix, and lattice defects etc. For the temperature shift—also called the thermal red shift—in a mono-atomic lattice $\overline{v^2}$ can be expressed by the kinetic part of the specific heat (1.11). Applying the Dulong-Petit law one obtains at elevated temperatures ($T \gtrsim \theta_D$) for Fe^{57} a temperature shift of $\delta_T \approx 7 \cdot 10^{-4}$ mm (sec $\cdot$ K) or the shift becomes comparable with the natural line width at $\Delta T \approx 150$ K.

Soon after the discovery of the Mössbauer effect it was realized that the sharpness of the resonance line can be used to verify Einstein's mass-energy equivalence in a terrestrial experiment [1.58, 59]. By the gravitational red shift the apparent weight of the photon travelling between source and absorber of different gravitational potential is measured. The gravitational red shift is given by

$$\delta_g = \frac{g_g d}{c^2} E_\gamma , \qquad (1.38)$$

where g_g is the acceleration of the photon in the gravitation field, and d the distance between source and absorber. The experiments were carried out using the isotope Fe^{57} over a distance of $d = 22.5$ m. The rather small shift of only a fraction of a line width allowed the prediction of Einstein's mass-energy equivalence to be verified within an accuracy of a few percent. For a shift of a full line width the distance of source and absorber has to be in the order of $d \approx 3000$ m when the experiments become unfeasible. However, other isotopes, like Ta^{181}, might be good examples for future studies because of their very small natural line width.

In the theory of general relativity the fields of gravitation and acceleration are considered to be equivalent and should produce the same effects. Shifts originating from the acceleration have been measured [1.60] with an ultracentrifuge.

Intensity, width, position, and splitting are the parameters characterizing the Mössbauer line. A physical interpretation of these parameters and a discussion on the kind of information these parameters yield have been given in preceding sections. The Mössbauer parameters and effects in the simple source-absorber arrangement are summarized in Table 1.2 and a schematic representation is given. The Mössbauer periodic table taken from the 1972 Mössbauer Effect Data Index [1.17] is shown in Fig. 1.10. A large number of isotopes (80) in which the effect has been demonstrated is now available. The number of resonance transitions has just reached 100. However, Fe^{57} remains the favorite candidate with a share of about 50% of the literature in this field.

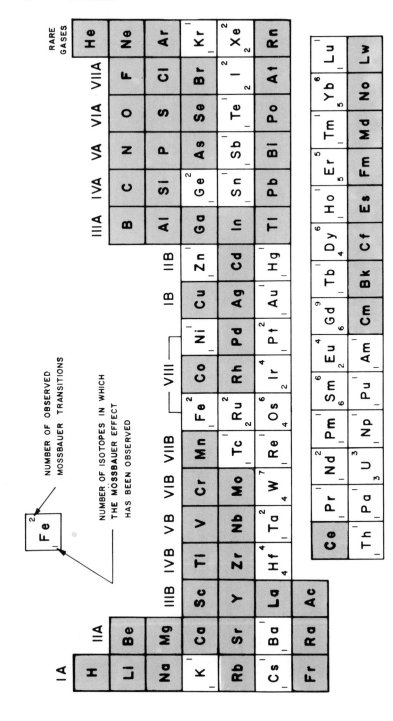

Fig. 1.10. Mössbauer periodic table [1.17]

1.8. Methodology

So far the discussion has been concentrated on the underlying principle of the Mössbauer effect and the parameters determining the resonance lines. Now the question of how the effect can be measured and developed to a spectroscopy will be discussed. Figure 1.11 shows the four basic

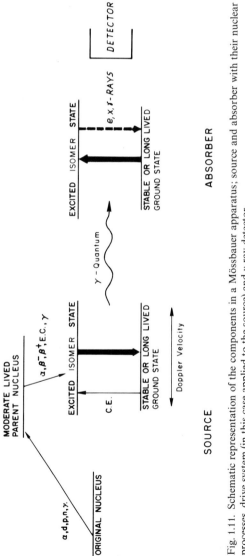

Fig. 1.11. Schematic representation of the components in a Mössbauer apparatus; source and absorber with their nuclear processes, drive system (in this case applied to the source) and γ-ray detector

components necessary for the measurement of a Mössbauer spectrum: source, absorber, drive system (indicated by the Doppler-velocity arrow), and detector.

1.8.1. Source

To obtain an effect a fraction of the emitted γ-rays from transitions between excited and ground nuclear states have to occur in a recoil-free fashion. This process combined with the reverse process in an absorber is the resonance phenomenon indicated by the bold arrows connecting the ground and excited states. At the source the excited state can be populated by various modes: α, β^+, β^-, γ, electron capture (E.C.) decay of radioactive isotopes, Coulomb excitation (C.E.) [1.61, 62] and nuclear reaction [1.63, 64] etc. In some cases the excited nuclei have been implanted into a solid [1.65, 66]. The decay scheme and the nuclear parameters determine to a great extent the usefulness of an isotope. The decay scheme for Fe^{57} is shown in Fig. 1.12. Experiments with both excited states, indicated by the bold arrows [14.41 and 136.46 keV), have been carried out.

The radiation emitted from a source is rather complex. It consists of:
1) Resonant γ-rays from an excited to a ground state (recoil-free).
2) Non-resonant γ-rays from the same transitions (involving recoil).

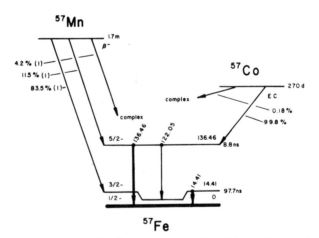

$^{57}_{26}Fe$ (14.4 keV, 136.5 keV)

Fig. 1.12. Decay scheme of Fe^{57} indicating the population of the two levels and transitions (14.41 and 136.46 keV) of this isotope [1.17]

3) Radiation from all other transitions.

4) Secondary radiation produced in the matrix (mainly X-rays).

The radiation from 1) produces the Mössbauer effect, the radiation from 2–4) contributes to the background.

In some cases even the nuclear processes in the formation of the parent isotope have to be considered because they are often associated with high recoil energies leading to lattice defects in the environment of the resonance isotope.

For the sources, mostly metallic matrices with high coordination symmetry are chosen in which the parent isotopes are diffused, implanted, Coulomb-excited, or produced by nuclear reaction. Metals have various advantages: non-magnetic cubic metals (bcc, fcc) with low impurity concentration produce single-line emission spectra, the effective Debye-Waller factor is relatively high for most metals and electronic relaxation processes are extremely fast, thus localized charge states as found in insulators resulting from the foregoing decay, existing over long periods of time compared to the lifetime of the excited state [1.67], do not exist in metals. Common sources are commercially available. Sources emitting polarized γ-rays are discussed below. The isotopes with some of their properties are listed in Table 1.1. Knowing these values one can estimate how useful an isotope is from an experimental point of view. Of course, in addition other properties such as lifetime of the parent isotope, difficulties in preparing appropriate sources and absorbers etc. must be considered. The abundance of rare earth isotopes is significant (Fig. 1.10 and Table 1.1), e.g. six isotopes are available for the element Gd with three excited states for Gd^{155}.

1.8.2. Absorber

In most cases the absorber is the material to be investigated, thus, most spectra shown in this book are "absorber spectra" taken with a single line source. Of course, there are exceptions where the resonance in the source is of interest, particularly in cases where defects associated with the resonance isotope are studied. The absorber thickness plays a significant role in the quantitative analysis of the spectra. The effective absorber thickness t_A (for a single line absorber) is usually defined by

$$t_A = \sigma_0 f_A n_a d_A a_a , \tag{1.39}$$

where σ_0 is the maximum absorption cross section (1.25), f_A is the recoil-free fraction in the absorber, n_a the number of atoms/cm^3 of the particular element, d_A the physical thickness of the absorber in cm, and a_a the isotopic abundance of the resonance isotope. If $t_A \ll 1$ the intensities of the resonance lines are rather small, however, in this case the lines can be fitted, to a good approximation, by Lorentzian curves. If $t_A \gg 1$ the lines are broadened by saturation effects and fitting by a sum of Lorentzian lines of hyperfine pattern fails. Usually experiments are carried out with a thickness of $t_A \approx 1$. Under these conditions the deviation from the thin absorber approximation in split spectra can be significant because of overlap effects. For a quantitative analysis the so-called transmission integral has to be evaluated. Fitting procedures in conjunction with various computer programs have been discussed extensively in the literature [1.68]. On-line computer systems are of great convenience.

When Mössbauer spectroscopy is used as a standard analytical method of multiphase systems, the stripping technique is very helpful [1.69]. This analytical technique involves reference spectra in least-squares-fit Lorentzian representations that are subtracted by appropriate amounts from the measured spectrum. The iteration procedure is continued until the residuals become satisfactorily small, i.e. every part of the resonance spectrum has been quantitatively assigned to a specific phase.

The temperature dependence of the resonance line or of the hyperfine splittings is often of primary interest. Cryostats and furnaces for such experiments at temperatures ranging from a few millidegree K up to the melting point of various metals and other materials have been described in the literature [1.70]. Experiments with external magnetic fields of more than 100 kOe are usually carried out with superconducting solenoids.

1.8.3. Drive Systems

As shown previously, the resonance lines are extremely sharp. Obviously, even with the best γ-ray detector systems these lines cannot be resolved for measurement. However, the energy of the γ-ray can be slightly varied by a first-order Doppler effect (1.5). By an appropriate relative motion v the nuclear transitions in source and absorber can be accurately matched and resonance occurs. The convention has been adopted to plot the spectrum not as function of the Doppler energy E_D but rather as a function of the relative velocity v, and furthermore, positive velocity is usually defined as the motion of source and absorber toward each other, and negative velocity as the motion of source and absorber away from each other. The Doppler variation technique had already been realized by MÖSSBAUER in his first experiments and were accomplished by using a toy [1.3]. Sophisticated systems have been developed in the meantime in order to obtain high precision. Nowadays various drive systems are in use [1.70], partly built in the laboratories and tailored to the experimental conditions or bought commercially.

The Doppler velocity needed to obtain a spectrum is in the order of the line width or in the order of the hyperfine splitting. From the energy scale relevant to Mössbauer spectroscopy (Fig. 1.4) this is found to be in the order of mm/sec for Fe^{57}. Note again the contrast to the earlier nuclear fluorescence experiments of the pre-Mössbauer time where orders of magnitudes higher Doppler energies were required to compensate for the recoil energy E_R.

In Mössbauer spectroscopy the radiation pulses passing through an absorber (or a scatterer) are plotted as functions of Doppler velocity v. For convenience, the radiation is usually normalized to the off-resonance counting rate, thus, the resonance-effect magnitude of the relative transmission (or scattering) is obtained.

A large variety of velocity modulation systems have been developed which are based on various principles: mechanical, electromechanical, piezoelectric, and hydraulic, etc. A distinction between constant-velocity and sweep-velocity systems can be made. The constant-velocity system has the advantage that one can select a particular velocity of interest for the duty cycle, e.g. measuring the resonance signal as a function of temperature (thermal scan). A change in the count rate might indicate a transition (Curie, Neél, Morin, phase transitions etc.) which can be determined with high accuracy by this method. With a mechanical system the absolute velocities can be measured and calibrated directly. Sweep-velocity systems are usually of an electromechanical nature, e.g. a loudspeaker-type transducer in conjunction with a multichannel analyzer are commonly used. Mostly the source makes the motion and the functional forms are: constant velocity, constant acceleration, and sinusoidal or trapezoidal velocity, although other modes are sometimes used. The measured radiation is stored in the analyzer in such a way that each channel corresponds to a velocity increment. The calibration is chiefly made by a hyperfine spectrum (α-Fe) where the line positions are known accurately. Commercial Mössbauer spectrometer systems are available.

Velocity modulation is the common technique. However, with extremely sharp lines (Ta^{181}) it is conceivable that the spectrum is traced by a relativistic effect in changing the gravitational potential of source and absorber by rotation instead of a Doppler motion.

Frequency-modulation sidebands can be produced by acoustic [1.71, 72] and radio-frequency excitations [1.73–75].

1.8.4. γ-Ray Detectors

Three types of detectors are available for the registration of γ-rays: scintillation detectors, proportional counters, and lithium-drifted germanium and silicon detectors. One might also add the photographic

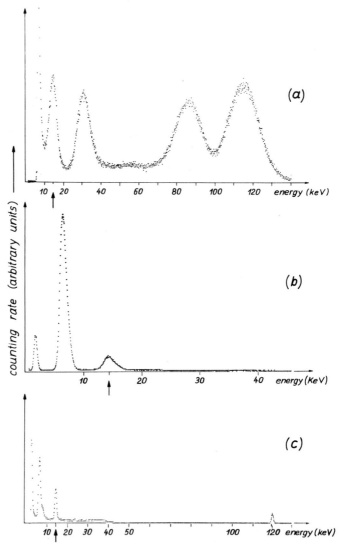

Fig. 1.13a-c. Pulse height spectra of γ-ray detectors: a) Proportional counter, b) NaI (Tl) scintillation counter, c) Solid state Si (Li) detector. Note the different energy scale. Arrows indicate 14.4 keV γ-rays.

emulsion which has been used in special cases. Pulse-height spectra from a Co^{57} source are shown in Fig. 1.13. From the figure the difference in resolution is clearly seen. However, the poor resolution of a detector is usually counterbalanced by the high count rate which can be achieved. γ-ray detectors should be carefully selected before an experiment is undertaken. Efficiency, resolution, count rate, and other technical data should be considered and, of course, the difference in price.

1.8.5. Scattering Technique

Most Mössbauer spectra are obtained in the transmission mode in which the γ-rays from a source are counted after passing through an absorber. However, another mode of operation exists: the scattering technique [1.76–78]. In the scattering technique the re-emission of radiation in the absorber is detected. Thus, the principle might be stated as an emission from an excited nuclear state, produced by a foregoing Mössbauer resonance. This is represented by the broken bold arrow in Fig. 1.11.

The scattering technique offers two advantages:

1) Different competing radiations accompanying the nuclear transition with their characteristic penetration depth can be used: γ-rays, X-rays, and conversion electrons.

2) Material of nearly any shape can be investigated in the original condition "in situ". The fabrication of thin foils or powder needed in the conventional transmission mode is tedious and often impractical because the properties one is interested in are significantly changed by the preparation. This difficulty is circumvented by the scattering technique and one might predict that it will become more important in the future as a non-destructive tool of investigation, particularly in physical metallurgy.

The Mössbauer back-scattering spectra shown in Fig. 1.14 of a pure α-Fe foil exposed to air at 800° C for one minute should serve as an example [1.79]. Most noticeable are the peaks instead of the dips observed with the transmission technique. The upper spectrum was obtained by detecting the $\approx 7\,keV$ electrons with an electron counter. The spectrum can be analyzed in terms of a superposition of a main contribution α-Fe_2O_3 (hematite), and minor contribution Fe_3O_4 (magnetite). When the $14.4\,keV$ γ-rays emitted from the same foil are measured only one line is observed which is characteristic of the FeO (wustite) lower spectrum. The differences in observation are due to the different path length of electrons and γ-rays in these materials. In the first case, electrons from a surface layer of a few hundred Å leaving the

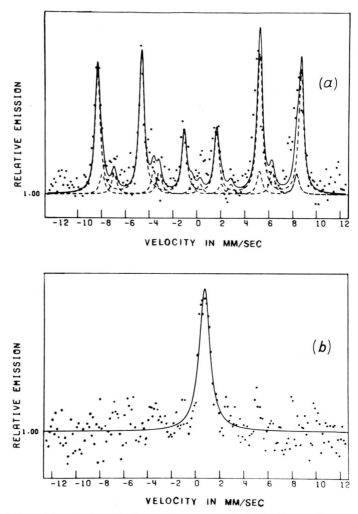

Fig. 1.14a and b. Mössbauer back-scattering spectra obtained with a $Co^{57} - Cu$ source at room temperature and an iron sheet after corrosion for one minute in air at 800 °C. a) Scattered electron spectrum, b) scattered 14.4 keV γ-ray spectrum

sample were counted while in the second case the 14.4 keV γ-rays penetrating layers of about 100000 Å (10 µm) were recorded. Thus, the Mössbauer spectrum measured with electrons is representative of less than 1 % of the layer which characterizes the γ-ray spectrum.

Sophisticated applications are concerned with thermal diffuse scattering of resonance γ-rays at the Bragg reflection [1.80], interference between electronic and nuclear resonance scattering to solve the phase problem in protein structures [1.81] and others.

1.8.6. Polarized Recoil-Free γ-Rays

Polarization effects in the hyperfine interaction and the convenient utilization of polarized recoil-free γ-rays were recognized [1.82–86], soon after the discovery of the resonance effect in Fe^{57}. If polarized recoil-free γ-rays are brought into resonance the matching of the polarization components in source and absorber nuclear transitions is required in addition to the usual appropriate Doppler motion. For instance, circularly polarized γ-rays from a source can only be resonantly absorbed if a transition with the same helicity is offered (conservation of angular momentum). By observing the helicity of circularly polarized γ-ray, the sign of the magnetic hyperfine field can be determined [1.87].

Linearly polarized γ-rays [1.88–90] are of particular interest. Three methods producing 14.4 keV linearly polarized γ-rays are briefly described:

1) The six lines emitted from a magnetized Co^{57}-α-Fe source are linearly polarized if observed perpendicular to the direction of the magnetic field $H(\theta_m = 90°)$. The plane of polarization of the γ-rays from transitions corresponding to $\Delta m = \pm 1$ is perpendicular to the plane of polarization of the γ-rays from the transition corresponding to $\Delta m = 0$.

If the γ-rays from such a Co^{57}-α-Fe source are offered to an absorber also consisting of α-Fe magnetized perpendicular to the γ-ray propagation direction, the resonance condition depends on the polarization of the corresponding transitions. This is clearly seen in Fig. 1.15, where the magnetic vectors of source, H_S, and absorber, H_A, were parallel or antiparallel ($H_S \| H_A$; Case a) and perpendicular ($H_S \perp H_A$; Case b) to each other. The location and the expected relative line intensities in the thin source-absorber approximation are indicated by the stick diagram. For the individual lines the resonant absorption condition changes from opaque to transparent or vice versa by rotating the source or absorber by 90° about the propagation direction of the γ-ray.

2) Linearly polarized γ-rays are also produced from a paramagnetic single-crystalline source exhibiting a quadrupole split spectrum. If the V_{zz} principal axis of the EFG is perpendicular to the direction of observation the γ-rays corresponding to the $m = \pm 3/2$ transition are totally linearly polarized and the γ-rays corresponding to the $m = \pm 1/2$

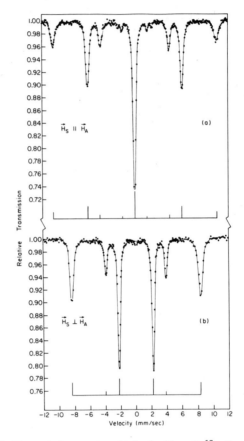

Fig. 1.15a and b. Transmission spectra obtained with a Co^{57}-α-Fe source and an α-Fe absorber both at room temperature and magnetized perpendicular to the γ-ray propagation direction. a) The magnetic fields in source and absorber were parallel or antiparallel ($H_S \parallel H_A$), and b) the magnetic fields in source and absorber were perpendicular to each other ($H_S \perp H_A$)

transition partly linearly polarized. The asymmetry parameter should be zero to ensure that the nuclear wave functions are pure $|m\rangle$ states.

3) The selective absorption of one plane polarized component of γ-radiation leads to linearly polarized γ-rays (dichroism). For instance, if a single-line γ-ray source is brought into resonance with one of the six lines of an α-Fe absorber magnetized perpendicular to the γ-ray propagation direction, the transmitted γ-rays are partially plane polarized. The methods can be refined by an appropriate filter technique [1.91].

1.8.7. Mössbauer Polarimetry

The applications of linearly polarized γ-rays are similar in nature to optical polarimetry. In the Mössbauer polarimeter the source and the absorber take the place of the polarizer and analyzer, respectively, as shown in Fig. 1.16. Such a polarimeter can be automatized by rotating the source continously with a synchronmotor [1.92]. The counts arriving at the detector are accumulated in a multichannel analyzer. In this case each channel corresponds to a defined angle between source-(polarizer) and absorber-(analyzer) polarization directions. The count rate $R(\omega)$ depends on the angle ω between the planes of polarization (H_S and H_A) and has a sinusoidal form in analogy to optics (Malus curve)

$$R(\omega) = R_0 - R_1 \cos(2\omega - 2\varrho),\tag{1.40}$$

where R_1 denotes the amplitude of the Malus curve, R_0 contains the background, non-resonant and non-rotating circularly polarized component, and ϱ is the birefringence rotation caused by a transmitter (see below).

The Malus curve exhibited in Fig. 1.17 is obtained from a rotating Co^{57}-α-Fe source and an α-Fe absorber both magnetized perpendicular to the propagation direction of the γ-radiation. No Doppler motion was applied to the source and the absorber.

1) Experiments without Transmitter. Linearly polarized γ-rays were used to measure the sign of the quadrupole constant [1.93], the orientation of the spin in magnetic materials [1.94], and the principal axes of the EFG [1.95]. Essentially, the technique consists of an analysis of the relative line intensities obtained from a single crystal cut in an arbitrary direction. From the maximum absorption or transmission in the $R(\omega)$ curve of a particular resonance transitions the orientations of principal axes and spins can be determined. (For further details see Chapter 3 by GRANT.)

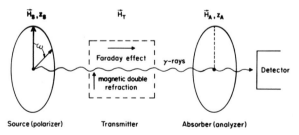

Fig. 1.16. Schematic representation of a Mössbauer polarimeter

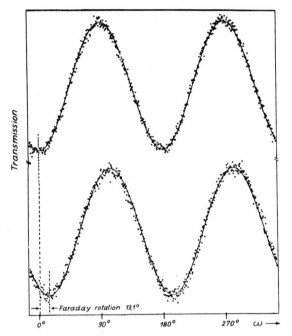

Fig. 1.17. Relative transmission of linearly polarized γ-radiation in a Mössbauer polarimeter as a function of rotating angle between source (polarizer) and absorber (analyzer). The transmission represents a Malus curve. With a transmitter of FeV the lower curve with a Faraday rotation of 13.1° was obtained [1.99]

2) Experiments with Transmitter. In this mode of operation one is interested in the dispersion associated with Mössbauer resonance absorption. In analogy to magneto-optics the following effects have been investigated: the Mössbauer-Faraday effect in a longitudinal magnetic field and the occurrence of magnetic double refraction in a transverse magnetic field. The experimental arrangements shown in Fig. 1.16 with the appropriate magnetic field are, in principle, the same as the one known in optical polarimetry, while the wavelength of the electro-magnetic radiation differ by nearly four orders of magnitude.

The Faraday effect was the great success of Faraday's long struggle to demonstrate an interaction of electric and magnetic forces on light. In 1839 Faraday wrote: "I have at last succeeded in magnetizing and electrifying a ray of light, and in illuminating a magnetic line of force" [1.96]. The rotation of the plane of linearly polarized light (γ-radiation) when transmitted through a medium with a magnetic field applied parallel or antiparallel to the propagation direction of the light (γ-radiation) beam is called the (Mössbauer)-Faraday effect [1.88, 97, 98]. The rotation "δ_F" observed by the Mössbauer-Faraday effect can be derived from classical theory of electromagnetic radiation and can be expressed approximately by

$$\delta_F \approx \frac{1}{4} t_T \sum_j \frac{(a_{1j}^2 - a_{2j}^2)(x_j - x_S)}{(x_j - x_S)^2 + 1}, \tag{1.41}$$

where t_T is the effective Mössbauer transmitter thickness (1.39), and x_S the position of the source line relative to the position of the transmitter resonance lines x_j. The sum takes all possible transmitter resonance lines into account. The quantities a_{1j}^2 and a_{2j}^2 give the relative contributions of the different lines to each polarization. These factors are products of the squares of the corresponding Clebsch-Gordan co-efficients and the angular dependence factors for the individual nuclear transitions.

The Mössbauer-Faraday effect is observed by the shift δ_F in the Malus curve, i.e. the maximum (or minimum) relative transmission as a function of the rotating angle ω of the polarimeter indicates the rotation of the plane of polarization by inserting the transmitter (Fig. 1.17) [1.99]. The Mössbauer-Faraday effect depends on the nuclear spin orientation while the optical Faraday effect is governed by the atomic spin (electrons). Therefore, the sign of the magnetic hyperfine interaction can be determined by observing the direction of rotation of linearly polarized γ-radiation (direction of shift in the Malus curve) in conjunction with the orientation of the transmitter external magnetic field [1.100]. For Fe^{57} in most cases the hyperfine interaction is negative (atomic and nuclear spin are antiparallel).

Recently the general theory of Mössbauer γ-ray optics has been worked out [1.101]. The observation of large dispersion in the 6.2 keV γ-ray transition of Ta^{181} could be explained as a interference of photo-electric and nuclear resonance absorption [1.102, 103]. One might predict that other optical phenomena like "Mössbauer optical rotation" will be demonstrated and applied in future investigations.

1.8.8. Measurements of Motions

In Mössbauer spectroscopy the positions of the resonance line are normally derived accurately from the known Doppler velocity. One can also reverse the objective and derive from the Mössbauer spectrum—split or unsplit—the corresponding velocities or accelerations in source or absorber. This procedure is suitable for measuring small motion and vibrational amplitudes in the Å range at audio frequencies. It was suggested that this technique should be used "*in vivo*" as a diagnostic tool, e.g. in checking the ear drum mechanism [1.104]. Naturally, the first experiment was performed on a guinea pig.

Another curious experiment was made on the collective motion of ants supplying the Doppler velocity as a function of temperature [1.105]. The analysis of the spectra allowed the determination of the mean velocity component in one direction of all the participating ants.

In the following chapters typical applications of Mössbauer spectroscopy are selected and discussed in greater details.

Acknowledgements

I am indebted to the Japanese Society for the Promotion of Sciences and to my friend Prof. Francis Eiichi Fujita for sponsoring my sabbatical at the University of Osaka. Furthermore, I wish to acknowledge valuable discussions with colleagues in Japan, at the "Universität des Saarlandes", and the Science Center of Rockwell International at Thousand Oaks, California. The preparation of various manuscripts in this book by Ms. R. Bubel is gratefully acknowledged.

References

1.1.   R. L. Mössbauer: Z. Physik **151**, 124 (1958).
1.2.   R. L. Mössbauer: Naturwissenschaften **45**, 538 (1958).
1.3.   R. L. Mössbauer: *Les Prix Nobel en 1961* (Nobel Foundation, Stockholm 1962), p. 136; and Science **137**, 731 (1962).
1.4.   H. Frauenfelder: *The Mössbauer Effect* (Benjamin, New York, 1962).
1.5.   A. J. F. Boyle, H. E. Hall: Rept. Progr. Phys. **25**, 441 (1962).
1.6.   A. Abragam: *L'Effet Mössbauer* (Gordon & Breach, New York, 1964).
1.7.   G. K. Wertheim: *Mössbauer Effect, Principles, and Applications* (Academic Press, New York, 1964).
1.8.   H. Wegener: *Der Mössbauer-Effect und seine Anwendungen in Physik und Chemie* (Bibliographisches Institut AG, Mannheim, 1965).
1.9.   I. J. Gruverman (Ed.): *Mössbauer Effect Methodology*, Vols. 1–9 (Plenum Press, New York, 1965–1974).
1.10.   "Applications of the Mössbauer Effect" (Intern. Atom Energy Agency, Techn. Repts., Vienna, 1966 and 1972).
1.11.   L. May (Ed.): *An Introduction to Mössbauer Spectroscopy* (Plenum Press, New York, 1971).
1.12.   V. I. Goldanskii, R. H. Herber, eds.: *Chemical Applications of Mössbauer Spectroscopy* (Academic Press, New York, 1968).
1.13.   E. Matthias, D. A. Shirley (Eds.): *Hyperfine Structure and Nuclear Radiation* (North-Holland Publishing Co., Amsterdam, 1968).

1.14.   C. JANOT: *L'Effet Mössbauer et ses Applications a la Physique du Solid et a la Metallurgie Physique* (Masson, Paris, 1972).

1.15.   N. N. GREENWOOD, T. C. GIBB: *Mössbauer Spectroscopy* (Chapman & Hall, London, 1971).

1.16.   H. J. LIPKIN: *Quantum Mechanics* (North-Holland Publishing Co., Amsterdam-London, 1973).

1.17.   A. H. MUIR, JR., K. J. ANDO, H. M. COOGAN: *Mössbauer Effect Data Index*, 1958–1965 (Interscience, New York, 1966); J. G. STEVENS, V. E. STEVENS: *Mössbauer Effect Data Index*, 1969–1973 (Adam Hilger, London).

1.18.   P. G. DEBRUNNER, H. FRAUENFELDER: In *An Introduction to Mössbauer Spectroscopy*, ed. by L. MAY (Plenum Press, New York, 1971).

1.19.   S. MARGULIES, J. R. EHRMAN: Nucl. Instr. Methods **12**, 131 (1961).

1.20.   K. S. SINGWI, A. SJOLANDER: Phys. Rev. **120**, 1093 (1960).

1.21.   R. C. KNAUER, J. G. MULLEN: Phys. Rev. **174**, 711 (1968).

1.22.   S. J. LEWIS, P. A. FLINN: Phil. Mag. **26**, 977 (1972).

1.23.   P. P. CRAIG, N. SUTIN: Phys. Rev. Letters **11**, 460 (1963).

1.24.   F. J. LYNCH, R. E. HOLLAND, M. HAMERMESH: Phys. Rev. **120**, 513 (1960).

1.25.   U. GONSER, H. WIEDERSICH: J. Phys. Soc. Japan **18**, Suppl. II, 47 (1963).

1.26.   D. C. KISTNER, A. W. SUNYAR: Phys. Rev. Letters **4**, 412 (1960).

1.27.   L. R. WALKER, G. K. WERTHEIM, V. JACCARINO: Phys. Rev. Letters **6**, 98 (1961).

1.28.   D. A. SHIRLEY: Rev. Mod. Phys. **36**, 339 (1964).

1.29.   R. L. MÖSSBAUER, M. J. CLAUSER: In *Hyperfine Interactions*, ed. by A. J. FREEMAN and R. B. FRANKEL (Academic Press, New York-London, 1967), p. 497.

1.30.   F. E. WAGNER, G. WORTMANN, G. M. KALVIUS: Phys. Letters **42** A, 483 (1973).

1.31.   P. H. BARRETT, R. W. GRANT, M. KAPLAN, D. A. KELLER, D. A. SHIRLEY: J. Chem. Phys. **39**, 1035 (1963).

1.32.   J. LEES, P. A. FLINN: Phys. Letters **19**, 186 (1965).

1.33.   R. L. COHEN, G. M. KALVIUS: Nucl. Instr. Methods **86**, 209 (1970).

1.34.   P. RÜEGSEGGER, W. KÜNDIG: Helv. Phys. Acta **46**, 165 (1973).

1.35.   S. S. HANNA, J. HEBERLE, G. J. PERLOW, R. S. PRESTON, D. J. VINCENT: Phys. Rev. Letters **4**, 513 (1960).

1.36.   K. ONO, A. ITO: J. Phys. Soc. Japan **19**, 899 (1964).

1.37.   R. L. COLLINS: J. Chem. Phys. **42**, 1072 (1965).

1.38.   J. R. GABRIEL, S. L. RUBY: Nucl. Instr. Methods **36**, 23 (1965).

1.39.   W. KÜNDIG: Nucl. Instr. Methods **48**, 219 (1967).

1.40.   V. I. GOLDANSKII, E. F. MAKAROV, V. V. KHRAPOV: Phys. Letters **3**, 334 (1963).

1.41.   S. V. KARYAGIN: Dokl. Akad. Nauk. SSSR **148**, 1102 (1963).

1.42.   P. A. FLINN, S. L. RUBY, W. L. KEHL: Science **143**, 1434 (1964).

1.43.   H.-D. PFANNES, U. GONSER: Appl. Phys. **1**, 93 (1973).

1.44.   U. GONSER, H.-D. PFANNES: In "Proc. Internat. Conf. Applications of the Mössbauer Effect", Bendor, France (1974) J. Physique C-6, 113 (1974).

1.45.   T. NAKAMURA, T. SHINJO, Y. ENDOH, N. YAMAMOTO, M. SHIGA, Y. NAKAMURA: Phys. Letters **12**, 178 (1964).

1.46.   W. KÜNDIG, H. BÖMMEL, G. CONSTABARIS, R. H. LINDQUIST: Phys. Rev. **142**, 327 (1966).

1.47.   U. GONSER, H. WIEDERSICH, R. W. GRANT: J. Appl. Phys. **39**, 1004 (1968).

1.48.   F. VAN DER WOUDE, A. J. DEKKER: Phys. Stat. Sol. **9**, 775 (1965).

1.49.   H. WEGENER: Z. Physik **186**, 498 (1965).

1.50.   M. BLUME, J. A. TJON: Phys. Rev. **165**, 446 (1968).

1.51.   H. H. WICKMAN, G. K. WERTHEIM: In *Chemical Applications of Mössbauer Spectroscopy*, ed. by V. I. GOLDANSKII and R. H. HERBER (Academic Press, New York, 1968).

1.52. H. Gabriel, J. Bosse, K. Rander: Phys. Stat. Sol. **27**, 301 (1968).
1.53. H. Schwegler: Phys. Stat. Sol. **41**, 353 (1970).
1.54. J. G. Dash, R. D. Taylor, P. P. Craig, D. E. Nagle, D. R. F. Cochran, W. E. Keller: Phys. Rev. Letters **5**, 152 (1960).
1.55. G. J. Ehnholm, T. E. Katila, O. V. Lounasmaa, P. Reivari: Phys. Letters **25** A, 758 (1967).
1.56. R. V. Pound, G. A. Rebka, Jr.: Phys. Rev. Letters **4**, 274 (1960).
1.57. B. D. Josephson: Phys. Rev. Letters **4**, 341 (1960).
1.58. R. V. Pound, G. A. Rebka, Jr.: Phys. Rev. Letters **4**, 337 (1960).
1.59. R. V. Pound, J. L. Snider: Phys. Rev. **140**, B 788 (1965).
1.60. H. J. Hay, J. P. Schiffer, T. E. Cranshaw, P. A. Egelstaff: Phys. Rev. Letters **4**, 165 (1960).
1.61. Y. K. Lee, P. W. Keaton, Jr., E. T. Ritter, J. C. Walker: Phys. Rev. Letters **14**, 957 (1965).
1.62. D. Seyboth, F. E. Obenshain, G. Czjzek: Phys. Rev. Letters **14**, 954 (1965).
1.63. S. L. Ruby, R. E. Holland: Phys. Rev. Letters **14**, 591 (1965).
1.64. D. W. Hafemeister, E. B. Shera: Phys. Rev. Letters **14**, 593 (1965).
1.65. G. Czjzek, J. L. C. Ford, J. C. Love, F. E. Obenshain, H. Wegener: Phys. Rev. Letters **18**, 529 (1967).
1.66. G. D. Sprouse, G. M. Kalvius, S. S. Hanna: Phys. Rev. Letters **18**, 1041 (1967).
1.67. G. K. Wertheim: In *The Electronic Structure of Point Defects*, ed. by S. Amelinckx, R. Gevers, J. Ninoul (North-Holland Publishing Co., Amsterdam-London, 1971).
1.68. G. K. Shenoy, J. M. Friedt, H. Maletta, S. L. Ruby: In *Mössbauer Effect Methodology*, Vol. 9, ed. by I. J. Gruverman (Plenum Press, New York, 1974).
1.69. A. H. Muir, Jr.: In *Mössbauer Effect Methodology*, Vol. 4, ed. by I. J. Gruverman (Plenum-Press, New York, 1968).
1.70. G. M. Kalvius, E. Kankeleit: *Mössbauer Spectroscopy and its Applications, Panel Proc. Series* (IAEC, Vienna, 1972).
1.71. S. L. Ruby, D. I. Bolef: Phys. Rev. Letters **5**, 5 (1960).
1.72. T. E. Cranshaw, P. Reivari: Proc. Phys. Soc. (London) **90**, 1059 (1967).
1.73. E. Matthias: In *Hyperfine Structure and Nuclear Radiation*, ed. by E. Matthias, D. A. Shirley (North-Holland Publishing Co., Amsterdam, 1968), p. 815.
1.74. G. Asti, G. Albanese, C. Bucci: Phys. Rev. **184**, 260 (1969).
1.75. L. Pfeiffer, N. D. Heiman, J. C. Walker: Phys. Rev. B **6**, 74 (1972).
1.76. J. H. Terrell, J. J. Spijkerman: Appl. Phys. Letters **13**, 11 (1968).
1.77. K. R. Swanson, J. J. Spijkerman: J. Appl. Phys. **41**, 3155 (1970).
1.78. R. A. Krakowski, R. B. Miller: Nucl. Instr. Methods **100**, 93 (1972).
1.79. W. Keune, U. Gonser, H. Vollmar: In *Handbuch der zerstörungsfreien Materialprüfung*, Vol. 10, ed. by E. H. W. Müller (Oldenbourg-Verlag, München-Wien, 1974).
1.80. G. Albanese, C. Ghezzi, A. Merlini, S. Pace: Phys. Rev. B **5**, 1746 (1972).
1.81. F. Parak, R. L. Mössbauer, W. Hoppe: Ber. Bunsenges. phys. Chemie **74**, 1207 (1970).
1.82. S. S. Hanna, J. Heberle, C. Littlejohn, G. J. Perlow, R. S. Preston, D. H. Vincent: Phys. Rev. Letters **4**, 177 (1960).
1.83. G. J. Perlow, S. S. Hanna, M. Hamermesh, C. Littlejohn, D. H. Vincent, R. S. Preston, J. Heberle: Rev. Letters **4**, 74 (1960).
1.84. H. Wegener, F. E. Obenshain: Z. Physik **163**, 17 (1961).
1.85. H. Frauenfelder, D. E. Nagle, R. D. Taylor, D. R. F. Cochran, W. M. Visscher: Phys. Rev. **126**, 1065 (1962).
1.86. A. Kastler: Compt. Rend. **255**, 3397 (1962).
1.87. N. Blum, L. Grodzins: Phys. Rev. **136**, A 133 (1964).

1.88. P. IMBERT: J. Physique **27**, 429 (1966).
1.89. U. GONSER: In *Hyperfine Structure and Nuclear Radiation*, ed. by E. MATTHIAS and D. A. SHIRLEY (North-Holland Publishing Co., Amsterdam, 1968), p. 343.
1.90. J. P. STAMPEL, P. A. FLINN: In *Mössbauer Effect Methodology*, Vol. 6, ed. by I. J. GRUVERMAN (Plenum Press, New York, 1971).
1.91. R. M. HOUSLEY: Nucl. Instr. Methods **62**, 321 (1968).
1.92. H.-D. PFANNES, U. GONSER: Nucl. Instr. Methods **114**, 297 (1974).
1.93. C. E. JOHNSON, W. MARSHALL, G. J. PERLOW: Phys. Rev. **126**, 1503 (1962).
1.94. U. GONSER, R. W. GRANT, H. WIEDERSICH, S. GELLER: Appl. Phys. Letters **9**, 18 (1966).
1.95. U. GONSER, R. W. GRANT: Phys. Stat. Sol. **21**, 331 (1967).
1.96. M. FARADAY: Phil. Trans. Roy. Soc. (London) **1846**, 1. — Poggendorfs Ann. **68**, 105 (1846); Phil. Mag. **29**, 153 (1846).
1.97. M. BLUME, O. C. KISTNER: Phys. Rev. **171**, 417 (1968).
1.98. R. M. HOUSLEY, U. GONSER: Phys. Rev. **171**, 480 (1968).
1.99. H.-D. PFANNES: Ph. D. dissertation, Universität des Saarlandes, Saarbrücken, Fed. Rep. Germany, 1973.
1.100. U. GONSER, R. M. HOUSLEY: Phys. Letters **26 A**, 157 (1968).
1.101. J. P. HANNON, N. J. CARRON, G. T. TRAMMELL: Phys. Rev. B **9**, 2791 and 2810 (1974).
1.102. C. SAUER, E. MATTHIAS, R. L. MÖSSBAUER: Phys. Rev. Letters **21**, 961 (1968).
1.103. G. KAINDL, D. SALOMON: Phys. Letters **32 B**, 364 (1970).
1.104. P. GILAD, S. SHTRIKMAN, P. HILLMAN, M. RUBENSTEIN, A. EVIATAR: J. Acoust. Soc. Am. **41**, 1232 (1967).
1.105. T. BONCHEV, I. VASSILEV, T. SAPUNDZHIEV, M. EVTIMOV: Nature **217**, 96 (1968).

2. Mössbauer Spectroscopy in Chemistry

P. GÜTLICH

With 12 Figures

KISTNER and SUNYAR's observation of a "chemical shift" in the ^{57}Fe Mössbauer spectrum of α-Fe_2O_3 in 1960 [2.1] initiated an overwhelming activity in applying the Mössbauer effect to many kinds of chemical problems. The rapidly growing number of communications on the successful application of the new nuclear resonance technique has witnessed its power and versatility in various areas of chemistry. Admittedly, by far the largest portion of Mössbauer research has been carried out in iron and tin chemistry; but fruitful work has also been on compounds of more than a dozen other Mössbauer active elements (Ni, Kr, Ru, Sb, Te, I, Xe, W, Ir, Au, Np, and some of the rare earth elements), as has been covered in a good number of review articles [2.1–12] and books, the more recent ones are given in [2.13–16].

It is the primary goal of this chapter to assist the inexperienced scientist to enter the field and learn first of all how to read a Mössbauer spectrum. We shall try to do this by first giving a short, hopefully comprehensive, introduction to the physics of the hyperfine interactions and the relevant Mössbauer parameters. Thereafter the kind of chemically interesting information being reflected by isomer shifts and quadrupole splittings, particularly with respect to bonding and structural properties, will be highlighted by discussing a few representative examples. In no instance an attempt will be made for complete coverage.

It is hoped that the first three sections will furnish the reader with the basic knowledge and a feeling for the kind of problems which may be clarified by use of the Mössbauer effect technique. A short survey of special applications in chemistry concludes the chapter.

2.1. Hyperfine Interactions and Mössbauer Parameters

A nucleus may interact with electric and magnetic fields in the region of the nucleus. The appropriate Hamiltonian contains a number of terms, which represent different kinds of interactions depending on the multipolarity of both the nuclear moments and the interacting fields:

$$\mathcal{H} = \mathcal{H}(e0) + \mathcal{H}(m1) + \mathcal{H}(e2) + \cdots. \tag{2.1}$$

The first term stands for the Coulombic interaction between the nucleus and electrons at the nuclear site. This so-called monopole interaction affects the nuclear energy levels without altering their degeneracies. The second term $\mathcal{H}(m1)$ refers to the coupling between the nuclear magnetic dipole moment and an effective magnetic field at the nucleus. The third term $\mathcal{H}(e2)$ expresses electric quadrupole interactions. $\mathcal{H}(m1)$ and $\mathcal{H}(e2)$ split the nuclear energy level into sublevels without shifting the center of gravity of the multiplet. In Mössbauer spectroscopy, only these three kinds of interactions have to be considered. Interactions of higher order ($m3$, $e4$, etc.) can be neglected, because their energies are several orders of magnitude smaller than $e0$, $m1$, and $e2$ interactions, respectively. Electric dipole interaction, represented by $\mathcal{H}(e1)$ in (2.1), is parity-forbidden.

A Mössbauer spectrum, in general, reflects the nature and the strengths of the hyperfine interactions between the Mössbauer nucleus and the surrounding fields. The $e0$ interactions affect the position of the resonance lines on the velocity (energy) scale giving rise to the so-called isomer shift δ.

The $m1$ and $e2$ interactions, respectively, together with the multipolarity of the γ-transition are responsible for the number of components and the intensities of a resonance multiplet. As we shall see in the following three subsections, the energy for each of the three hyperfine interactions is, to a first approximation, proportional to a product containing a factor governed by nuclear properties, and a factor that depends solely on the electronic environment of the nucleus. It is the second factor which is of major interest to a chemist studying substances containing a particular Mössbauer nuclide (e.g., ^{57}Fe). In what follows, we shall see how the chemical environment of a Mössbauer nuclide influences the fields at the nucleus and consequently affects the nuclear energy levels. Our discussion will be concentrated on the electric monopole and electric quadrupole interactions, because the isomer shift and the quadrupole splitting are the two Mössbauer parameters which yield the most valuable chemical information. The magnetic hyperfine interaction, which may be most informative in the study of metals, alloys and nonstoichiometric compounds, is treated in detail in the Chapters 3 and 6 by Grant and Fujita and will only be sketched briefly here. With respect to other Mössbauer parameters like line width, line shape, and the magnitude of the resonance effect the reader is referred to Chapter 1 by Gonser.

2.1.1. Electric Monopole Interaction; Isomer Shift

The isomer shift (other names which are sometimes used in the literature "chemical isomer shift" and "center shift") arises from the fact that an atomic nucleus occupies a finite volume, and s-electrons have the ability of penetrating the nucleus and spending a fraction of their time inside the nuclear region. (p-, d-, and f-electrons do not have this ability; only if relativistic effects are considered, $p_{1/2}$-electrons can spend a very small fraction of their time inside the nucleus.) The nuclear charge interacts electrostatically with the s-electron charge cloud inside the nuclear dimensions. As a result the level of the nuclear energy will be shifted by the very small amount δE (Fig. 2.1).

The energy shift δE can be computed classically. WERTHEIM et al. [2.17] have given a somewhat restricted analysis assuming a) the nucleus to be a uniformly charged sphere with radius R, and b) the electron cloud to be uniformly distributed over the nuclear range. δE then represents the energy difference between the Coulombic (electrostatic) interaction of a (hypothetical) point nucleus and one of actual

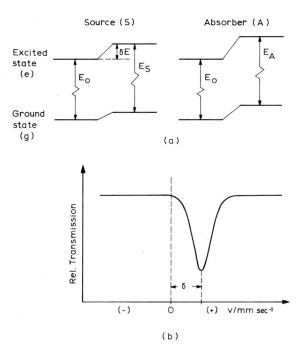

Fig. 2.1a and b. Origin of isomer shift. (a) Electric monopole interaction shifts nuclear energy levels without lifting the degeneracy, (b) resultant Mössbauer spectrum (schematic)

radius R, both possessing the same charge Ze,

$$\delta E = \int_0^\infty \varrho_{el}(V_f - V_p)\, 4\pi r^2\, dr, \tag{2.2}$$

where

$$V_p(r) = Ze/r \quad 0 \leq r \leq \infty \tag{2.3}$$

is the electrostatic potential for a point-charge nucleus at a distance r, and

$$V_f(r) = (Ze/R)\,[3/2 - (r^2/2R^2)] \quad \text{for} \quad r \leq R$$
$$V_f(r) = Ze/r \quad \text{for} \quad r \geq R \tag{2.4}$$

the electrostatic potential of a nucleus of finite size. ϱ_{el} is the electron density at the nucleus, which is expressed in terms of the electron wave function Ψ by $-e|\Psi(0)|^2$. Substituting (2.3) and (2.4) into (2.2) and evaluating the integral, one obtains

$$\delta E = (2\pi/5)\, Ze^2 R^2 |\Psi(0)|^2. \tag{2.5}$$

As the nuclear volume will, in general, be different in each state of excitation, the electrostatic shift δE will be different in each nuclear state. Thus, in a transition of a nucleus between its ground state and an excited state the energy change of a gamma ray due to this "volume effect" will be (relative to a point-charge nucleus)

$$\Delta E = (\delta E)_e - (\delta E)_g = (2\pi/5)\, Ze^2 |\Psi(0)|^2\, (R_e^2 - R_g^2). \tag{2.6}$$

In a Mössbauer experiment, however, where an appropriate Doppler velocity is applied to either the source (S) or the absorber (A) in order to bring the emitted gamma ray into coincidence with the absorption energy in an absorber, one actually observes the difference of the electrostatic shift (2.6) in a source and an absorber. If the absorber material is chemically and/or physically different from the source material, the electron density at the nucleus in the source and the absorber, respectively, will have different values. From (2.6) the difference in the electrostatic shift between source and absorber is then

$$\delta = \Delta E_A - \Delta E_S = (E_A - E_0) - (E_S - E_0) = E_A - E_S$$
$$= (2\pi/5)\, Ze^2 (R_e^2 - R_g^2)\, [|\Psi(0)|_A^2 - |\Psi(0)|_S^2]. \tag{2.7}$$

This expression is more frequently written in the form

$$\delta = (4\pi/5)\, Z e^2\, R^2 (\delta R/R)\, [|\Psi(0)|^2_A - |\Psi(0)|^2_S] \tag{2.8}$$

where $\delta R = R_e - R_g$ is the change in the nuclear radius in going from the excited state to the ground state.

Equations (2.7) and (2.8) are the fundamental expressions for the isomer shift δ in nonrelativistic form. The corresponding resonant Doppler velocity in a Mössbauer experiment is

$$v = (4\pi c/5 E_\gamma)\, Z e^2\, R^2 (\delta R/R)\, [|\Psi(0)|^2_A - |\Psi(0)|^2_S] \tag{2.9}$$

and can readily be computed from a Mössbauer spectrum as the distance of the resonance line (or centroid of a resonance multiplet) from zero Doppler velocity (Fig. 2.1).

In heavy elements the wave function Ψ is subject to considerable modification, particularly near the nucleus, by relativistic effects. Therefore, the electron density at the nucleus will be modified as well and the above equations for the isomer shift require a relativistic correction. In a somewhat restricted approach using Dirac wave functions and first-order perturbation theory (references are given in [2.18]), it has been shown that this correction simply consists of a dimensionless factor $S(Z)$, which is introduced into the above expressions for δ,

$$\delta = (4\pi/5)\, Z e^2\, S(Z)\, R^2 (\delta R/R)\, [|\Psi(0)|^2_A - |\Psi(0)|^2_S] . \tag{2.10}$$

Values of the "relativity factor" $S(Z)$ for $Z = 1$ to 96 are tabulated in [2.18]. For example, $S(Z) = 1.32$ for iron ($Z = 26$), 2.48 for tin ($Z = 50$), 19.4 for Np ($Z = 93$).

In Mössbauer effect studies, where one compares compounds of a given Mössbauer nuclide, the problem of relativistic corrections does not arise, since the relativity factor $S(Z)$ is constant for all compounds of a given Mössbauer nuclide. Furthermore, if one uses a standard source and looks at various absorbers of a given Mössbauer nuclide, $|\Psi(0)|^2_S = C$ is constant and the isomer shift δ will be a linear function of the charge density $|\Psi(0)|^2_A$ in the absorber,

$$\delta = \mathrm{const}(\delta R/R)\, [|\Psi(0)|^2_A - C] . \tag{2.11}$$

The ratio $\delta R/R$ is known, but not to any great accuracy, for many Mössbauer nuclides [2.19]. It can be positive or negative. For $\delta R/R$ positive, a positive isomer shift indicates an increase in the electron density at the nucleus in going from source to absorber whereas, when

$\delta R/R$ is negative, a positive isomer shift implies a decrease of the electron density at the nucleus.

The Mössbauer spectra of a particular compound measured with different sources under otherwise constant conditions (in ^{57}Fe spectroscopy, for example, ^{57}Co in metal foils of Pd, Pt, Cr, Cu, and stainless steel are commonly used sources), will show different isomer shifts, because $|\Psi(0)|_S^2$ changes with the chemical environment of the Mössbauer nuclide. Therefore, isomer shift data must always be reported with respect to a given standard material. This can be the Mössbauer source used in a particular experiment or any absorber material (in ^{57}Fe spectroscopy metallic iron and sodium nitroprusside dihydrate, $Na_2[Fe(CN)_5NO] \cdot 2H_2O$ (SNP), are commonly used as standard reference materials).

As mentioned earlier in this section, the electron density at the nucleus is mainly due to s-electrons. The total s-electron density at the nucleus of an atom in a compound can be assumed as being composed of two contributions, one from filled s-orbitals in inner electron shells and one from partially filled outer orbitals (valence orbitals), where the Mössbauer atom's own valence electrons as well as electrons from surrounding ligands are accommodated constituting the chemical bond. It is this valence electron contribution to the s-electron density at the nucleus, that is very sensitively affected by changes in the electronic structure of the valence shell as a consequence of chemical influences (e.g. change of charge state, change of bond properties by electron delocalization etc.). Such changes in the valence shell structure will inevitably influence the s-electron density at the nucleus, generally in two ways:

a) directly, by altering the s-electron population in the valence shell (increasing the s-electron density in the valence shell will directly increase $|\Psi(0)|^2$,

b) indirectly, via shielding s-electrons by electrons of p-, d-, and f-character (increasing the valence electron density of p-, d-, and f-character, respectively, will cause the s-electron cloud to expand and thus decrease $|\Psi(0)|^2$).

In Section 2.2 we shall see that the Mössbauer isomer shift can provide very useful information about the bond properties, valency, and oxidation state of a Mössbauer atom.

2.1.2. Electric Quadrupole Interaction; Quadrupole Splitting

Our discussion of the electric monopole interaction and isomer shift has assumed the nuclear charge distribution to be uniform and spherically symmetrical. In many nuclei, however, the nuclear charge distribution deviates more or less from spherical symmetry; the deviation may be different in each state of excitation. A measure of the deviation from spherical symmetry is given by the electric quadrupole moment eQ, which is a tensor quantity with elements

$$Q_{ij} = \int \varrho_n(r) \, x_i x_j \, dv \tag{2.12}$$

(ϱ_n: nuclear charge, x_i, x_j: cartesian coordinates of r). The sign of Q refers to the shape of the distorted nucleus: Q is negative for a flattened nucleus and positive for an elongated one. Nuclei with spin $I = 0, 1/2$ do not possess an observable quadrupole moment. Any nuclear state with $I > 1/2$ has a non-zero quadrupole moment ($Q \neq 0$) and can interact with an inhomogeneous electric field described by the electric field gradient (EFG) at the nucleus. This so-called electric quadrupole interaction may be expressed by the quadrupole Hamiltonian in the general form

$$\mathcal{H}(e2) = \hat{Q} \cdot (\hat{V}\hat{E}) . \tag{2.13}$$

$\hat{Q}$ denotes the operator of the nuclear electric quadrupole moment, and $(\hat{V}\hat{E})$ the EFG tensor operator. As Q is constant for a given Mössbauer nuclide in different compounds, changes in the quadrupole interaction energy observed under constant conditions can only arise from changes of the EFG. In order to understand the observed differences in quadrupole splitting in compounds of the same Mössbauer nuclide, it is necessary to know how the EFG is altered by chemical and physical influences. Because of the importance of the EFG in chemical applications of the Mössbauer effect we shall digress into a discussion of the essential concepts of the EFG and shall return to the quadrupole coupling later.

Electric Field Gradient (EFG)

A point charge q at a distance $r = (x^2 + y^2 + z^2)^{1/2}$ from the nucleus gives rise to a potential $V(r) = q/r$ at the nucleus. The electric field E at the nucleus is the negative gradient of the potential, $-\nabla V$, and the gradient of the electric field, finally, is given by

$$\text{EFG} = \nabla E = -\nabla\nabla V = - \begin{bmatrix} V_{xx} & V_{xy} & V_{xz} \\ V_{yx} & V_{yy} & V_{yz} \\ V_{zx} & V_{zy} & V_{zz} \end{bmatrix}, \tag{2.14}$$

where

$$V_{ij} = \frac{\partial^2 V}{\partial i\,\partial j} \ (i, j = x, y, z).$$

The EFG is a 3×3 second-rank tensor. Only five of the nine EFG components are independent parameters. Three of the off-diagonal elements are dependent because of the symmetric form of the EFG tensor, i.e. $V_{xy} = V_{yx}$, $V_{xz} = V_{zx}$, $V_{yz} = V_{zy}$. One diagonal element is dependent, because it can be expressed by the other two by Laplace's equation, which requires that the EFG be a traceless tensor,

$$V_{xx} + V_{yy} + V_{zz} = 0 . \tag{2.15}$$

It would still be rather laborious to work out the five independent EFG elements for a compound of interest. Fortunately, however, a unique axis system of the Mössbauer atom, called the "principal axes of the EFG tensor", can be defined such that the off-diagonal elements vanish and the diagonal elements are ordered as

$$|V_{zz}| \geq |V_{yy}| \geq |V_{xx}| . \tag{2.16}$$

With respect to the principal axes, the EFG tensor is described by only two independent parameters, usually chosen as $V_{zz} = eq$, and the asymmetry parameter η, defined by

$$\eta = (V_{xx} - V_{yy})/V_{zz} . \tag{2.17}$$

With the above ordering for the diagonal elements the asymmetry parameter η is restricted to $0 \leq \eta \leq 1$. For a fourfold or threefold axis passing through the Mössbauer nucleus, $V_{xx} = V_{yy}$ and therefore $\eta = 0$, and the EFG is called axially symmetric. Furthermore, it can be shown that two mutually perpendicular axes of threefold or higher symmetry give rise to a vanishing EFG.

In general, there are two fundamental sources which can contribute to the total EFG:

a) charges on distant atoms or ions, surrounding the Mössbauer atom in non-cubic symmetry, usually called the *ligand/lattice contribution*;

b) non-cubic electron distribution in partially filled valence orbitals of the Mössbauer atom, usually denoted as the *valence electron contribution*.

If the distances r_i and the angles ϕ_i and θ_i of all n ions i with respect to the Mössbauer atom are known from a crystal structure determination, and if effective charges q_i can be assigned to the pertinent ions, the ligand/lattice contributions to V_{zz} and η can be readily computed using the formulae

$$(V_{zz})_L = \sum_i^n q_i r_i^{-3} (3\cos^2\theta_i - 1),\tag{2.18}$$

$$\eta_L = 1/(V_{zz})_L \sum_i^n q_i r_i^{-3} 3\sin^2\theta_i \cos 2\phi_i .\tag{2.19}$$

However, $(V_{zz})_L$ is not the EFG contribution felt by the Mössbauer nucleus. Instead, as was shown by STERNHEIMER [2.20], the electron shell of a Mössbauer atom distorts in the presence of a non-cubic charge distribution in the surrounding crystal lattice in such a way as to greatly amplify the lattice quadrupole interaction. This phenomenon is known as "Sternheimer antishielding" and is accounted for by multiplying $(V_{zz})_L$ by the factor $(1 - \gamma_\infty)$, where γ_∞ is called the Sternheimer antishielding factor; $(1 - \gamma_\infty)$ has been estimated to be in the order of 10 for iron compounds.

The valence electron contribution to V_{zz} is evaluated simply by taking the expectation value of the quantity $-e(3\cos^2\theta - 1)r^{-3}$ for each electron in the valence orbital state $|l_i m_i\rangle$ and summing over all valence electrons i (using Dirac notation),

$$(V_{zz})_{val} = -e\sum_i \langle l_i m_i|(3\cos^2\theta - 1)/r^3|l_i m_i\rangle .\tag{2.20}$$

The expectation value for $1/r^3$, $\langle r^{-3}\rangle = \int R(r) r^{-3} R(r) r^2 dr$ is generally not calculable with satisfactory precision, but may be obtained from experiments [2.21]. Therefore, by factorizing out $\langle r^{-3}\rangle$ from the above integral, (2.20) becomes

$$(V_{zz})_{val} = -e\sum_i \langle l_i m_i|3\cos^2\theta - 1|l_i m_i\rangle \langle r_i^{-3}\rangle .\tag{2.21}$$

Due to the screening of the valence electrons from the nucleus by inner shell electrons, the value of $(V_{zz})_{val}$ given by (2.21) will not be the actual valence contribution to the EFG at the nuclear site. STERNHEIMER has shown that in this case $(V_{zz})_{val}$ has to be corrected by multiplying it by $(1 - \mathscr{R})$. The Sternheimer shielding factor $\mathscr{R}$ has been estimated to be $0.2 - 0.3$ for iron and tin.

In general, the z-component of the total effective EFG at the nucleus may be written as

$$V_{zz} = (1 - \gamma_\infty)(V_{zz})_L + (1 - \mathscr{R})(V_{zz})_{val} \tag{2.22}$$

and the asymmetry parameter is given by

$$\eta V_{zz} = V_{xx} - V_{yy} = (1 - \gamma_\infty)(V_{zz})_L \eta_L + (1 - \mathscr{R})(V_{zz})_{val} \eta_{val}. \tag{2.23}$$

Similar expressions exist for the other two diagonal EFG tensor elements,

$$(V_{xx})_{val} = -e \sum_i \langle l_i m_i | 3 \sin^2 \theta \cos^2 \phi - 1 | l_i m_i \rangle \langle r_i^{-3} \rangle$$

$$(V_{yy})_{val} = -e \sum \langle l_i m_i | 3 \sin^2 \theta \sin^2 \phi - 1 | l_i m_i \rangle \langle r_i^{-3} \rangle. \tag{2.21a}$$

By using these expressions one can calculate the EFG elements and η for electrons of different angular momenta. In most chemical applications only p- and d-electrons are considered. s-electrons are always arranged in spherical symmetry and therefore do not contribute to the EFG. The f-electrons rarely participate in chemical bonding to any significant extent, because they are accommodated much closer to the nucleus than the d-, p-, and s-valence electrons of a particular complex ion and are therefore well shielded by them from

Table 2.1. Magnitude of the diagonal $(EFG)_{val}$ tensor elements and η for p- and d-electrons

Orbital	$\dfrac{(V_{xx})_{val}}{e\langle r^{-3}\rangle}$	$\dfrac{(V_{yy})_{val}}{e\langle r^{-3}\rangle}$	$\dfrac{(V_{zz})_{val}}{e\langle r^{-3}\rangle}$	η
p-electrons				
p_x	$-4/5$	$+2/5$	$+2/5$	-3^a
p_y	$+2/5$	$-4/5$	$+2/5$	$+3$
p_z	$+2/5$	$+2/5$	$-4/5$	0
d-electrons				
d_{xy}	$-2/7$	$-2/7$	$+4/7$	0
d_{xz}	$-2/7$	$+4/7$	$-2/7$	$+3$
d_{yz}	$+4/7$	$-2/7$	$-2/7$	-3
$d_{x^2-y^2}$	$-2/7$	$-2/7$	$+4/7$	0
d_{z^2}	$+2/7$	$+2/7$	$-4/7$	0

[a] In those cases, where $\eta > 1$, the ordering (2.16) is not fulfilled. To restrict η to $0 \leq \eta \leq 1$ requires proper choice of the principal axis system.

ligand influences. Consequently f-orbitals are hardly expected to undergo ligand field splitting and therefore electrons in the quasi degenerate f orbital set do not contribute to the EFG. The contributions to $(V_{zz})_{val}$ from d- and p-electrons are listed in Table 2.1.

Quadrupole Splitting

We finally return to the coupling of the nuclear electric quadrupole moment and the EFG at the nucleus and express the interaction by the quadrupole Hamiltonian in the well-known form [2.22]

$$\mathscr{H}(e2) = \frac{eQV_{zz}}{4I(2I-1)} \left[3\hat{I}_z^2 - \hat{I}^2 + \eta(\hat{I}_+^2 + \hat{I}_-^2)/2 \right]. \tag{2.24}$$

Here, I is the nuclear spin quantum number, $\hat{I}$ is the nuclear spin operator, $\hat{I}_\pm = \hat{I}_x \pm i\hat{I}_y$ are shift operators (raising and lowering operators), and $\hat{I}_x$, $\hat{I}_y$, $\hat{I}_z$ are the nuclear spin component operators. Using the first-order perturbation theory, the eigenvalues of $\mathscr{H}(e2)$ can be found as

$$E_Q = \frac{eQV_{zz}}{4I(2I-1)} \left[3m_I^2 - I(I+1) \right] (1 + \eta^2/3)^{1/2}, \tag{2.25}$$

where $m_I = I, I-1, \ldots, -I$ is the nuclear magnetic spin quantum number. From (2.25) the effect of the electric quadrupole interaction is obvious: a nuclear state with $I > 1/2$, which is $(2I+1)$-fold degenerate, will be split into substates $|I, \pm m_I\rangle$ without shifting the center of gravity. The substates are characterized by the magnitude of the magnetic spin quantum number $|m_I|$, but cannot be distinguished by the sign of m_I, because (2.25) contains only the second power of the magnetic spin quantum number. Therefore, the nuclear substates arising from nuclear quadrupole splitting remain doubly degenerate and we shall denote them by $|I, \pm m_I\rangle$. The two-fold degeneracy of the substates can only be removed by magnetic perturbation (see Subsection 2.1.3).

As an example, the effect of the electric quadrupole interaction in a Mössbauer nucleus with $I = 3/2$ in the excited and $I = 1/2$ in the ground state, as is the case, for example, in ^{57}Fe and ^{119}Sn, is pictured in Fig. 2.2a. The isomer shift is also shown, because the electric monopole interaction is always present. The nuclear ground state ($I = 1/2$) is not split, because $Q = 0$. The excited state ($I = 3/2$) is split into two doubly degenerate substates $|3/2, \pm 3/2\rangle$ and $|3/2, \pm 1/2\rangle$. The perturbation energies $E_Q(\pm m_I)$ for the substates can be readily written down using

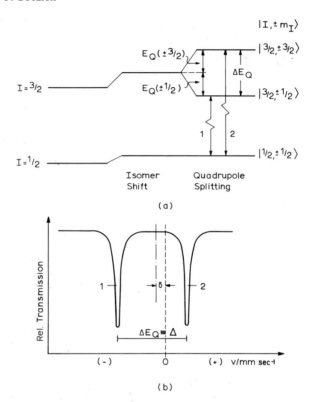

Fig. 2.2a and b. Quadrupole splitting for a nucleus with spin $I = 3/2$ in the excited state (e.g. ^{57}Fe, ^{119}Sn). (a) $I = 3/2$ level is split into two sublevels by electric quadrupole interaction, (b) resultant Mössbauer spectrum (schematic)

(2.25). Assuming, for simplicity, an axially symmetric EFG ($\eta = 0$), one obtains

$$E_Q(\pm 3/2) = 3eQV_{zz}/12 \quad \text{for} \quad I = 3/2, \, m_I = \pm 3/2$$
$$E_Q(\pm 1/2) = -3eQV_{zz}/12 \quad \text{for} \quad I = 3/2, \, m_I = \pm 1/2. \tag{2.26}$$

(The magnitude of the perturbation energy is the same for both doubly degenerate substates, which indicates that the center of gravity is not affected.) For the difference in energy ΔE_Q between the two substates one finds

$$\Delta E_Q = E_Q(\pm 3/2) - E_Q(\pm 1/2) = eQV_{zz}/2. \tag{2.27}$$

In a Mössbauer experiment gamma transitions are possible between the nuclear ground state and both substates $|I, \pm m_I\rangle$ of the $I = 3/2$ level. Using a single-line source one would therefore observe two resonance lines of equal intensities (except for the occurence of an anisotropic recoilless fraction f in polycrystalline material, termed the Goldanskii-Karyagin effect [2.13]) in the Mössbauer spectrum with the assignment shown in Fig. 2.2. The distance Δ between the two lines corresponds exactly to the energy splitting (quadrupole interaction energy) ΔE_Q. The observable quantity Δ, called the "quadrupole splitting", is another Mössbauer parameter of great significance in chemical applications of the Mössbauer effect. As the quadrupole interaction energy is proportional to the product of the nuclear quadrupole moment and the EFG, one can never derive values for both quantities Q and V_{zz} from a measurement of the quadrupole splitting energy. Values for the quadrupole moment are accessible only if, in connection with measurements of the quadrupole interaction energy, the EFG tensor can be evaluated independently.

2.1.3. Magnetic Dipole Interaction; Magnetic Splitting

A nucleus with spin $I > 0$ has a magnetic dipole moment μ, which can interact with a magnetic field H at the nucleus. The interaction is described by the Hamiltonian

$$\mathscr{H}(m1) = -\mu \cdot H = -g_N \beta_N I \cdot H, \tag{2.28}$$

where g_N is the nuclear Landé splitting factor and $\beta_N = eh/2Mc$ (M: mass of the nucleus) is the nuclear Bohr magneton. Using first-order perturbation theory one finds the eigenvalues of $\mathscr{H}(m1)$ as

$$E_m(m_I) = -\mu H m_I/I = -g_N \beta_N H m_I. \tag{2.29}$$

From (2.29) it is obvious that the magnetic dipole interaction splits a nuclear state $|I\rangle$ into $2I + 1$ equally spaced substates, each of these being characterized by the nuclear magnetic spin quantum number $m_I = I, I - 1, \ldots, -I$ (nuclear Zeeman effect). The magnetic dipole splitting is shown in Fig. 2.3 for ^{57}Fe with $I_e = 3/2$ and $I_g = 1/2$. Each of the two states has a magnetic dipole moment and will therefore be split by magnetic interaction. Gamma transitions between the sublevels of the ground state and those of the excited state are subject to selection rules. For magnetic dipole radiation (as in ^{57}Fe) only transitions with $\Delta I = 1$, $\Delta m = 0, \pm 1$ are allowed, giving six altogether in ^{57}Fe.

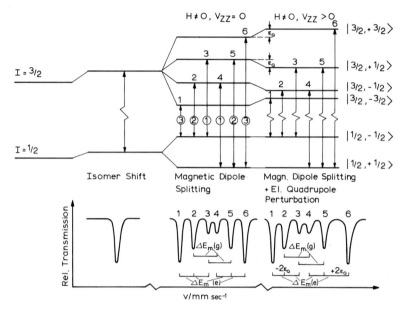

Fig. 2.3. Magnetic dipole splitting without ($H \neq 0$, $V_{zz} = 0$) and with electric quadrupole perturbation ($H \neq 0$, $V_{zz} \neq 0$) and resultant Mössbauer spectra (schematic). $\Delta E_m(g) = g_g \beta_N H$ (ground state splitting); $\Delta E_m(e) = g_e \beta_N H$ (excited state splitting)

The six transitions are shown in Fig. 2.3 (diagram for $H \neq 0$, $V_{zz} = 0$) together with their relative intensities for a polycrystalline material (circled numbers, which are given by the square of the Clebsch-Gordan coefficients). Using a single-line source one would expect a resonance sextet in the Mössbauer spectrum, the centroid of which may be shifted from zero velocity by electric monopole interaction (isomer shift).

Pure nuclear magnetic dipole interactions are rarely encountered in chemical applications of the Mössbauer effect. Metallic iron is an exception. Quite frequently one finds that a nuclear state is simultaneously perturbed by both magnetic dipole and electric quadrupole interactions. In this case the sublevels of the $I = 3/2$ state of ^{57}Fe are no longer equally spaced, as shown in the right-hand diagram of Fig. 2.3 ($H \neq 0$, $V_{zz} > 0$). Assuming $\mathscr{H}(e2) \ll \mathscr{H}(m1)$ the quadrupole coupling may be treated as a first-order perturbation on the magnetic dipole interaction and one finds the quadrupolar perturbation energy $E_Q(\pm m_I) = \Delta/2$, by which the sublevels $|+3/2\rangle$ and $|-3/2\rangle$ of the excited state are raised (lowered) and the sublevels $|+1/2\rangle$ and $|-1/2\rangle$ are lowered (raised) if $V_{zz} > 0$ ($V_{zz} < 0$). This opens the possibility of determining the sign of the quadrupole coupling constant and hence the sign of V_{zz}, which is very desirable in studies of the electronic and molecular structure of compounds containing Mössbauer nuclides.

If $\mathscr{H}(e2) \ll \mathscr{H}(m1)$ and if the EFG tensor is axially symmetric and its principal axis makes an angle β with the axis of the magnetic field, first-order perturbation theory yields the general expression for the eigenvalues

$$E = -g_N \beta_N H m_I + (-1)^{|m_I| + 1/2}(eQV_{zz}/8)(3\cos^2\beta - 1). \qquad (2.29a)$$

2.2. Chemical Information from Isomer Shift

As stated briefly in Subsection 2.1.1 the isomer shift δ will reflect changes in the electron density at the nucleus due to changes in the valence orbital populations of a Mössbauer atom. These factors in turn are subject to various influences such as different σ-donor and π-acceptor strengths of surrounding ligands, covalency effects, oxidation/reduction processes, differences in electronegativity of ligands coordinated to a Mössbauer atom, etc. From the chemical point of view the study of a single compound may not be very informative unless data from similar compounds are available for comparison. It is then possible to correlate isomer shift data with the oxidation state and spin state of the Mössbauer atom in a complex ion, electronegativity of ligands, coordination number, and other empirical parameters. Simple arguments from molecular orbital theory and atomic structure calculations are very often helpful in understanding bond properties and electron configurations derived from isomer shift correlations. A few representative examples will now be discussed to demonstrate the usefulness of isomer shift studies in chemistry.

2.2.1. Correlation of Isomer Shift with Oxidation State and Electron Configuration

The observation of an isomer shift in Fe_2O_3 (with respect to a $^{57}Co/$ stainless steel source) by KISTNER and SUNYAR in 1960 [2.1] has initiated extensive systematic Mössbauer studies of compounds with different Mössbauer nuclides. Already from early investigations of iron compounds one readily found a correlation of the isomer shift with the formal oxidation state of the iron. Moreover, the isomer shift has turned out to be quite sensitive to the spin state of the iron in a complex compound. As an example, the isomer shift values of high spin iron(II)

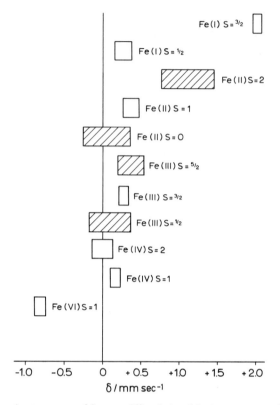

Fig. 2.4. Approximate ranges of isomer shifts observed in iron compounds (relative to metallic iron at room temperature). Shadowed ranges belong to more frequently met configurations (adapted from [2.15])

compounds (with spin quantum number $S = 2$) appear in a region of the velocity scale well separated from that of low spin iron(II) compounds ($S = 0$).

Figure 2.4 (after [2.15]) shows approximate ranges of the isomer shifts observed in iron complexes with different oxidation and spin states of the central metal ion.

The shadowed areas refer to the most common iron compounds. The diagram demonstrates that for ionic (high spin) iron compounds the δ values become more positive with decreasing formal oxidation state. Fortunately, the δ-ranges for the different oxidation states in ionic iron compounds hardly overlap with one another which offers the possibility of determining the oxidation state of iron in unknown complexes. Low spin iron(II) and iron(III) compounds, however, show very similar isomer shifts, and it is therefore not possible to distinguish between iron(II) and iron(III) in such compounds from δ-values alone. Nevertheless, a distinction in such cases can be made by considering the data of the quadrupole splitting Δ in addition, which are generally rather small $(0 \leq \Delta \lesssim 0.8 \text{ mm sec}^{-1})$ in low spin iron(II), but substantially greater $(\sim 0.7 \lesssim \Delta \lesssim 1.7 \text{ mm sec}^{-1})$ in low spin iron(III) compounds. In many instances both the oxidation state and spin state can readily be derived from a single Mössbauer measurement.

The dependence of the isomer shift on the electron configuration, as shown in Fig. 2.4, can be understood on the basis of results from Hartree-Fock atomic structure calculations by WATSON [2.23]. WATSON found radial functions $R(r)$ for the first transition metal ion series in convenient analytical expressions as accurate solutions to the Hartree-Fock equations. From these wave functions it can be seen that the s-orbitals are the only ones which directly contribute to the electron density at the nucleus $(r = 0)$. Thus we need consider only s-functions, which may be written as

$$\psi_{ns} = R_{ns}(r)/2\sqrt{\pi}. \tag{2.30}$$

The total electron density at $r = 0$ is then given by

$$|\Psi(0)|^2 = \frac{1}{2\pi} \sum_n [R_{ns}(r)]_r^2 = 0. \tag{2.31}$$

Using Watson's wave functions one obtains the electron densities at the iron nucleus for different configurations as given in Table 2.2.

The differences in going from one configuration to another primarily originate from changes in the $3s$ shell, whereas the contributions from the filled $1s$ and $2s$ orbitals remain practically constant for all configurations of Table 2.2. The removal of $3d$ electrons leads to an increase of the electron density at the nucleus. This result has been interpreted as being due to shielding of the $3s$ electrons from the nuclear charge by $3d$ electrons. Adding $4s$ electrons, e.g. in going from $Fe^{2+}(3d^6)$ to metallic iron $(3d^6 4s^2)$, increases the electron density at the nucleus and—since $\delta R/R$ is negative for ^{57}Fe—causes the isomer shift to become more negative than for Fe^{2+} (taken with respect to the same standard). The more or less wide-spread ranges of the δ values for each oxidation state is a direct consequence of the nature of the chemical bond. The electron distribution in the molecular orbitals is the result of the variable abilities of the ligands to donate electrons to the metal ion via σ-bonding and to accept electrons from the metal ion via π-bonding. Later on we shall discuss in more detail how these mechanisms affect the isomer shift.

Table 2.2. s-electron densities at the iron nucleus for various valence electron configurations of the iron atom (in atomic units: electrons per cubic Bohr radius)

	Partial electron densities $|\psi_{ns}|^2_{r=0} = \dfrac{1}{4\pi} \sum\limits_{n} |R_{ns}(r)|^2_{r=0}$ for the configuration				
	$3d^8$	$3d^7$	$3d^6$	$3d^5$	$3d^6 4s^2$ (free atom)
From one electron in $1s$	5378.005	5377.973	5377.840	5377.625	5377.873
From one electron in $2s$	493.953	493.873	493.796	493.793	493.968
From one electron in $3s$	67.524	67.764	68.274	69.433	68.028
From one electron in $4s$					3.042
$|\Psi(0)|^2 = 2 \sum\limits_{n} |\psi_{ns}|^2_{r=0}$	11878.9	11879.2	11879.8	11881.7	11885.8

(The numbers were taken from [2.24].)

Isomer shift scales as a function of the oxidation state of a Mössbauer atom similar to the one shown in Fig. 2.4 are now available for a number of other Mössbauer active nuclides, like ^{119}Sn, ^{127}I, ^{129}Xe, ^{99}Ru, ^{151}Eu, ^{197}Au, ^{237}Np, and others. Such diagrams are extremely helpful in characterizing unknown substances and in identifying different species of a certain Mössbauer nuclide in a mixture.

2.2.2. Correlation of Isomer Shift with Bonding Properties

From the large number of compounds with different Mössbauer atoms studied so far one has learned that there is no unique bonding model which allows the interpretation of all the observed trends in isomer shifts. In some cases observed changes in the isomer shift can be rationalized simply by considering p orbital participation in chemical bonding, in other cases the assumption of spd hybrid orbitals (Valence Bond Theory [2.25, 26]) as being most important for the chemical bond is more successful. More complicated bonding phenomena finally require more or less sophisticated molecular orbital descriptions [2.27] as a basis for the interpretation of observed isomer shifts.

Iodine Compounds

PASTERNAK et al. have shown for a series of iodine compounds (Fig. 2.5) that the observed isomer shifts can be linearly correlated with the number h_p of electron holes in the $5p$ orbitals [2.28]. Assuming, on the one hand, a $5p^5$ electron configuration for each iodine atom in the

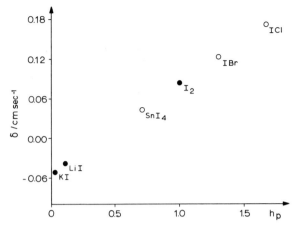

Fig. 2.5. Isomer shift (relative to ZnTe source) as a function of the number of $5p$ holes, h_p, for some iodine compounds at ca. 80 K (from [2.28]). ● reference data; ○ calculated from (2.32)

covalent I_2 molecule, the isomer shift for I_2 would then correspond to one p hole in the $5p$ shell. Taking, on the other hand, the iodine in the alkali iodides as being I^- with approximately the $5p^6$ electron configuration, the isomer shifts in alkali iodides should be related to $h_p \approx 0$. The very small values of h_p for alkali iodides were calculated from NMR chemical shift data. (According to Pauling electronegativities [2.25] for K and I, the bond in KI has nearly 50% covalent character, and therefore one cannot expect h_p to be equal to zero.) Assuming a linear dependence of the isomer shift with h_p one obtains the following equation

$$\delta = 0.136\, h_p - 0.054\ [\text{cm sec}^{-1}], \tag{2.32}$$

where

$$h_p = 6 - (N_{p_x} + N_{p_y} + N_{p_z}) \tag{2.33}$$

(the N's give the number of electrons in the p_x, p_y, and p_z orbitals, respectively). Equation (2.32) allows the calculation of h_p for other iodine compounds employing observed δ values. Because of the shielding of $5s$ electrons by $5p$ electrons the electron density at the ^{129}I nucleus is expected to increase with increasing h_p (removal of $5p$ electrons), and— since $\delta R/R$ is positive for ^{129}I—the isomer shift will become more positive. Furthermore, from the ordering of the compounds in Fig. 2.5 as a function of δ and h_p it is to be concluded that the electron population in the $5p$ shell of the iodine atom is directly related to the electronegativity of the atoms which are bonded to iodine, i.e. h_p and δ increase with increasing electronegativity of the ligand. The $5s$ electron population, however, is assumed to be nearly constant in the above compounds. If $5s$ electrons played a major role in the chemical bonding, e.g. via participation of sp hybrid orbitals, the dependence of the isomer shift on the electronegativity of the bonded atoms would then be expected to be the other way round (δ would be most positive for the least electronegative ligand). The removal of valence electrons with equal amounts of both s and p character will cause the electron density at the nucleus to decrease, because changes in the s valence orbital population generally are more effective than changes in the p population.

Very similar observations have been made in Mössbauer studies on xenon compounds, which can also be accounted for by changes of the population in the $5p$ shell [2.31].

Tin(IV) Compounds

In tin(IV) compounds correlations between the isomer shift and the electronegativity of the ligands bound to the tin atom have been found for tetrahalides SnX_4 ($X = Cl$, Br, I) and for pure and mixed hexa-halogenates, $SnX_6^=$ and $SnX_4Y_2^=$. In the framework of Pauling's valence bond picture the tetrahedral four-coordinated tetrahalides are believed to use $5(sp^3)$ hybrid orbitals and the octahedral six-coordinated hexa-halogenates to use $5(sp^3 d^2)$ hybrid orbitals in bond formation. From many systematic measurements of the ^{119}Sn Mössbauer effect there is sufficient evidence that the electron density at the tin nucleus is most sensitive to changes in the population of s-valence electrons. It is there-fore expected, that—having in mind that $\delta R/R$ is positive for ^{119}Sn—the isomer shift should decrease with increasing electronegativity of the ligand. Figure 2.6 shows this effect for both types of tin(IV) compounds, SnX_4 and $SnX_4Y_2^=$. For the majority of the $SnX_4Y_2^=$ complexes the isomer shift is nearly independent of the cation. The least-squares lines through the points of Fig. 2.6 yield the equations

$$\delta(SnX_4)/mm\ sec^{-1} = 4.82 - 1.27\ \overline{\chi}_P, \tag{2.34}$$

$$\delta(SnX_6^=)/mm^{-1} = 4.27 - 1.16\ \overline{\chi}_P, \tag{2.34a}$$

which can be used for estimating unknown values of the Pauling electronegativities of the ligands, e.g. O in SnO_2: $\delta = 0.00$ mm sec^{-1}, $\overline{\chi}_P = 3.7$; $-CH_3$ in $(CH_3)_4Sn$: $\delta = 1.31$ mm sec^{-1}, $\overline{\chi}_P = 2.8$; $-N(CH_3)_2$ in $Sn[N(CH_3)_2]_4$: $\delta = 0.84$ mm sec^{-1}, $\overline{\chi}_P = 3.1$ [2.32].

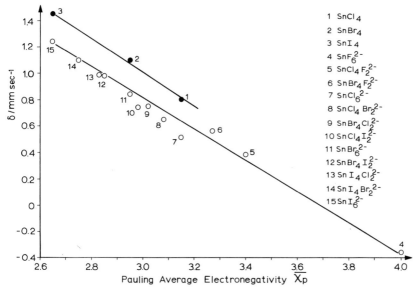

Fig. 2.6. Isomer shift (relative to SnO_2) versus average of Pauling electronegativities for SnX_4 and $(Et_4N)_2SnX_4Y_2$ (average isomer shift data from [2.29, 30])

Iron(II) High Spin Compounds

The isomer shifts observed in high spin iron compounds generally do not impose serious difficulties in giving a qualitative interpretation. Again, there is a strong correlation between δ and the electronegativity of coordinated ligands. Recalling that $\delta R/R$ is negative for ^{57}Fe, δ is expected to become more positive with increasing electronegativity of the ligands. This is the case e.g. for the ferrous halides FeX_2 (X = F, Cl, Br, I) [2.33]. It is still possible to rationalize such variations of δ in high spin iron compounds on the grounds of the valence bond picture, assuming $4(sp^3d^2)$ hybrid orbitals in bond formation. The electron density at the nucleus is most sensitive to changes in the 4s charge, but relatively insensitive to changes in the electron population of the 4p and 4d shell because of their ineffective shielding ability versus 4s electrons. Therefore, removal of valence electrons of $4(sp^3d^2)$ character by electronegative ligands will effectively reduce the electron density at the nucleus.

Intermetallic Compounds

Good correlations between the isomer shift and the electron withdrawing power (electronegativity) of neighboring atoms have also been found in alloys of various Mössbauer active nuclides. As an example

we shall describe briefly the results of Mössbauer measurements on
^{197}Au in Li$_2$AuX (X = Ga, In, Tl, Ge, Sn, Pb, Bi) [2.34].

The ternary alloys Li$_2$AuX are cubic and have O_h local symmetry at
the gold atoms [2.35, 36]. A single resonance line for each appears in
the positive velocity region (with respect to metallic gold as absorber),
thus indicating a substantial increase of the electron density at the gold
nucleus when alloyed with the main group elements X. The answer to
the question whether the increase in $|\Psi(0)|^2$ at the gold nucleus is
primarily due to an increase in charge in the 6s band or a depletion of
5d charge upon alloy formation may be found in correlating the isomer
shifts of Li$_2$AuX with the electronegativity per valence electron of
surrounding atoms X, $\overline{EN(X)}/VE(X)$. The plot in Fig. 2.7 shows a
nearly linear change of δ in positive direction with increasing
$\overline{EN(X)}/VE(X)$. This suggests a net charge flow from the 5d band of gold
onto the surroundings. Very similar observations have been made in

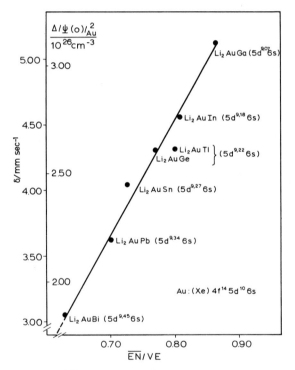

Fig. 2.7. Isomer shift of ^{197}Au (relative to ^{197}Au/Pt source at 4.2 K) and relative electron
densities at the ^{197}Au nucleus in Li$_2$AuX (X = Ga, In, Tl, Ge, Sn, Bi; at 4.2 K) as a function
of average electronegativity (Allred-Rochow) per valence electron, $\overline{EN}/VE$

$Li_2Au_{2-x}In_x$ $(1.0 < x < 1.75)$ [2.34], where gold is gradually substituted by indium while retaining the cubic structure [2.36]. A charge flow off the gold atom in these alloys is also to be concluded from the crystallographically observed contraction of the gold atom in these alloys as compared to the pure metal. These results have been parallelled by conclusions from a study of other gold alloys by WATSON et al. [2.37]. Using the results of Dirac-Fock atomic structure calculations by FALTENS [2.38] it is possible to correlate the observed isomer shifts with the amount Δn of the charge flow off the $5d$ band with practically constant charge density in the $6s$ band: $5d^{9-\Delta n}6s^1$ (see Fig. 2.7).

Covalent Transition Metal Complexes

Pauling's valence bond theory is a very useful and simple model in predicting the structure of a molecule and—as we have seen earlier in the discussion of iron(II) halides—in understanding the observed isomer shifts in compounds with predominantly σ-bonding and negligible amounts of π-interaction (a bond between two atoms, say a metal atom and a ligand atom, is of σ-type, if it is symmetric about the internuclear axis M-L, it is of π-type, if it is symmetric about a nodal plane which contains the internuclear axis M-L; cf. Fig. 2.8). Pauling's valence bond model uses σ-type hybrid orbitals, which are obtained from linear combinations of sterically appropriate atomic orbitals. As an example, mixing the $4s$, $4p_x$, $4p_y$, $4p_z$, $4d_{z^2}$, and $4d_{x^2-y^2}$ atomic orbitals of the central iron atom in say the complex ion $Fe(H_2O)_6^{2+}$ with nearly pure σ-interaction between Fe and H_2O yields six equivalent sp^3d^2 hybrid orbitals pointing at the apices of a regular octahedron. The six sp^3d^2 orbitals are assumed to be populated entirely by ligand electrons, two from each ligand (or less depending on the electronegativity of the ligands, cf. iron(II) halide series). The $3d$ shell of the central iron ion will be undisturbed, the $3d$ electrons are allowed to align themselves according to Hund's first rule of maximum spin multiplicity (cf. Fig. 2.9). Complexes of this type are called outer-orbital, electrovalent, or high spin complexes and exhibit paramagnetic behaviour. The diamagnetic (or nearly diamagnetic) behaviour in octahedral complexes such as e.g. $[Fe(CN)_6]^{4-}$ is explained on the basis of Pauling's picture by ligand electrons penetrating more deeply into the iron core and populating now d^2sp^3 hybrid orbitals (which differ from the above type of sp^3d^2 in that they now use $3d_{z^2}$ an $3d_{x^2-y^2}$ orbitals rather than the corresponding ones from the N shell). The $3d$ electrons are forced in this way to spin-pair—against Hund's first rule—in the orbitals $3d_{xy}$, $3d_{xz}$, $3d_{yz}$, which do not take part in hybridization.

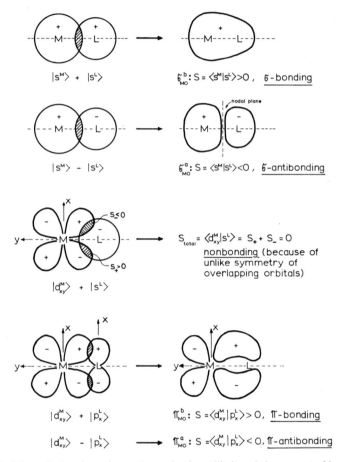

Fig. 2.8. Schematic drawings of σ- and π-molecular orbitals and the concept of bonding, antibonding, and non-bonding orbitals. (S: overlap integral, a: antibonding, b: bonding, MO: molecular orbital). The signs shown in the drawing refer to the sign of the interacting orbital functions. Only overlapping orbitals of like symmetry contribute to chemical bonding

	3d					4s	4p			4d		
free Fe^{2+} Ion	↑↓	↑	↑	↑	↑							
Fe^{II} high spin complex	↑↓	↑	↑	↑	↑	••	•• •• ••	•• ••				sp^{3}d^2 hybridization
Fe^{II} low spin complex	↑↓	↑↓	↑↓	••	••	••	•• ••	•• ••				d^{2}sp^3 hybridization

↑ 3d electron of iron
• ligand electron

Fig. 2.9. Valence bond orbital diagram for octahedral high spin and low spin iron(II) complexes

Nevertheless, the chemical bond in such complexes—called inner-orbital, covalent, or low spin complexes—is still considered to be purely of σ-type in Pauling's picture. The π-interaction, which does play an important role in such compounds, is completely ignored. As a consequence one can not understand within this model e.g. why the observed isomer shifts in $K_4[Fe(CN)]_6 \cdot 3H_2O$ and $K_3[Fe(CN)_6]$ are nearly equal [2.39]. One would expect a considerable change of δ in the positive direction by putting one more electron into the $3d$ shell (in going from Fe^{III} to Fe^{II}), because of the increase in the shielding effect for the $3s$ electrons. The concomitant phenomenon, however, of a charge-flow from the $3d$ shell backwards onto the ligands via π-interaction, called π-back donation, cannot be accounted for in Pauling's model, but can adequately be handed in molecular orbital theory [2.27].

To give the inexperienced reader a feeling of what one does in molecular orbital theory we shall outline here very briefly the most essential steps in molecular orbital calculations:

1) Valence atomic orbitals for the atoms under consideration are picked out forming a basis set of functions.

2) The functions are classified with respect to symmetry making use of group theoretical tools ([2.40] and references given therein) and projection operators.

3) Following the so-called LCAO-MO method (*l*inear *c*ombination of *a*tomic *o*rbitals to *m*olecular *o*rbitals) proper linear combinations of symmetry-adapted functions are formed to yield molecular wave functions of the general form

$$\Psi_{MO} = C_M \Phi_M + C_L \Phi_L . \qquad (2.35)$$

Φ_M and Φ_L are the proper metal and ligand orbital combinations entering the molecular orbital under consideration. The coefficients C_M and C_L are subject to the normalization and orthogonality conditions.

4) The energy of each molecular orbital wave function Ψ_{MO} is calculated and along with it the values of the C_M and C_L coefficients. The methods of self-consistent field calculations devised by WOLFSBERG and HELMHOLZ [2.41] and ROOTHAAN [2.42] have been successfully used in calculating molecular orbital energies of octahedral transition metal complexes (see e.g. [2.43]).

Figure 2.10 shows the molecular orbital energy level diagram for octahedral metal complexes containing ligands which possess π-orbitals ready to interact with metal π-orbitals [2.44]. Examples of such ligands are the isoelectronic systems CN^-, CO, NO^+, which all have the same molecular orbital diagram by themselves with filled π^b-orbitals and empty π^a-orbitals [2.45]. The most important conclusions that can be

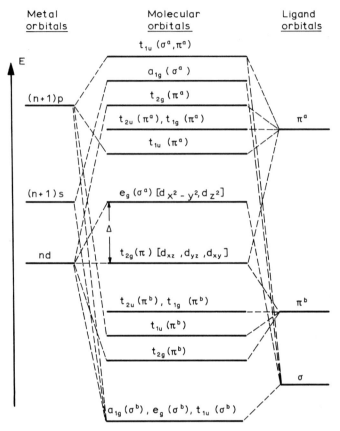

Fig. 2.10. Molecular orbital energy level diagram for octahedral metal complexes containing ligands with π^b(bonding) and relatively stable π^a(antibonding) orbitals

extracted from Fig. 2.10 are the following: The most stable molecular orbitals are the σ^b-orbitals a_{1g}, e_g, and t_{1u} (a, e, and t refer to the Mulliken symbols for one-, two-, and three-dimensional irreducible representations, respectively; g and u stand for *gerade* and *ungerade*; the indices 1 and 2 are added if a certain irreducible representation occurs more than once). These MO's are predominantly of ligand character with some relatively small contributions from the metal e_g ($3d_{x^2-y^2}$, $3d_{z^2}$), a_{1g} ($4s$), and t_{1u} ($4p_x$, $4p_y$, $4p_z$) orbitals. (A general rule [2.46] is that the amount of mixing of atomic orbitals in the molecular orbitals is directly proportional to the magnitude of the atomic orbital overlap and inversely proportional to the difference of their Coulomb energies.) Accordingly, the electrons in these MO's being entirely donated from filled ligand σ-orbitals (of a_{1g}, e_g, and t_{1u} type) take on some metal character. This so-called ligand-to-metal σ-donation makes by far the biggest contribution (some 80–90% in low-spin complexes, nearly 100% in high spin complexes) to the stability of the bond. By evaluating the C_M coefficients in the MO wave function one obtains a measure of the relative partial influences on the Mössbauer isomer shift of the fractional charge being donated into the metal valence orbitals.—The strength of metal-ligand π-interactions is, in general, considerably weaker than σ-interactions. The t_{2u} and t_{1g} ligand π-orbitals are non-bonding orbitals, because there are no counterparts of like symmetry on the metal atom. The t_{2g} ligand π-orbitals do have t_{2g} counterparts on the metal to interact with (as can be seen from Fig. 2.10); it is assumed, however, that π-bonding employing filled ligand orbitals (like in CN^-, CO, NO^+)—so-called ligand-to-metal π-donation—is not likely to be very important, because the overlap is not good, and the metal gains more than enough electrons from the ligands via σ-bonding to satisfy its charge requirements. What remains is the interaction of the metal $t_{2g}(\pi)$ orbitals (d_{xy}, d_{xz}, d_{yz}, which accomodate the d_{π} electrons in complexes with filled ligand π^b-orbitals and empty ligand π^a-orbitals) with ligand π^a-orbitals, which results in a stabilization of the molecular orbital mainly based on the metal; this way the strength of the chemical bond will increase by 10–20%. Such an interaction is called π-back-bonding (or π-back-donation) and the appropriate ligands are referred to as π-acceptor ligands. π-back-bonding offers the possibility to the metal atom to get rid of excess charge, accumulated on the metal through σ-bonding, by delocalizing a fraction of the $t_{2g}(\pi)$ electrons into empty ligand π^a-orbitals. The reader will now easily grasp the idea of covalency, which in molecular orbital theory is arrived at by the fact that the molecular orbitals—σ and π-type, bonding and antibonding—are always mixtures of both metal and ligand orbitals.

Molecular orbital theory allows us to interpret isomer shift changes mainly by two mechanisms: ligand-to-metal σ-donation ($\sigma_{L \to M}$) and π-back-donation ($\pi_{M \to L}$). The other two mechanisms, $\sigma_{M \to L}$ and $\pi_{L \to M}$, do not play significant roles neither in bonding nor in isomer shift changes. $\sigma_{L \to M}$ results in an increase in $|\Psi(0)|^2$, because the electron density at the nucleus is more sensitive to electron augmentation in the ns-shell than to np- and nd-electron augmentations. $\pi_{M \to L}$ also increases $|\Psi(0)|^2$ because of a decrease in the shielding effect on ns-electrons due to donation of nt_{2g} metal electrons into π^a ligand orbitals. The observed δ values for the selected list of covalent Fe^{II} and Ru^{II} compounds given in Table 2.3 illustrate these tendencies and reflect orderings of the various ligands with respect to their relative power of the combined effects ($\sigma_{L \to M} + \pi_{M \to L}$). For the series of $[Fe^{II}(CN)_5 X^{n-}]^{(3+n)-}$ compounds ($\sigma_{L \to M} + \pi_{M \to L}$) increases, and—since $\delta R/R$ is negative for ^{57}Fe—

Table 2.3. Isomer shifts and quadrupole splittings of covalent Fe(II) compounds (295 K, δ relative to $Na_2[Fe(CN)_5NO] \cdot 2H_2O$) and Ru(II) compounds (4.2 K, δ relative to Ru metal)

Complex	δ/mm sec^{-1}	Δ/mm sec^{-1}
$[Fe^{II}(CN)_5NO]^{2-}$	0.00[a]	+1.73
$[Fe(CN)_5CO]^{3-}$	0.15	(+)0.43
$[Fe(CN)_5SO_3]^{5-}$	0.22	(+)0.80
$[Fe(CN)_5NO_2]^{4-}$	0.26	(+)0.89
$[Fe(CN)_5NH_3]^{3-}$	0.26	+0.67
$[Fe(CN)_5H_2O]^{3-}$	0.31	+0.80
$[Ru(NH_3)_5NO]Cl_3 \cdot H_2O$	−0.18[b]	0.36
$[Ru(NH_3)_5CO]Br_2$	−0.54	small
$[Ru(NH_3)_5SO_2]Cl_2$	−0.61	0.30
$[Ru(NH_3)_5N_2]Cl_2$	−0.62	0.24
$[Ru(NH_3)_6]Cl_2$	−0.82	small
$K_2[Ru(CN)_5NO]$	−0.06	0.42
$Rb_2[Ru(NCS)_5NO]$	−0.30	0.24
$Rb_2[RuCl_5NO]$	−0.37	0.24
$Cs_2[RuBr_5NO]$	−0.47	0.08

[a] Data of iron complexes were taken from [2.52–55].
[b] Data of ruthenium complexes were taken from [2.56, 57].

δ becomes more negative in the order $H_2O < NH_3 < NO_2 < SO_3^=$ $< CO \ll NO^+$. H_2O is a rather weak σ-donor ligand with negligible π acceptor capability. CO and NO^+, however, are known to be strong π-acceptor ligands. For the $[Ru^{II}(NH_3)_5X^{n-}]^{(n-2)-}$ compounds δ becomes more positive with increasing $(\sigma_{L \to M} + \pi_{M \to L})$ in the order $NH_3 < SO_2 < CO \ll NO^+$ (note that $\delta R/R$ is positive for ^{99}Ru). Similarly, in the $[RuX_5(NO)]^{2-}$ series, δ changes in a more positive direction with increasing $(\sigma_{L \to M} + \pi_{M \to L})$ in the order $X = Br^- < Cl^-$ $< NCS^- < CN^-$. The reader will notice the close correlation with the ranking of these ligands in the spectrochemical series [2.47].

Bonding properties have also successfully been studied in Au(I) and Au(III) compounds using the Mössbauer effect technique [2.48, 49].

It is obvious from the above discussion that isomer shift studies are enormously valuable in classifying new ligands with respect to their $(\sigma_{L \to M} + \pi_{M \to L})$ ability. It is desirable, of course, to get reliable information about the independent effects of $\sigma_{L \to M}$ and $\pi_{M \to L}$. Despite major difficulties, this is possible by considering in addition to δ-values the quadrupole coupling constants. Information from other spectroscopic methods as well as results from theoretical approaches along the line of self-consistent charge and configuration MO calculations (SCCC-LCAO-MO) [2.50, 51] are also important.

Partial Isomer Shift

The concept of *partial isomer shift* (p.i.s.) was first been introduced by
HERBER et al. [2.58] and has its roots essentially in the observation that
   a) isomer shifts correlate linearly with average electronegativities of
surrounding ligands, as has been observed for many iron and tin
compounds,
   b) a characteristic bonding distance between the metal atom and a
given ligand occurs in a variety of related compounds.
   The p.i.s. concept is an additivity model and suggests that the
isomer shift of a Mössbauer atom in a given compound be composed of
the p.i.s. values of all coordinated ligands i: $\delta = \Sigma_i (\text{p.i.s.})_i$. The model
has been extensively tested for iron(II) and tin(IV) compounds.
BANCROFT et al. [2.59] have calculated p.i.s. values for a large number
of ligands in iron(II) low spin compounds; a small selection thereof
is listed in Table 2.4. With these values and employing the formula

$$\delta = 0.16 + \sum_{i=1}^{6} (\text{p.i.s.})_i \tag{2.36}$$

it is possible to predict the isomer shift of iron(II) low spin compounds.
BANCROFT et al. have done this for a variety of iron(II) compounds
[2.59]. Some of their results are given in Table 2.5, which clearly
demonstrate that the p.i.s. concept operates successfully. It is particu-

Table 2.4. Partial isomer shift (p.i.s.) values (relative to $Na_2[Fe(CN)_5NO] \cdot 2H_2O$ at
295 K) for ligands in low spin iron(II) compounds. (Data from [2.59][a])

Ligand	p.i.s. [mm sec^{-1}]	Ligand	p.i.s. [mm sec^{-1}]
NO$^+$	−0.20	NCO$^-$	0.06
H$^-$	−0.08	depe/2[b]	0.06
SiH$_3^-$	−0.05	bipy/2[b]	0.06
ArNC[b]	0.00	phen/2[b]	0.07
MeNC	0.00	py[b]	0.07
EtNC	0.00	NH$_3$	0.07
CO	0.00	N$_3^-$	0.08
CN$^-$	0.01	H$_2$O	0.10
SnCl$_3^-$	0.04	Cl$^-$	0.10
pc/2[b]	0.05	Br$^-$	0.13
NCS$^-$	0.05	I$^-$	0.13

   [a] The error is estimated to be ±0.01 mm sec^{-1}.
   [b] ArNC ≐ *p*-methoxyphenyl isocyanide; pc ≐ phthalocyanine; depe ≐ *bis*(diethylphos-
phino)ethane; bipy ≐ 2,2′-bipyridyl; phen ≐ 1,10-phenanthroline; py ≐ pyridine.

Table 2.5. Observed and predicted isomer shifts (relative to $Na_2[Fe(CN)_5NO] \cdot 2H_2O$ at 295 K) for iron(II) low spin compounds (from [2.59])

Compound	δ [mm sec^{-1}]	
	Observed	Predicted (p.i.s. model)
cis-FeCl$_2$(ArNC)$_4$[a]	+0.28	+0.36
cis-Fe(SnCl$_3$)$_2$(ArNC)$_4$	+0.27	+0.24
[FeCl(ArNC)$_5$]ClO$_4$	+0.23	+0.26
trans-FeHCl(depe)$_2$	+0.39	+0.42
trans-FeCl(SnCl$_3$)(depe)$_2$	+0.55	+0.54
trans-Fe(CN)$_2$(MeNC)$_4$	+0.16	+0.18
cis-Fe(CN)$_2$(MeNC)$_4$	+0.16	+0.18
trans-Fe(CN)$_2$(EtNC)$_4$	+0.21	+0.18
Na$_3$[Fe(CN)$_5$NH$_3$] $\cdot$ H$_2$O	+0.26	+0.28

[a] See footnote b of Table 2.4.

larly useful in predicting isomer shifts of unknown iron(II) compounds which may only exist as unstable intermediates. The p.i.s. values, just like the isomer shifts in iron(II) compounds, decrease with increasing σ-bonding and π-backbonding (cf. Table 2.4).

2.3. Chemical Information from Quadrupole Splitting

As we have seen in Subsection 2.1.3, non-zero electric field gradients essentially arise from two sources:

a) An aspherical distribution of electrons in the valence orbitals, denoted as $(V_{zz})_{val}$ in the principal axis system,

b) an aspherical charge distribution in the ligand sphere and/or lattice surrounding with symmetry lower than cubic, denoted as $(V_{zz})_L$.

The electronic influence $(V_{zz})_{val}$ may be further subdivided into a contribution arising from an aspherical population of the d-orbitals due to crystal field splitting, $(V_{zz})_{CF}$, and a contribution from anisotropic bond properties (anisotropic population of molecular orbitals), $(V_{zz})_{MO}$. Equation (2.22) for the total effective EFG may therefore be written as

$$V_{zz} = (1 - \gamma_\infty)(V_{zz})_L + (1 - \underline{R})[(V_{zz})_{CF} + (V_{zz})_{MO}]. \tag{2.22a}$$

$(V_{zz})_{CF}$ will be zero in octahedral complexes of transition metal ions with filled or half-filled t_{2g} and/or e_g subshells, e.g. Fe(II) low spin (t_{2g}^6), Fe(III) high spin $(t_{2g}^3 e_g^2)$, Ir(III) (t_{2g}^6); also in compounds of main group ions, e.g. Sn(IV) $(4d^{10})$, Te(VI) (d^{10}). Any observed quadrupole splitting in such compounds will arise from $(V_{zz})_L$ and/or the aspherical electron distribution in the valence molecular orbitals, $(V_{zz})_{MO}$. $(V_{zz})_{CF}$ will be significant in high spin compounds $(t_{2g}^4 e_g^2)$ and Fe(III) low spin (t_{2g}^5) with some admixture of $(V_{zz})_{MO}$. A quantitative separation of the various contributions to any great satisfaction is generally not easy; it requires skilful calculational techniques to do this, particularly with compounds such as $[Fe^{II}(CN)_5 X^{n-}]^{(3+n)}$, where all three contributions are effective.

According to the different origins of quadrupolar interaction, it is expected that observed quadrupole splittings may reflect information about the electronic structure, bond properties, and molecular symmetry.

2.3.1. Effect of $(V_{zz})_{CF}$; Electronic Structure

$(V_{zz})_{CF}$ dominates the EFG in iron(II) high spin and iron(III) low spin compounds. This is illustrated in Fig. 2.11 with 6 different orbital splittings and electronic arrangements for d^6 and d^5 systems. The d-orbital diagrams shown were obtained by considering the effect of a ligand field potential of O_h symmetry (regular octahedron), D_{4h} symmetry (tetragonally distorted octahedron, $\varepsilon < 0$ and $\varepsilon > 0$) and tetragonally distorted T_d-symmetry, respectively, on the five-fold degenerate set of d-orbitals (one-electron model or in ligand field theory termed "strong-field approximation" [2.60, 61]). High spin complexes are characterized by the crystal field parameter Δ_o (octahedral complexes) or Δ_t (tetrahedral complexes) being smaller than the mean spin pairing energy Π. Low spin complexes have $\Delta_o > \Pi$ (tetrahedral low spin complexes of first-row transition metal complexes are not known, because $\Delta_t = 4\Delta_o/9 < \Pi$). In a ligand field of O_h symmetry the five-fold degenerate set of d-orbitals is split into a doubly-degenerate set (e_g), comprising the orbitals $|x^2 - y^2\rangle$ and $|z^2\rangle$, and a three-fold degenerate set (t_{2g}) containing the orbitals $|xy\rangle$, $|xz\rangle$, and $|yz\rangle$. The two degenerate groups, taken separately, are symmetrical and contribute nothing to $(V_{zz})_{CF}$, independent of the electronic population of the individual orbitals (Cases a and d of Fig. 2.11). This can easily be verified by summing the $(V_{zz})_{val}$ components of the d-orbitals (cf. Table 2.1) of each subgroup, multiplied by the number of electrons in each orbital. In doing so one has to keep in mind that in Case a with strict O_h symmetry the extra electron above the half-filled t_{2g} shell is equally spread over the three t_{2g} orbitals making the average population to be $1\frac{1}{3}$ electron in each t_{2g} orbital. In Case d one electron hole spends, on the average, an equal length of time in each

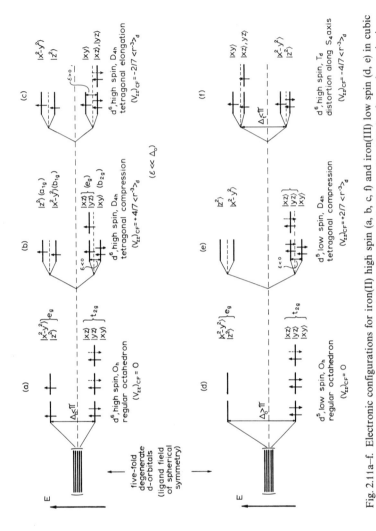

Fig. 2.11a–f. Electronic configurations for iron(II) high spin (a, b, c, f) and iron(III) low spin (d, e) in cubic ligand fields without (a, d) and with tetragonal distortion (b, c, e, f). The resultant $(V_{zz})_{CF}$ for each case is given in the comments

t_{2g} orbital causing $(V_{zz})_{CF}$ to be zero. The same situation holds for an Fe(II) complex with T_d symmetry (regular tetrahedron); again $(V_{zz})_{CF} = 0$.

$(V_{zz})_{CF}$ will be non-zero in Fe(II) high spin and Fe(III) low spin compounds only if the molecule is (slightly) distorted from cubic symmetry. The effect of tetragonal distortion (along the C_4 axis in octahedral molecules, along the S_4 axis in tetrahedral molecules, $0 \lesssim \varepsilon \ll \Delta_{o,t}$) is shown in Cases b, c, e of Fig. 2.11. The degeneracy of the $t_{2(g)}$ space (the index g = gerade is added only in O_h, but not in T_d symmetry because of the lack of a center of inversion) is partly lifted;

the degeneracy of the $e_{(g)}$ space is completely removed. Case b of Fig. 2.11 represents a tetragonal compression of an octahedron. This is in accordance with the Jahn-Teller theorem[1]. The most stable electron configuration here is $b_{2g}^2 e_g^2 b_{1g}^1 a_{1g}^1$ (the superscripts denote the number of electrons, the symbols b_{2g} etc. characterize the symmetry properties of the orbital functions in the Mulliken notation); the corresponding ground term is $^5B_{2g}$. The resultant $(V_{zz})_{CF} = +(4/7)\langle r^{-3}\rangle_d$ (cf. Table 2.1) entirely stems from the non-cubic electron distribution in the split t_{2g} space; no contribution comes from the split e_g space because of equal population. In Case c the direction of the tetragonal distortion is reversed ($\varepsilon > 0$) as compared to Case b. The resultant electron configuration is $e_g^3 b_{2g}^1 a_{1g}^1 b_{1g}^1$ with a ^5E_g ground term and a net $(V_{zz})_{CF} = -(2/7)\langle r^{-3}\rangle_d$, again entirely arising from the unbalanced electron population in the split t_{2g} space. (Notice here that the extra electron above the half-filled e_g space is equally spread among the $|xz\rangle$ and $|yz\rangle$ orbitals, whereas in Case b the most stable $|xy\rangle$ orbital is fully populated by two electrons; this causes the factor of 2 and the sign reversal in $(V_{zz})_{CF}$ between the Cases b and c. The origin of $(V_{zz})_{CF} = 0$ in octahedral iron(III) low spin and tetrahedral iron(II) high spin is explained similarly in Cases e and f, and needs no further comment.

The quadrupole splitting energy in compounds with a dominating $(V_{zz})_{CF}$ contribution to the EFG is generally temperature-dependent, because the distortion parameter (ε in Fig. 2.11) is very often of the order of a few hundred wave numbers (200–600 cm^{-1}) and therefore allows thermal electronic population of low-lying orbitals according to Boltzmann's law. For instance, the electron distribution, as shown in Case b of Fig. 2.11, strictly occurs only at very low temperatures (near absolute zero). With increasing temperature the probability of exciting the ($\downarrow$) electron from the $|xy\rangle$ ground orbital into the doubly degenerate $|xz\rangle$ and $|yz\rangle$ orbitals, solely due to thermal energy, also increases. This does not alter the net spin and therefore does not affect the balance of the quantum mechanical exchange energy. The fractional population P_i of the ith level with energy E_i, out of a total of n levels with energy E_k, is given by the Boltzmann equation

$$P_i = \exp(-E_i/k_B T) \Big/ \sum_{k=1}^{n} \exp(-E_k/k_B T) \tag{2.37}$$

(k_B: Boltzmann's constant). Choosing the ground state as reference level with zero energy, the fractional population of the ith level compared to

---

[1] The Jahn-Teller theorem states that a non-linear molecule with an orbitally degenerate ground state is not stable and should distort itself so as to remove the orbital degeneracy of the ground state.

that of the ground state is

$$P_i/P_o = \exp(-E_i/k_B T). \tag{2.38}$$

For a molecule at temperature T, the components V_{ij} of the EFG tensor are obtained by weighting the contributions V_{ij} from each orbital $|r\rangle$ with their relative population P_r and taking the sum over all states $|r\rangle$

$$\begin{aligned}
V_{ij} &= \sum_{r=1}^{n} P_r \cdot (V_{ij})_r \\
&= \sum_{r=1}^{n} (V_{ij})_r \exp(-E_r/k_B T) \Big/ \sum_{k=1}^{n} \exp(-E_k/k_B T).
\end{aligned} \tag{2.39}$$

In particular, $(V_{zz})_{CF}$ of Case b (Fig. 2.11) as a function of temperature will be (using Table 2.1)

$$(V_{zz})_{CF} = (2/7)(e\langle r^{-3}\rangle_d)[2 - 2\exp(-\varepsilon/k_B T)]/[1 + 2\exp(-\varepsilon/k_B T)]. \tag{2.40}$$

A similar expression is obtained for Case c, where the orbital doublet lies lowest,

$$(V_{zz})_{CF} = (-2/7)(e\langle r^{-3}\rangle_d)[2 - 2\exp(-\varepsilon/k_B T)]/[2 + \exp(-\varepsilon/k_B T)]. \tag{2.41}$$

It is obvious from this description that a study of the temperature dependence of the quadrupole splitting allows the determination of the distortion parameter ε, which is in many compounds so small that it escapes detection by other methods (like X-ray diffraction). The direction of the distortion and along with it the sign of $(V_{zz})_{CF}$ can, in many instances (with comparatively small $(V_{zz})_L$ contributions which oppose and thus diminish $(V_{zz})_{CF}$ [2.62]), readily be extracted from the size of the quadrupole splitting; compare e.g. $(V_{zz})_{CF}$ in Cases b and c. Otherwise spectra taken in an applied magnetic field will yield the sign of the total EFG [2.63]. JOHNSON et al. [2.64] have measured the temperature dependence of the quadrupole splitting in the tetrahedral iron(II) high spin compounds $(NMe_4)_2[FeCl_4]$, $(NEt)_4[FeCl_4]$, and $(NMe_4)[Fe(NCS)_4]$ and found that the tetrahedron of the ferrous complex ion is slightly distorted along the z-axis with distortion energy of $100–135 \text{ cm}^{-1}$ and the d_{z^2} orbital being lowest.

More rigorous treatments of the temperature dependence of the quadrupole splitting involve, beside distortions from cubic symmetry (primary effect of the crystalline field), calculations of spin-orbit coupling, covalency effects, and the underlying temperature-independent contribution $(V_{zz})_L$ to the EFG (secondary effect of the crystalline field), as has been carried out by INGALLS [2.62] and other authors [2.65–67]. INGALLS [2.62] suggests that the quadrupole splitting Δ for ferrous compounds can be written as

$$\Delta = (2/7)\,e^2\,Q(1 - \underline{R})\langle r^{-3}\rangle_0\alpha^2 F(\varepsilon_1, \varepsilon_2, \alpha^2\lambda_0, T) \qquad (2.42)$$

where $\langle r^{-3}\rangle_0$ denotes the expectation value of $1/r^3$ in the free (gaseous) ion, $\alpha^2 = \langle r^{-3}\rangle/\langle r^{-3}\rangle_0$ is the covalency parameter (which expresses the extent of radial expansion of the $3d$ orbitals upon complex formation, α^2 usually takes values between 0.6 and 0.9), F is a function depending on the field distortion parameters ε_1 and ε_2 as explained in Fig. 2.12, the effective spin-orbit coupling constant $\alpha^2\lambda_0$ (where λ_0 refers to the free ion), and the temperature T. The dependence of F on the various parameters is given in graphical form in [2.62].

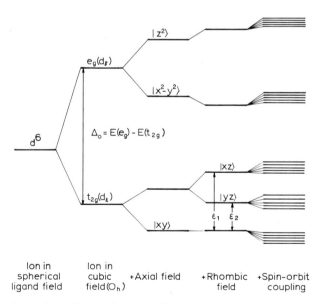

Fig. 2.12. Energy level diagram for Fe(II) high spin under the action of the crystalline field and spin-orbit coupling (cf. [2.62]). Spin-orbit interaction lifts the five-fold spin degeneracy of each orbital state and mixes the orbital wave functions; this decreases the value of F defined in (2.42) and thus the quadrupole splitting

2.3.2. Effect of $(V_{zz})_{MO}$; Bonding Properties

Iodine and Xenon Compounds

As discussed in Subsection 2.2.2, the observed trends of isomer shifts in iodine and xenon compounds may be explained solely by changes in the electronic population of the $5p$ orbitals. Furthermore, the isomer shifts in these compounds correlate linearly with observed quadrupole splittings [2.68, 69, 31]. Unbalanced electron population in the $5p_x$, $5p_y$, and $5p_z$ orbitals is considered responsible for this observation. On the basis of the simple Townes-Dailey approach [2.70, 71], $(V_{zz})_{val}$ may be expressed by (cf. Table 2.1)

$$(V_{zz})_{val} = \tfrac{4}{5} e \langle r^{-3} \rangle_p [-N_{p_z} + \tfrac{1}{2}(N_{p_x} + N_{p_y})]. \qquad (2.43)$$

The fractional populations N in the $5p_x$, $5p_y$, and $5p_z$ orbitals of iodine and xenon will be influenced by both σ- and π-bonding between iodine (xenon) and the attached ligand. For ICl and IBr e.g. one has found that, due to the more electronegative halogens Cl and Br, N_{p_z} (the p_z orbital coincides with the molecular axis) is considerably less than 1, the value taken for N_{p_z} in I_2, by σ-interaction; N_{p_x} and N_{p_y}, however, deviate only very little from the I_2 values of 2 because of negligible π-interaction. Consequently, $V_{zz} \approx (1 - \underline{R})$ $(V_{zz})_{MO} > 0$.

Covalent Iron(II) and Ru(II) Compounds

The metal-to-ligand bonds in strongly covalent Fe(II) and Ru(II) compounds are influenced by both σ- and π-interaction. It is therefore anticipated that both mechanisms will affect $(V_{zz})_{MO}$. Consider the series of $[Fe^{II}(CN)_5 X^{n-}]^{(3+n)-}$ complexes as an example (cf. Table 2.3). The plus signs of Δ in these complexes have been determined using the applied magnetic field technique [2.63]; those given in brackets have been predicted. To a first approximation, one assumes that a) any quadrupole splitting arises mainly from an unbalanced $3d$ orbital population, b) any change in the EFG is due to the varied ligand X and not to a change in the bonding properties in the $Fe(CN)_5$ moiety, and c) lattice contributions $(V_{zz})_L$ from neighboring anions and cations are negligible. In $[Fe(CN)_6]^{4-}$, where $X = CN^-$, both the valence electron structure and the molecular symmetry about the iron atom are cubic (O_h); all three contributions in (2.22a) (at the beginning of Section 2.3) are zero and no quadrupole splitting is observed. If X is different from CN^- (cf. Table 2.3), the two mechanisms, σ-donation and π-acceptance, enter the game and create $(V_{zz})_{MO} \neq 0$, the sign of which being determined by their relative strengths compared to $X = CN^-$. If X is a stronger σ-donor than CN^-, then $N(d_{z^2}) > N(d_{x^2-y^2})$ (the Fe−X axis is chosen to be the z-axis) and a negative contribution to $(V_{zz})_{MO}$ results. If X is a more effective π-acceptor than CN^-, then $N(d_{xy}) > [N(d_{xz}) + N(d_{yz})]/2$ because of a more pronounced charge delocalization from the metal onto X, and a positive contribution to $(V_{zz})_{MO}$ is expected. The combined effect is to make $(V_{zz})_{MO}$ more negative with increasing $(\sigma - \pi)$. It turns out that all X-ligands in the Fe^{II} pentacyanide series given in Table 2.3 are less effective $(\sigma - \pi)$ ligands than CN^-; the measured values for Δ indicate that σ increases and/or π decreases in the order $NO^+ < NO_2^- < SO_3^= \sim H_2O < NH_3 < CO$. NO^+ is an extremely good π acceptor ligand and gives the most positive Δ value.

What is most desirable in this context is a separation of σ- and π-interactions, as already pointed out in Subsection 2.2.2. In fact, this has been done, at least qualitatively, by plotting the isomer shift versus quadrupole splitting for several series of Fe^{II} compounds [2.72, 73]. BANCROFT et al. [2.72] have found that e.g. the N_2 ligand (which is of great interest in nitrogen fixation chemistry) apparently is a comparable $(\sigma + \pi)$ ligand to the nitriles, but an appreciably better π-acceptor and poorer σ-donor than the nitriles.

More rigorous analyses of the quadrupole splittings in the Fe^{II} pentacyanide series recently carried out by several investigators [2.51, 74] using self-consistent field molecular orbital approaches [2.50] show that the above approximations a, b, and c are somewhat crude. The treatment by TRAUTWEIN et al. [2.74] includes EFG contributions from the Fe valence electrons (d and p) and from net atomic charges q_a/e on other atoms a:

$$\Delta E_Q = \tfrac{1}{2} e Q V_{zz} (1 + \tfrac{1}{3}\eta^2)^{1/2}, \qquad (2.44)$$

with

$$
\begin{aligned}
V_{zz} = e \Big[& (1 - \underline{R})_{3d} \langle r^{-3} \rangle_{3d} \sum_{3d} P_{3d,3d} f_{3d} \\
& + (1 - \underline{R})_{4p} \langle r^{-3} \rangle_{4p} \sum_{4p} P_{4p,4p} f_{4p} \\
& + (1 - \gamma_\infty) \sum_a \frac{1}{e} q_a (3z_a^2 - r_a^2)/r_a^5 \Big]
\end{aligned}
\qquad (2.45)
$$

and similarly for the asymmetry parameter

$$\eta = \frac{e}{V_{zz}}\left[(1 - \underline{R})_{3d}\langle r^{-3}\rangle_{3d}(P_{3d_{yz},3d_{yz}} - P_{3d_{xz},3d_{xz}})\tfrac{6}{7}\right.$$
$$+ (1 - \underline{R})_{4p}\langle r^{-3}\rangle_{4p}(P_{4p_y,4p_y} - P_{4p_x,4p_x})\tfrac{6}{5} \qquad (2.46)$$
$$\left. + (1 - \gamma_\infty)\sum_a \frac{3}{e} q_a(x_a^2 - y_a^2)/r_a^5\right].$$

P_m, P_m are the bond order matrix elements for the orbital states $|m\rangle$ of the $3d$ and $4p$ subshells, f_{3d} and f_{4p} refer to the $(V_{zz})_{val}$ components as given in Table 2.1, the other symbols have been explained in Subsection 2.1.2.

The most important results of TRAUTWEIN et al. [2.74] may be summarized as follows: 1) The EFG in the Fe (II) pentacyanide series is substantially influenced not only by the population of the $|xy\rangle$, $|xz\rangle$, and $|yz\rangle$ orbitals of the iron $3d$ subshell, but also by those in the $|z^2\rangle$ and $|x^2 - y^2\rangle$ orbitals. The latter occupancies cancel in their effect on the EFG only if they are equal. 2) The EFG is also influenced by departures of the electronic distribution from axial symmetry (Fe$-$NO axis apparently is bent and fixed in a certain position, as has also been found in MO calculations by DORN [2.51]). 3) Net charges from surrounding atoms contribute to the EFG as well as, to some extent, asymmetric electron populations in the $4p$ subshell. 4) On reduction of $[Fe(CN)_5 NO]^{2-}$ to $[Fe(CN)_5 NO]^{3-}$ the added electron is distributed, on the average, to ca. 70% on the NO ligand, which is indicative of the very strong π-acceptor capacity of NO^+, and to ca. 30% on the iron central ion, in good agreement with calculations by other authors [2.51, 75].

Ru (II) compounds, like those listed in Table 2.3, also yield satisfactory correlations between the isomer shift and quadrupole splitting. In the Ru ammine series there will be no quadrupole splitting, if X is substituted for NH_3. Otherwise the quadrupole splitting becomes more negative with increasing $(\sigma - \pi)$ of X, relative to $X = NH_3$. For the $RuX_5 NO$ series Δ is assumed to be positive because of the strong π-acceptor properties of NO^+ relative to X. Δ becomes more positive in the order $X = Br^- < Cl^- \sim NCS^- < CN^-$.

A simple molecular orbital approach has been suggested to rationalize the observed 2: -1 ratio for the quadrupole splitting in octahedral trans- and cis-MA_2B_4 compounds [2.59]. According to the different nature of the ligands A and B, the M$-$A and M$-$B bonds will be different; i.e. the electron populations of the σ- and π-molecular orbitals will not be the same for the M$-$A and M$-$B bonds in one compound. This anisotropic electron structure creates a $(V_{zz})_{MO}$ contribution to the EFG, which is different for the *cis*-MA$_2$B$_4$ and *trans*-MA$_2$B$_4$ isomers by a factor of -2. The simple calculational method of finding this factor of -2 is described in detail in [2.12, 16].

2.3.3. Effect of $(V_{zz})_L$; Molecular Symmetry

Non-cubically distributed charges on atoms and/or ligands about the Mössbauer nucleus give rise to an EFG contribution $(V_{zz})_L$. Predictions about the relative magnitude and the sign of $(V_{zz})_L$ can be made using the simple *point-charge formalism* under the assumption that the additivity concept holds, i.e. that the quadrupole splitting can be regarded, to a first approximation, as the sum of independent contributions, one for each ligand X. It is assumed that a particular ligand X in a certain position of the principal axis system always gives the same contribution to the EFG tensor for a given central atom with a certain coordination number. We call this contribution *partial field gradient* (p.f.g.); it gives rise to a *partial quadrupole splitting* p.q.s. $= (1/2)eQ[X]$, where $[X]$ is calculated using (2.18).

The point-charge model has been applied successfully to interpret the quadrupole splitting in a wide range of iron (II) low spin complexes of the types FeA$_2$B$_4$ and FeAB$_5$ [2.76, 77]. Some representative results are listed in Table 2.6. There is no quadrupole splitting in Compound 1 because of the cubic molecular symmetry. For the other compounds in Table 2.6 the point-charge model, using (2.18), predicts

a) $(V_{zz})_L$ (*trans*-FeA$_2$B$_4$) $= (4[A] - 4[B])$,   (2.47a)

b) $(V_{zz})_L$ (*cis*-FeA$_2$B$_4$) $= (-2[A] + 2[B])$,   (2.47b)

c) $(V_{zz})_L$ (FeAB$_5$) $= (2[A] - 2[B])$ (2.47c)

where

$$[A] = q_A/r_A^3, \ [B] = q_B/r_B^3.$$

One notices the excellent agreement between experiment and prediction concerning the ratios of $(a):(b):(c) = 2:-1:1$. There will always be, to some extent, a $(V_{zz})_{MO}$ effect, as described in Subsection 2.3.2, going along with $(V_{zz})_L$. A separation of the two contributions is possible, but not to any great precision, and only in connection with rather tedious MO calculations. The two contributions may be of comparable magnitude and opposite sign, so that they fortuitously cancel.

Table 2.6. Quadrupole splittings for some Fe(II) low spin complexes

Compound	Δ [mm sec^{-1}]	Ref.
1. $[Fe(CNEt)_6](ClO_4)_2$	0.00	[2.76]
2. cis-$[Fe(CN)_2(CNEt)_4]$	(+)0.29[a]	[2.76]
3. trans-$[Fe(CN)_2(CNEt)_4]$	− 0.60	[2.76]
4. $[FeCl(ArNC)_5](ClO_4)$	+ 0.70	[2.77]
5. cis-$[FeCl_2(ArNC)_4]$	− 0.78	[2.77]
6. trans-$[FeCl_2(ArNC)_4]$	+ 1.55	[2.77]

[a] Sign predicted.

The point-charge formalism has also been extensively applied to rationalizing the quadrupole splitting in 6-, 5-, and 4-coordinate tin (IV) compounds of various geometries (octahedral, trigonal-bipyramidal, tetrahedral) [2.78–81]. BANCROFT and PLATT have collected, from various sources, the point-charge expressions for the components of the EFG tensor for the most common structures [2.12]; their compilation is extremely useful in predictive calculations concerning $(V_{zz})_L$.

2.4. Conclusion

In Sections 2.2 and 2.3 we have seen how to deduce information about the electronic structure and bonding properties of a Mössbauer atom and the molecular symmetry from a measured spectrum. Once the chemically important Mössbauer parameters of a substance are known, it is then rather easy, to use the Mössbauer technique to identify a chemical species or even a number of species containing the same Mössbauer atom in a mixture. It is of great advantage that the Mössbauer effect operates selectively, i.e. only hyperfine interactions felt by the particular Mössbauer nuclide, which is being used as a probe in the source-absorber pair, are reflected in the Mössbauer spectrum. Furthermore, the Mössbauer effect, to be successfully observed, does not require a crystallographically ordered state; amorphous and glasseous samples may also be studied. Quantitative analysis is possible after appropriate calibration. Finally, it should be emphasized that the chemical and physical state of a material is not noticeably altered by the γ-radiation during the measurement, because the γ-dose given to the sample is too small to cause any observable radiation damage.

The most important Mössbauer parameters in chemical investigations are undoubtedly a) the isomer shift and b) the quadrupole splitting. Yet there are other observable parameters, which may be of great value in the study of chemical problems: c) internal magnetic field, d) shape, width at half-maximum, and intensity of the resonance lines, e) effect of an applied magnetic field, f) angular dependence in single crystals, g) temperature and pressure dependence of a)–d).

There are essentially two kinds of applications of the Mössbauer effect in chemistry:

1) Fundamental studies of compounds with respect to

a) electronic structure of the Mössbauer atom, e.g. oxidation state and spin state;

b) bond properties, e.g. σ- and π-interaction between the Mössbauer atom and bonded ligands, influence of the electronegativity of the ligands;

c) structural properties, e.g. molecular geometry, distortion from cubic symmetry (Jahn-Teller theorem), effect of polymerization;

d) magnetic properties in "diluted" systems (diamagnetism, para-magnetism, temperature-dependent spin change) and cooperative phenomena (ferro-, ferri-, antiferromagnetism);

e) dynamic processes, e.g. electron-hopping in spinels, spin-spin and spin-lattice relaxation.

2) Use of the Mössbauer effect as an analytical tool for identifying chemical species (qualitative and quantitative analysis) in various fields of chemistry, e.g.

a) solid state reactions, e.g. ligand exchange in transition metal complexes, thermal and radiation induced decompositions, electron exchange reactions;

b) surface studies, e.g. corrosion on iron and steel surfaces, adsorption properties of ion exchange resins, surface reactions on catalysts;

c) frozen solution studies, e.g. ligand exchange reactions, solvent effects, ions in ice, polymerization;

d) phase transitions, e.g. magnetic ordering, change in crystal structure;

e) chemical reactions associated with nuclear decay processes (decay after-effects).

Acknowledgments

The author expresses his thanks to his colleagues, associates, and students for stimulating discussions and for reading the manuscript. He is also indebted to the "Deutsche Forschungsgemeinschaft", the "Bundesministerium for Forschung und Technologie", and the "Fonds der Chemischen Industrie" for financial support of his research in this field.

References

2.1. O. C. KISTNER, A. W. SUNYAR: Phys. Rev. Letters **4**, 229 (1960).
2.2. E. FLUCK: Advan. Inorg. Chem. Radiochem. **6**, 433 (1964).
2.3. J. F. DUNCAN, R. M. GOLDING: Quart. Rev. **19**, 36 (1965).
2.4. I. J. GRUVERMAN (ed.): *Mössbauer Effect Methodology*, Vol. 1 (Plenum Press, New York, 1965) and annually afterwards.
2.5. E. FLUCK: Fortschr. chem. Forsch. **5**, 399 (1966) (German).
2.6. J. R. DE VOE, J. J. SPIJKERMAN: Anal. Chem. **38**, 382 R (1966); **40**, 472 R (1968); **42**, 366 R (1970).
2.7. R. H. HERBER: Ann. Rev. Phys. Chem. **17**, 261 (1966).
2.8. R. H. HERBER: Prog. Inorg. Chem. **8**, 1 (1967).
2.9. N. N. GREENWOOD: In *"Spectroscopic Properties of Inorganic and Organometallic Compounds"*, Chem. Soc., Specialist Periodical Report 1967 and periodically afterwards.
2.10. D. A. SHIRLEY: Ann. Rev. Phys. Chem. **20**, 25 (1969).
2.11. M. L. GOOD: In *"Coordination Chemistry"*, Vol. 1, ACS Monograph, ed. by A. E. MARTELL (Van Nostrand Reinhold Comp., New York, 1971).
2.12. G. M. BANCROFT, R. H. Platt: Advan. Inorg. Chem. Radiochem. **15**, 59 (1972).
2.13. V. I. GOLDANSKII, R. H. HERBER (eds.): *Chemical Applications of Mössbauer Spectroscopy* (Academic Press, New York, 1968).
2.14. L. MAY (ed.): *An Introduction to Mössbauer Spectroscopy* (Adam Hilger, London, 1971).
2.15. N. N. GREENWOOD, T. C. GIBB: *Mössbauer Spectroscopy*, 1st ed. (Chapman & Hall Ltd., London, 1971).
2.16. G. M. BANCROFT: *Mössbauer Spectroscopy*, An Introduction for Inorganic Chemists and Geochemists (McGraw-Hill, London-New York, 1973).
2.17. L. R. WALKER, G. K. WERTHEIM, V. JACCARINO: Phys. Rev. Letters **6**, 98 (1961); G. K. WERTHEIM: *Mössbauer Effect:* Principles and Applications, 1st ed. (Academic Press, New York-London, 1964), pp. 49–58.
2.18. D. A. SHIRLEY: Rev. Mod. Phys. **36**, 339 (1964).
2.19. J. G. STEVENS, V. E. STEVENS: *Mössbauer Effect Data Index*, Volumes 1969, 1970, 1971 (Adam Hilger, London).
2.20. R. M. STERNHEIMER: Phys. Rev. **80**, 102 (1950); **84**, 244 (1951); **130**, 1423 (1963); H. M. FOLEY, R. M. STERNHEIMER, D. TYCKO: Phys. Rev. **93**, 734 (1954); R. M. STERNHEIMER, H. M. FOLEY: Phys. Rev. **102**, 731 (1956).
2.21. R. G. BARNES, W. V. SMITH: Phys. Rev. **93**, 95 (1954).
2.22. A. ABRAGAM: *The Principles of Nuclear Magnetism* (Oxford University Press, Clarendon, London-New York, 1961), p. 161.
2.23. R. E. WATSON: Phys. Rev. **118**, 1036 (1960); **119**, 1934 (1960); Techn. Rep. 12, M.I.T., Solid State and Molecular Theory Group, Cambridge, Mass. (1959).
2.24. J. DANON: In *"Chemical Applications of Mössbauer Spectroscopy"*, ed. by V. I. GOLDANSKII, R. H. HERBER (Academic Press, New York, 1968), p. 169.
2.25. L. PAULING: *The Nature of the Chemical Bond*, 3rd ed. (Cornell University Press, Ithaca, N.Y., 1967), p. 26.
2.26. C. A. COULSON: *Valence*, 2nd ed. (Oxford University Press, Oxford, 1965).
2.27. C. J. BALLHAUSEN, H. B. GRAY: *Molecular Orbital Theory*, 1st ed. (W. A. Benjamin Inc., New York, 1965).
2.28. M. PASTERNAK, A. SIMOPOULOS, Y. HAZONY: Phys. Rev. **140** A, 1892 (1965).
2.29. C. A. CLAUSEN, M. L. GOOD: Inorg. Chem. **9**, 817 (1970).
2.30. A. G. DAVIES, L. SMITH, P. J. SMITH: J. Organomet. Chem. **23**, 135 (1970).
2.31. G. J. PERLOW, H. YOSHIDA: J. Chem. Phys. **49**, 1474 (1968).

2.32. R. V. PARISH: Prog. Inorg. Chem. **15**, 101 (1972).

2.33. R. C. AXTMANN, Y. HAZONY, J. W. HURLEY: Chem. Phys. Letters **2**, 673 (1968).

2.34. P. GÜTLICH, S. ODAR, A. WEISS: To be published.

2.35. H. PAULY, A. WEISS, H. WITTE: Z. Metallkde. **59**, 47 (1968).

2.36. H. PAULY, A. WEISS, H. WITTE: Z. Metallkde. **59**, 554 (1968).

2.37. R. E. WATSON, J. HUDIS, M. L. PERLMAN: Phys. Rev. B **4**, 4139 (1971).

2.38. M. O. FALTENS: Ph. D. Thesis, University of California, Berkeley (1969) UCRL 18706.

2.39. W. KERLER, W. NEUWIRTH: Z. Physik **167**, 176 (1962).

2.40. F. A. COTTON: *Chemical Applications of Group Theory*, 2nd ed. (Wiley Interscience, New York-London, 1971).

2.41. M. WOLFSBERG, L. HELMHOLZ: J. Chem. Phys. **20**, 837 (1952).

2.42. C. C. J. ROOTHAAN: Rev. Mod. Phys. **23**, 69 (1951).

2.43. C. J. BALLHAUSEN, H. B. GRAY: Inorg. Chem. **1**, 831 (1962).

2.44. H. B. GRAY: J. Chem. Educ. **41**, 2 (1964).

2.45. H. B. GRAY: *Electrons and Chemical Bonding* (W. A. Benjamin, Inc., New York-Amsterdam, 1965).

2.46. H. B. GRAY, C. J. BALLHAUSEN: J. Am. Chem. Soc. **85**, 260 (1963).

2.47. C. K. JØRGENSEN: *Absorption Spectra and Chemical Bonding in Complexes* (Pergamon Press, Oxford, 1964).

2.48. H. D. BARTUNIK, W. POTZEL, R. L. MÖSSBAUER, G. KAINDL: Z. Physik **240**, 1 (1970).

2.49. M. O. FALTENS, D. A. SHIRLEY: J. Chem. Phys. **53**, 4249 (1970).

2.50. A. TRAUTWEIN, F. E. HARRIS: Theor. Chim. Acta **30**, 45 (1973).

2.51. W. DORN: Dissertation, Universität Hamburg, 1974.

2.52. E. FLUCK, W. KERLER, W. NEUWIRTH: Angew. Chem. Internat. Ed. **2**, 277 (1963).

2.53. N. L. COSTA, J. DANON, R. M. XAVIER: J. Phys. Chem. Solids **23**, 1783 (1962).

2.54. E. FLUCK, P. KUHN: Z. Allg. Anorg. Chem. **350**, 263 (1967).

2.55. N. E. ERICKSON: Ph. D. Thesis, University of Washington, Seattle, USA, 1964.

2.56. W. POTZEL, F. E. WAGNER, U. ZAHN, R. L. MÖSSBAUER, J. DANON: Z. Physik **240**, 306 (1970).

2.57. R. GREATREX, N. N. GREENWOOD, P. KASPI: J. Chem. Soc. (A), 1873 (1971).

2.58. R. H. HERBER, R. B. KING, G. K. WERTHEIM: Inorg. Chem. **3**, 101 (1964).

2.59. G. M. BANCROFT, M. J. MAYS, B. E. PRATER: J. Chem. Soc. (A), 956 (1970).

2.60. H. L. SCHLÄFER, G. GLIEMANN: *Einführung in die Ligandenfeldtheorie* (Akademische Verlagsgesellschaft, Frankfurt/Main, 1967).

2.61. C. J. BALLHAUSEN: *Introduction to Ligand Field Theory* (McGraw-Hill, London-New York, 1962).

2.62. R. INGALLS: Phys. Rev. **133** A, 787 (1964).

2.63. R. L. COLLINS: J. Chem. Phys. **42**, 1072 (1965).

2.64. P. R. EDWARDS, C. E. JOHNSON, R. J. P. WILLIAMS: J. Chem. Phys. **47**, 2074 (1967).

2.65. P. GÜTLICH, W. MÜLLER, K. M. HASSELBACH: J. Physique (in press).

2.66. W. MÜLLER: M. S. Thesis, Technische Hochschule Darmstadt, Fed. R. Germany (1974).

2.67. J. L. K. F. DE VRIES: Ph. D. Dissertation, Catholic University of Nijmegen, Netherlands, 1972.

2.68. M. PASTERNAK, T. SONNINO: J. Chem. Phys. **48**, 1997 (1968).

2.69. S. BUKSHPAN, R. H. HERBER: J. Chem. Phys. **46**, 3375 (1967).

2.70. C. H. TOWNES, B. P. DAILEY: J. Chem. Phys. **17**, 782 (1949).

2.71. B. P. DAILEY, C. H. TOWNES: J. Chem. Phys. **23**, 118 (1955).

2.72. G. M. BANCROFT, M. J. MAYS, B. E. PRATER, F. P. STEFANINI: J. Chem. Soc. (A), 2146 (1970).

2.73. B. W. Dale, R. J. P. Williams, P. R. Edwards, C. E. Johnson: Trans. Faraday Soc. **64**, 620 (1968); **64**, 3011 (1968).

2.74. A. Trautwein, F. E. Harris, I. Dézsi: Theor. Chim. Acta (in press).

2.75. P. T. Manoharan, H. B. Gray: J. Am. Chem. Soc. **87**, 3340 (1965).

2.76. R. R. Berrett, B. W. Fitzsimmons: J. Chem. Soc. (A), 525 (1967).

2.77. G. M. Bancroft, M. J. Mays, B. E. Prater: Chem. Commun. **1968**, 1374.

2.78. R. V. Parish, R. H. Platt: Inorg. Chim. Acta **4**, 65 (1970).

2.79. B. W. Fitzsimmons, N. J. Seeley, A. W. Smith: J. Chem. Soc. (A), 143 (1969).

2.80. G. M. Bancroft, K. D. Butler, A. T. Rake, B. Dale: J. Chem. Soc. (Dalton), 2025 (1972).

2.81. J. Ensling, P. Gütlich, K. M. Hasselbach, B. W. Fitzsimmons: J. Chem. Soc. (A), 1940 (1971).

3. Mössbauer Spectroscopy in Magnetism: Characterization of Magnetically-Ordered Compounds

R. W. GRANT

With 21 Figures

3.1. Introduction

Before the Mössbauer effect was discovered, the possibility of directly observing gamma ray transitions between individual nuclear magnetic substates seemed to be unlikely because of the very small energy differences involved; an internal magnetic field H_{int} of 150 kOe at a spin one-half nucleus with a nuclear moment of 1 μ will produce a hyperfine splitting on the order of 10^{-6} eV. If the gamma ray connecting two nuclear levels has a nominal energy of 10 keV, one would need an energy resolution of about 1 part in 10^{10} to directly resolve individual transitions between magnetic substates. Mössbauer spectroscopy not only makes it possible to obtain this rather phenomenal energy resolution, but, in fact, for many Mössbauer isotopes considerably better resolution is achieved. It is the ability to directly observe and study magnetic hyperfine structure that makes Mössbauer spectroscopy a valuable tool for investigating magnetically-ordered substances.

The study of the magnetic properties of materials has been one of the most frequent applications of Mössbauer spectroscopy. For this purpose the isotope Fe^{57} has been used far more often than all other Mössbauer isotopes. There are several reasons for the popularity of Fe^{57} in magnetic material investigations. Certainly, one of the most important reasons is the common occurrence of iron as a constituent of many of the most interesting and technologically important magnetic materials. Even in those magnetic materials where iron is not a normal constituent, it is often possible to incorporate small amounts of Fe^{57} (or the parent isotope Co^{57}) as a substitutional impurity in small enough amounts that the basic properties of the material are not substantially altered. An additional reason for the popularity of Fe^{57} in magnetic materials studies is that many magnetically-ordered iron compounds (including the oxides of iron which are of particular technological importance) have fairly large effective Debye temperatures; consequently, the Fe^{57} resonance in these materials usually can be observed easily at temperatures even well above room temperature. Also, the relatively long lifetime ($\sim 10^{-7}$ sec) of the Fe^{57} 14.4 keV excited nuclear state and the corresponding narrow resonant line width ($\sim 10^{-8}$ eV) coupled with the small values of the relevant nuclear spins and sizeable nuclear moments often make it possible to study completely resolved hyperfine structure; the use of many Mössbauer isotopes for magnetic materials investigations is severely complicated by grossly overlapping hyperfine transitions. Finally, the relatively long half-life of the parent isotope Co^{57} and the commercial availability of high-quality sources are important practical considerations for many experimenters.

Because Fe^{57} Mössbauer spectroscopy is used so extensively for magnetic materials studies, the experimental illustrations and discussions of hyperfine structure given in this chapter will be specific for this isotope. Mössbauer isotopes other than Fe^{57} can, of course, be used to investigate magnetic materials. In principle at least, information analogous to that obtained by Fe^{57} Mössbauer spectroscopy can be obtained from such investigations; the analysis of these experiments would differ only in that for the specific transition being employed, appropriate nuclear moments, nuclear spins and gamma ray multipolarities would have to be used. In practice, no other isotope as yet has all of the attractive features, mentioned above, which are associated with Fe^{57}.

This chapter will begin with a general discussion of hyperfine structure observed in Fe^{57} Mössbauer spectroscopy of magnetically-ordered compounds. A procedure is outlined to evaluate hyperfine parameters in the presence of mixed electric monopole, magnetic dipole and electric quadrupole interactions. The second section of this chapter will discuss some of the more common applications of Mössbauer spectroscopy for characterizing magnetic compounds. These will include the determination of magnetic transition temperatures, phase analysis and transitions and site distribution studies. The results of several experimental studies will be used to illustrate these applications. The final section of this chapter contains a discussion on the use of Mössbauer spectroscopy for magnetic structure investigations-particularly by making use of polarized radiation. The magnetic structure determination of $Ca_2Fe_2O_5$ (a colinear antiferromagnet) and FeOCl (a noncolinear antiferromagnet) are discussed; also, the determination of the spin reorientation mechanism in the rare earth orthoferrite $ErFeO_3$ is reviewed. Much of the material presented in this chapter was drawn from two previously published papers [3.1, 2].

3.2. Analysis of Fe^{57} Hyperfine Structure

In the study of magnetic materials by Mössbauer spectroscopy, it is frequently desirable to evaluate accurately the hyperfine parameters. These parameters contain information on the properties of ions and the local environment of Mössbauer isotopes; it is often of interest to compare experimentally measured hyperfine parameters with theoretical calculations. The detailed analysis of hyperfine structure in magnetically-ordered materials is not always completely trivial. In the presence of mixed magnetic dipole and electric quadrupole interactions, the nuclear magnetic quantum number m_I may not be a good quantum number and the nuclear wave functions become mixed expressions of $|m_I\rangle$. A nucleus with spin I greater than zero may have a nonzero magnetic dipole moment; in addition, a nucleus with $I > 1/2$ may have a nonzero electric quadrupole moment. The 14.4 keV state of Fe^{57} has a spin of 3/2 while the ground state has $I_g = 1/2$; thus both magnetic dipole and electric quadrupole interactions may occur in the excited state. The origin of hyperfine interactions was already mentioned in Chapters 1 and 2.

There are many useful literature references which discuss the derivation of hyperfine parameters. The calculation of eigenvalues and eigenvectors is thoroughly discussed in [3.3, 4]. Several computer programs have been developed for this purpose, see, for example [3.5–7], and appropriate analytical techniques have been obtained [3.8]. In addition, KÜNDIG [3.9] has published extensive graphs which describe solutions for many interesting cases of mixed hyperfine interactions. Because much of the valuable information to be learned about magnetic compounds is contained in the hyperfine parameters, this section will discuss the analysis of Fe^{57} hyperfine structure.

3.2.1. Mixed Magnetic Dipole and Electric Quadrupole Interactions

When the crystallographic point symmetry at a lattice site is sufficiently low, the magnetic dipole and electric quadrupole hyperfine inter-actions may have an arbitrary spacial relation. It is necessary to adopt convenient coordinate systems to relate H_{int} to the electric field gradient (EFG) and the gamma-ray propagation direction k; one such system of coordinates is shown in Fig. 3.1. Because the electric field is a vector, the gradient of the electric field is a symmetric 3×3 second-rank tensor which can be diagonalized in a principal axis system and specified by the diagonal elements V_{xx}, V_{yy}, and V_{zz} ($V_{xx} \equiv \partial^2 V/\partial x^2$ etc., where V is the electric potential). Only s electrons

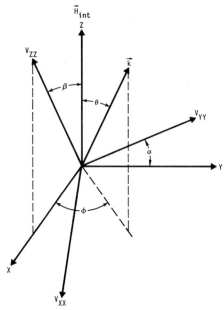

Fig. 3.1. Definition of coordinate systems relating the internal magnetic field (H_{int}), the electric field gradient parameters (V_{jj}), and the gamma ray propagation direction (k)

have finite charge density at the nucleus and because these electrons have a spherically symmetric spacial distribution, they do not contribute to the EFG. Thus, the EFG is produced by non-s electrons and charges external to the ion. Because there is no non-spherical charge in the nuclear vicinity, Laplace's equation requires the EFG to be a traceless tensor; i.e.,

$$V_{xx} + V_{yy} + V_{zz} = 0 \tag{3.1}$$

and, therefore, only two of the three diagonal elements are independent. The conventional description of the EFG defines two slightly different parameters

$$q = V_{zz}/e \tag{3.2}$$

and

$$\eta = (V_{xx} - V_{yy})/V_{zz}, \tag{3.3}$$

where e is the charge of the proton. The elements of the diagonalized EFG are normally defined so that $|V_{zz}| \geq |V_{yy}| \geq |V_{xx}|$; this definition restricts η to $0 \leq \eta \leq 1$. In Fig. 3.1 and below the notation that V_{zz} specifies the z principal axis of the EFG, etc., is used. The x axis of Fig. 3.1 is in the plane defined by H_{int} and V_{zz} and is perpendicular to H_{int}; the y axis is perpendicular to both x and H_{int} and is in the plane defined by V_{xx} and V_{yy}. The angles α and β are Euler angles relating the EFG principal axes to the xyz coordinate system. By arbitrarily choosing x, V_{zz}, and H_{int} to be coplanar, only two of the three Euler angles are necessary to relate the EFG and H_{int} coordinate systems. To transform the xyz coordinate system into the V_{jj} system, one first rotates by β about y (to align z and V_{zz}) and then by α about the new position of z. The quantization axis is parallel to z. The angles θ and ϕ are the polar and azimuthal angles which relate k to the xyz coordinate system of H_{int}.

The matrix elements of the total interaction Hamiltonian have been derived by MATTHIAS et al. [3.3]. The nonzero elements are given by

$$H_{m_I m_I} = -\omega_H \hbar m_I + 0.5 \omega_Q \hbar (3 \cos^2 \beta - 1 + \eta \sin^2 \beta \cos 2\alpha)$$
$$[3 m_I^2 - I(I+1)], \tag{3.4}$$

$$H_{m_I m_I \pm 1} = 1.5 \omega_Q \hbar \sin \beta \{ \cos \beta \mp \eta \, [(1 \pm \cos \beta) \exp(2i\alpha)$$
$$- (1 \mp \cos \beta) \exp(-2i\alpha)]/6 \} \, (2m_I \pm 1) \tag{3.5}$$
$$\cdot [(I \mp m_I)(I \pm m_I + 1)]^{1/2}$$

and

$$H_{m_I m_I \pm 2} = 0.75 \omega_Q \hbar \{ \sin^2 \beta + \eta \, [(1 \pm \cos \beta)^2 \exp(2i\alpha)$$
$$+ (1 \mp \cos \beta)^2 \exp(-2i\alpha)]/6 \} \, [(I \pm m_I + 2) \tag{3.6}$$
$$\cdot (I \pm m_I + 1)(I \mp m_I)(I \mp m_I - 1)]^{1/2}.$$

The parameters ω_H and ω_Q are defined as

$$\omega_H \hbar = g_N H_{int} \mu \tag{3.7}$$

and

$$\omega_Q \hbar = e^2 q Q / 4I (2I - 1), \tag{3.8}$$

where g_N is the nuclear g-factor, μ is the nuclear moment, $h (= 2\pi\hbar)$ is Planck's constant, eQ is the nuclear quadrupole moment and $i = (-1)^{1/2}$.

The problem of calculating the eigenvalues and corresponding eigenvectors from the above matrix is treated in standard texts on matrix algebra (see, e.g., [3.10]). The problem is trivial for the Fe[57] ground state because no quadrupole interaction exists, and by choosing the quantization axis to be parallel to H_{int}, the ground state interaction Hamiltonian is always diagonal. For the Fe^{57} excited state the problem involves diagonalizing a 4×4 Hermitian matrix. Since one usually wants to compare several calculations with experiment in order to derive hyperfine parameters, computer methods are very helpful.

Once the eigenvalues of excited and ground states are obtained, the relative transition energies are calculated trivially (an isomer shift increases or decreases all relative transition energies by the same amount). One next wants to be able to calculate the transition probabilities associated with the various transitions. The gamma transition connecting the 14.4 keV excited state of Fe^{57} to the ground state is essentially pure magnetic dipole ($M1$) radiation, [3.11, 12]; that is, each gamma-ray is associated with one unit ($\hbar$) of angular momentum and there is no nuclear parity change. The selection rules for magnetic dipole radiation are $\Delta m_I = \pm 1$ or 0; $\Delta m_I = \pm 2$ is forbidden. For this radiation field, HOUSLEY et al. [3.13] have derived an appropriate expression for the amplitude of the electric field vector $\varepsilon(r)$ by using the formulation of BLATT and WEISSKOPF [3.14]. This expression is given by

$$\varepsilon(r) \sim [a(1, 1) \exp(i\phi) + a(1, -1) \exp(-i\phi)] \hat{\theta}$$
$$+ i[a(1, 1) \cos\theta \exp(i\phi) + a(1, 0) \sqrt{2} \sin\theta - a(1, -1) \qquad (3.9)$$
$$\cdot \cos\theta \exp(-i\phi)] \hat{\phi},$$

where $\hat{\theta}$ and $\hat{\phi}$ are orthogonal spherical unit vectors defined by the angles θ and ϕ of Fig. 3.1. The coefficients $a(1, \Delta m_I)$ for a particular transition between magnetic substates of the Fe^{57} 14.4 keV and ground nuclear states are defined in terms of Clebsch-Gordan coefficients and the eigenvector coefficients which are calculated as outlined above. The appropriate expression is given by

$$a(1, \Delta m_I) = \alpha_i C_{1, 1/2}(3/2, m_3, \Delta m_I, m_1). \qquad (3.10)$$

The eigenvector expressions for the excited state have the form

$$\psi_i = \sum_{m_3 = -3/2}^{3/2} \alpha_i |m_3\rangle \qquad (3.11)$$

and $m_1 = \pm 1/2$ specifies the ground magnetic substates; Δm_I is defined as $\Delta m_I = m_3 - m_1$. The Clebsch-Gordan coefficients necessary for calculations involving $M1$ radiation are

$$C_{1,1/2}(3/2, -3/2, -1, -1/2) = C_{1,1/2}(3/2, 3/2, 1, 1/2) = 1$$
$$C_{1,1/2}(3/2, -1/2, 0, -1/2) = C_{1,1/2}(3/2, 1/2, 0, 1/2) = \sqrt{2/3} \qquad (3.12)$$
$$C_{1,1/2}(3/2, 1/2, 1, -1/2) = C_{1,1/2}(3/2, -1/2, -1, +1/2) = \sqrt{1/3}.$$

Clebsch-Gordan coefficients involving $\Delta m_I = \pm 2$ are zero. In the most general case of arbitrary orientation of H_{int} and the EFG principal axes the eigenvector coefficients α_i will be complex numbers. The relative transition probabilities are proportional to the dot product $\varepsilon^*(r) \cdot \varepsilon(r)$ where the * refers to the complex conjugate. One possible general form in which this product can be expressed is

$$
\begin{aligned}
\varepsilon^*(r) \cdot \varepsilon(r) \sim &[a^*(1,1)\,a(1,-1)\exp(-2i\phi) \\
&+ a^*(1,-1)\,a(1,1)\exp(2i\phi) + 2a^*(1,0)\,a(1,0)]\sin^2\theta \\
&+ [a^*(1,1)\,a(1,1) + a^*(1,-1)\,a(1,-1)](1+\cos^2\theta) \qquad (3.13) \\
&+ \sqrt{2}\,\{[a^*(1,1)\,a(1,0) - a^*(1,0)\,a(1,-1)]\exp(-i\phi) \\
&+ [a^*(1,0)\,a(1,1) - a^*(1,-1)\,a(1,0)]\exp(i\phi)\}\sin\theta\cos\theta.
\end{aligned}
$$

With the above expressions, one can now calculate transition energies and probabilities for any mixed magnetic dipole and electric quadrupole interaction observed in the hyperfine structure of Fe^{57}. By comparing calculated and experimental spectra, the hyperfine field, EFG parameters and orientational parameters α and β can be derived. For single-crystal experiments where k is known relative to the crystal axes, the orientation of axes associated with the hyperfine parameters relative to the crystal axes can be determined directly. Several effects may need to be considered in comparing calculated hyperfine spectra with actual experiments. In particular, crystallographically-equivalent sites may have inequivalent orientations relative to k which requires averaging the intensities over the possible orientations; polycrystalline specimens require averaging intensities over all possible orientations. Hyperfine spectra from crystallographically inequivalent sites must, of course, be treated individually.

In deriving hyperfine parameters from experimental data, maximum use should usually be made of absorption-line position data before relative intensity data are considered. This is because additional effects; e.g., saturation and anisotropy of the recoil-free fraction can affect relative absorption intensities. In studying polycrystalline specimens, it may also be difficult to obtain completely randomly oriented specimens; this preferential orientation or texture can also

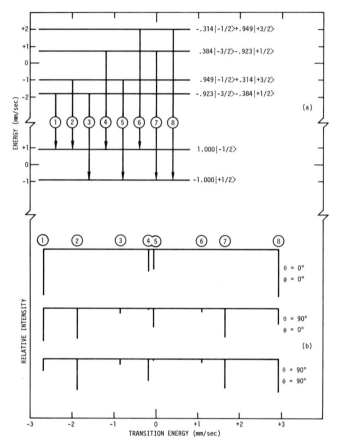

Fig. 3.2a and b. Calculation of Fe⁵⁷ hyperfine structure in $FeC_2O_4 \cdot 2H_2O$ at liquid He temperature based on experimental results of ÔNO and ITO [3.15]. Transitions are labeled numerically in order of increasing energy. (a) Eigenvalues and eigenvectors. (b) Transition energies and intensities for three gamma-ray propagation directions

affect relative absorption intensities. These latter complications are discussed in Chapter 6 by FUJITA.

A simple example of the use of the above expressions is the calculation of the hyperfine spectra observed in $\alpha - $ Fe as discussed in Chapter 1. With some effort, the transition probabilities and angular dependence for the six allowed transitions of the $\alpha - $ Fe spectrum can be derived from (3.13). The calculation of transition energies from (3.4)–(3.6) is trivial in this case because the electric quadrupole interaction is absent due to the essentially cubic site symmetry and thus the interaction Hamiltonian for both excited and ground states is diagonal. To illustrate a slightly more complicated example of this type of calculation, one may consider the hyperfine pattern found in the Fe^{57} Mössbauer spectrum of $FeC_2O_4 \cdot 2H_2O$. Ôno and Ito [3.15] measured and analyzed the hyperfine spectrum of this compound at liquid He temperature. Their results are $H_{int} = 154$ kOe, $e^2qQ/2 = -1.7$ mm/sec, $\eta = 0.63$, $\alpha = 0°$, and $\beta = 90°$. With these hyperfine parameters and values for the Fe^{57} excited and ground state nuclear moments of $\mu_{1/2} = +0.09024$ and $\mu_{3/2} = -0.1547\,\mu$ the above expressions can be used to calculate the expected hyperfine structure. Figure 3.2a shows the excited and ground state level structure with the associated eigenvectors and Fig. 3.2b illustrates the calculated transition energies and intensities for three different orientations of k. To compare directly the relative transition intensities with the experimental spectrum of a polycrystalline sample, one would have to average k over a spherical surface and shift all the transition energies by the appropriate isomer shift δ. For the purposes of calculating Fig. 3.2, δ was assumed to be zero. An interesting feature to note in Fig. 3.2 is the strong mixing of the nuclear wave functions. This produces a significant relative transition intensity for all eight possible transition lines indicated in Fig. 3.2 rather than the more usually observed six-line Fe^{57} hyperfine spectrum. One of the two additional "forbidden" lines present in the Mössbauer spectrum of $FeC_2O_4 \cdot 2H_2O$ was easily observed by Ôno and Ito [3.15].

3.2.2. Isomer Shift Determination in Complex Spectra

As discussed in Chapter 2, the isomer shift observed in Mössbauer spectroscopy provides a measure of the relative s electron density at the nucleus and consequently can be used as a measure of the oxidation state of a Mössbauer isotope. For Fe^{57} the correlation of isomer shift and oxidation state has been discussed by WALKER et al. [3.16]. The determination of the isomer shift from a Fe^{57} hyperfine spectrum of arbitrary complexity has been discussed by WERTHEIM [3.17]. The main point to consider in this determination is that the centroid of a nuclear level remains unshifted by the combined effects of magnetic dipole and electric quadrupole interactions. A simple means of demonstrating this point can be given [3.18]. If one combines the nuclear, hyperfine, and orientational parameters used to express the matrix elements given in [3.4] into two constants C_A and C_B, the diagonal elements of the mixed interaction Hamiltonian are just

$$H_{m_I m_I} = C_A m_I + C_B [3m_I^2 - I(I+1)] . \tag{3.14}$$

The trace of a matrix determines the sum of its eigenvalues so that it can be shown that the centroid of a nuclear level remains unshifted in the presence of arbitrarily complex hyperfine interactions by proving that

$$\sum_{m_I=-I}^{I} H_{m_I m_I} = C_A \sum_{m_I=-I}^{I} m_I + C_B \sum_{m_I=-I}^{I} [3m_I^2 - I(I+1)] = 0. \quad (3.15)$$

The sum involving C_A is obviously equal to zero. With some algebra one can show that the sum involving C_B is also zero.

WERTHEIM [3.17] gives a prescription to obtain δ by choosing a minimum set of four transitions which simultaneously eliminate the excited and ground state splittings. An alternative, which would be useful for Fe^{57} if the magnetic dipole and electric quadrupole interaction energies were roughly equal so that the proper four transitions were not easily identified initially, would be to obtain δ by averaging the eight possible transition energies (including the "forbidden" transitions) connecting the two nuclear levels. In any case, it is interesting to note that δ can always be determined from arbitrarily complex hyperfine spectra without explicitly determining the other hyperfine parameters.

3.2.3. Sign of the Internal Magnetic Field

An additional hyperfine parameter which is often of interest to determine is the sign of the internal magnetic field; i.e., whether the field at the nucleus is parallel $(+)$ or antiparallel $(-)$ to the direction of an applied external magnetic field. The internal magnetic field originates from several terms. In the absence of an externally-applied magnetic field, H_{int} is usually expressed as

$$H_{int} = H_c + H_{orb} + H_{dip}. \quad (3.16)$$

The origin and calculation of these terms are discussed in the literature, see, e.g., [3.19–22]. The Fermi contact term H_c arises from the unbalanced spin density of s-electrons at the nucleus and for ionic iron compounds, this term is large and negative. The term H_{orb} arises from the orbital angular momentum of the ion. For high spin ferric compounds, this term is 0 because ferric iron is an S-state ion, ^6S. In ferrous iron this term can be large and of opposite sign to H_c. The dipolar term H_{dip} is the field produced at the nucleus under considera-tion by the arrangement of atomic moments throughout the crystal. For most iron compounds this term is somewhat smaller than the other two terms. Because $H_{orb}=0$ in high-spin ferric compounds, the hyperfine field at low temperatures in these compounds is always negative and on the order of 500–600 kOe. In ferrous compounds where H_{orb} can be large, the sign of the hyperfine field may be difficult to predict particularly when the observed H_{int} is small. To compare theoretical calculations with experiment, it is, therefore, often useful to experimentally determine the sign of H_{int}.

Several approaches can be taken to measure the sign of H_{int}. The most common approach involves applying a large external magnetic field (typically 20–50 kOe is needed) to the specimen under investigation and observing whether H_{int} increases or decreases. This was the approach first used [3.23] to show that H_{int} in $\alpha - Fe$ was negative rather than positive, as had been theoretically predicted. Other approaches may also be used to determine the sign of H_{int}; for example, circularly-polarized radiation [3.24] (see discussion of Section 3.3) or the Mössbauer Faraday effect [3.25] may be used.

As an example of a material in which it was of interest to determine the sign of H_{int}, the Mössbauer spectrum of polycrystalline ilmenite ($FeTiO_3$) at 5 K is shown in Fig. 3.3 [3.26]. Ilmenite crystallizes in the trigonal space group $R\bar{3}$ [3.27]. All Fe^{2+} sites are crystallo-

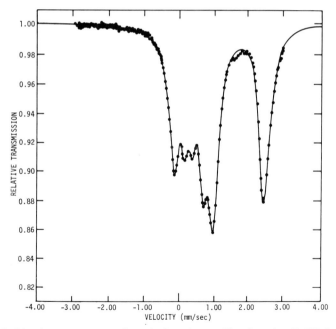

Fig. 3.3. Mössbauer spectrum of synthetic polycrystalline ilmenite ($FeTiO_3$) at 5 K. Source was Co^{57} in Cu ($\approx 22°$ C). Data are from [3.26]

graphically equivalent and have point symmetry 3. Several types of measurements have been used to show that the material orders antiferromagnetically below about 57 K with spin directions parallel to the crystallographic c axis. The point symmetry of the Fe^{2+} sites requires that H_{int} is parallel to V_{zz} and that $\eta = 0$; thus the hyperfine pattern is particularly easy to analyze. The curve shown through the data of Fig. 3.3 is an unconstrained least-squares fit to six Lorentz line shapes. The typical six-line hyperfine pattern observed for non-magnetized, randomly-oriented powders of magnetically-ordered Fe^{57}-containing materials has relative absorption intensities 3:2:1:1:2:3 in order of ascending energy. The small H_{int} and large e^2qQ observed in ilmenite at 5 K shifts the $|-3/2\rangle \rightarrow |-1/2\rangle$ transition to higher energy than the $|+1/2\rangle \rightarrow |+1/2\rangle$ transition and leads to relative intensities 2:1:1:2:3:3 in order of ascending energy. With the line positions measured from the data of Fig. 3.3 the hyperfine parameters of Fe^{2+} in $FeTiO_3$ at 5 K were derived as $|H_{int}| = 43 \pm 3$ kOe, $e^2qQ/2 = +1.44 \pm 0.01$ mm/sec and δ (relative to $\alpha - Fe$ at room temperature) $= +1.22 \pm 0.01$ mm/sec. Okiji and Kanamori [3.21] have calculated H_{orb} and H_{dip} for this case and by assuming a negative value for previously-reported $|H_{int}|$ data they evaluated H_c. Since H_{int} is quite small, it was of interest to experimentally determine the sign of H_{int}. The fact that ilmenite orders antiferromagnetically poses an added problem; in this case an external magnetic field H_{ext} applied parallel to the crystallographic c axis in the antiferromagnetic state will increase H_{int} for half the sites and decrease H_{int} for the others at least for relatively modest values of H_{ext}. This difficulty was avoided by applying H_{ext} parallel to the c axis of a single crystal of $FeTiO_3$ at 87 K which is in the paramagnetic state where the anti-ferromagnetic interaction does not exist. An applied field of 55 kOe produced an internal field of 41 ± 3 kOe which established the negative sign of H_{int}. In ilmenite at 5 K the internal field contributions calculated by the method described by Okiji and Kanamori [3.21] are $H_{orb} = +420$, $H_{dip} = +59$ and $H_c = -522$ kOe. For more details of this experiment and calculations the reader may consult the original references [3.21, 26].

3.3. Some Typical Magnetic Material Characterization Studies

Almost all magnetic compounds have some unique properties which frequently can be studied by Mössbauer spectroscopy. To review all possible applications of Mössbauer spectroscopy for magnetic compound investigations would not be appropriate for an introduction to the subject because several types of studies would have limited applicability or be appropriate only for a specific material.

To obtain information on specific compounds, the reader might best consult the detailed indexes of the Mössbauer literature [3.28, 29] or the exhaustive tabulation of hyperfine interactions in magnetic materials which was compiled several years ago [3.30]. Also, the fairly recent work of GREENWOOD and GIBB [3.31] provides summaries of results obtained from Mössbauer investigations of many magnetically-ordered compounds.

This section will discuss four types of studies which are often of fairly general interest for characterizing magnetically-ordered materials. These are the determination of magnetic transition temperatures, the identification of iron-containing phases, phase transition studies, and the determination of ion distributions in materials with crystallo-graphically inequivalent iron-containing sites. The experimental studies which are used to illustrate these applications were chosen primarily to provide clear illustrations without any specific regard to technological importance.

3.3.1. Magnetic Ordering Temperature and Type of Magnetic Ordering

Mössbauer spectroscopy can be used to determine the magnetic ordering temperature of materials by measuring the temperature variation of the internal magnetic field. Since no external magnetic field is required for this measurement, the method may on occasion have some advantages over more conventional techniques. There are three approaches which are usually used for this purpose. The magnitude of H_{int} can be determined at several temperatures below the ordering temperature. If one assumes that H_{int} is proportional to the magnetization, one can extrapolate to $H_{int} = 0$ in order to determine the transition temperature. As an example, the Néel temperature of $\alpha - Fe_2O_3$ was determined by this technique [3.32]. It is also possible to measure the total absorption area as a function of temperature for a relatively thick absorber. Because of saturation effects, a discontinuity will be observed at the transition temperature; this approach is illustrated in [3.33]. The above two methods are time-consuming since they involve obtaining several spectra. A third method which is much faster, involves following the absorption intensity of a resonance line in the paramagnetic state as a function of temperature. At the magnetic ordering temperature a sharp decrease in absorption intensity will occur due to the appearance of H_{int} (the rare possible complication

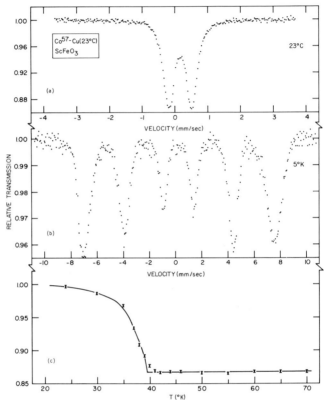

Fig. 3.4a–c. The Mössbauer spectra shown in (a) and (b) were obtained with a source of Co^{57} in Cu (23° C) and an absorber of polycrystalline $ScFeO_3$ at 23° C and 5 K, respectively. (c) Intensity of the highest energy absorption line in the paramagnetic region as a function of temperature

caused by an extremely small H_{int} in the magnetically-ordered state has been ignored).

As an example, Fig. 3.4 shows the determination of the magnetic-transition-temperature in $ScFeO_3$. Mössbauer spectra in both the paramagnetic and magnetically-ordered state are shown in this figure. Geller et al. [3.34] reported the existence of a possible magnetic transition at ≈ 35 K for this material based on magnetic measurements but the results were not conclusive. To determine the magnetic ordering temperature by Mössbauer spectroscopy, the intensity of the highest energy absorption line in the paramagnetic state was followed as a function of temperature (Fig. 3.4c). The sharp break in the curve at 39 ± 2 K indicates that the material magnetically orders at this point.

A novel variation of this last technique can be used in some cases. By choosing an appropriate source so that the maximum resonance in the paramagnetic state occurs at or near zero Doppler velocity, the transition temperature can be determined with a stationary source and absorber thus not requiring a spectrometer. This approach has been employed, see, e.g., [3.35].

The measurement of magnetic transition temperatures can be used to determine sample compositions in material systems if calibration points for the system have been determined. For example, in the growth of single crystals by melt techniques, the composition of the resulting crystals is often poorly known. By comparing measured values of the transition temperature with similar data on samples with known composition, chemical compositions can be determined. For materials in which the magnetic ordering temperature is a strong function of composition, the width of the transition region can be used to assess sample homogeneity. For example, an investigation of this nature in the $(Mn_{1-x}Fe_x)_2O_3$ system [3.36] was able to establish that earlier work on this solid solution system, interpreted as implying the existence of separate sublattice Néel temperatures, was really the result of sample inhomogeneity.

The Mössbauer effect can be used to investigate the general nature of magnetic coupling in a material; i.e., whether the material is ferromagnetic, ferrimagnetic, or antiferromagnetic. For this purpose one can apply an external magnetic field to a polycrystalline sample of the material and observe the variation of the hyperfine transition intensities. The spacial distribution of atomic moments in the external field can then be determined by making use of the angular dependence of the various hyperfine transitions. For example, the spin distribution of a ferromagnetic or ferrimagnetic material of low magnetic anisotropy (or high anisotropy if the polycrystalline particles are free to rotate) will be aligned parallel (or antiparallel) to an external magnetic field. If k is parallel to H_{ext}, and if we assume the absence of a sizeable quadrupole interaction, the $\Delta m_I = 0$ hyperfine transitions will vanish because of their $\sin^2 \theta$ angular dependence. If the hyperfine fields at the magnetic sublattices in a ferrimagnet have the same sign, the internal magnetic field at sublattices aligned parallel or antiparallel to H_{ext}, will increase and decrease, respectively, (or vice versa) which, coupled with the vanishing $\Delta m_I = 0$ line intensities, can be used to determine the ferrimagnetic nature of the magnetic ordering. The application of H_{ext} to a polycrystalline sample of an antiferromagnet will usually have little effect on the relative absorption line intensities (in the thin absorber limit) because no significant polarization of spins in general is obtained in modest external fields. The main effect on the spectrum of a polycrystalline sample will be to broaden absorption lines due to the random orientation of H_{ext} and H_{int}. When single crystals of magnetically-ordered materials are available, considerably more information about the type of magnetic ordering and, in particular, the spin orientation directions can often be obtained. This subject will be considered in Section 3.4.

3.3.2. Phase Analysis

A fairly common application of Mössbauer spectroscopy for characterizing magnetic materials involves the identification of solid phases. The characteristic hyperfine parameters observed in a Mössbauer spectrum can be used to identify a phase in much the same way as X-ray

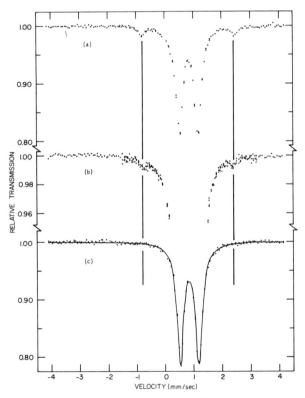

Fig. 3.5a–c. Mössbauer spectra obtained with a Co^{57} in Cu source (23° C) and polycrystalline absorbers (also at 23° C) with nominal compositions before firing of (a) $FeTiO_3$, (b) $Fe_{0.9}Mg_{0.1}TiO_3$, and (c) $FeTiO_3$. Traces of second phase with absorption lines at positions indicated by vertical lines are seen in (a) and (b)

diffraction patterns are used; of course, for this purpose, the applicability of Mössbauer spectroscopy is not nearly as general as X-ray diffraction. As an example of this type of application, data on the preparation and characterization of ilmenite will be discussed. In conjunction with Mössbauer spectroscopic studies of lunar samples [3.37, 38], synthetic ilmenite specimens containing small amounts of Fe^{3+} and Mg^{2+} were prepared. It is necessary to use a very low oxygen partial pressure pO_2 to obtain single phase materials in these solid solution systems [3.39]. If pO_2 is too high, a second phase of the Fe_2TiO_5-$(Fe, Mg)Ti_2O_5$ solid solution system is obtained. In Fig. 3.5a the Mössbauer spectrum of a specimen with nominal starting composition $FeTiO_3$ which was fired at 1200° C in relatively poor vacuum is shown. The two strong resonance lines are from Fe^{2+} in $FeTiO_3$. Absorption lines due to Fe^{2+} in the pseudobrookite (Fe_2TiO_5) structure are also clearly evident; this additional phase could easily be identified by powder X-ray diffraction. As the preparation procedure was improved to reduce pO_2, eventually it was no longer possible to detect the second phase by powder X-ray diffraction; although traces of it could still be observed by Mössbauer absorption. Figure 3.5b shows an example of such a case for a sample with nominal starting composition $Fe_{0.9}Mg_{0.1}TiO_3$. To obtain really single phase material it was necessary to fire specimens at 1200° C in a vacuum of about 10^{-8} Torr. The Mössbauer spectrum of a specimen with nominal starting composition $FeTiO_3$ which was fired under these conditions is shown in Fig. 3.5c. This spectrum has been least-squares-fit with two Lorentz line shapes and no trace of second phase is visible.

3.3.3. Phase Transition

Phase transitions can often be detected with Mössbauer spectroscopy by determining the temperature dependence of hyperfine parameters. As an example, the compositional dependence of the orthorhombic-to-cubic phase transition in the solid solution system $(Mn_{1-x}Fe_x)_2O_3$ was determined by this technique [3.36]. The room temperature Mössbauer spectra of a specimen with composition $(Mn_{0.9925}Fe_{0.0075})_2O_3$ are shown in Fig. 3.6. At room temperature this material is paramagnetic; the Néel temperature for this composition is about 80 K [3.36]. The cubic phase of this solid solution system has the bixbyite structure (see [3.40] and references therein) which has two crystallographically inequivalent cation positions, the 8b and 24d sites. A quadrupole splitting is observed at both Fe^{3+} sites in this material which accounts for the four line spectrum of Fig. 3.6. The smaller quadrupole splitting (inner two lines of the spectra) is associated with the b sites; the larger

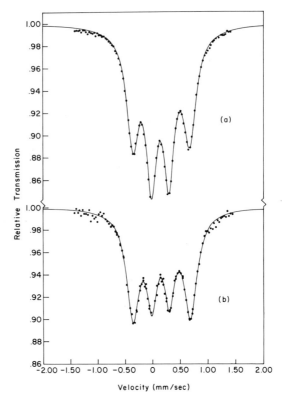

Fig. 3.6a and b. Mössbauer spectra of $(Mn_{0.9925}Fe_{0.0075})_2O_3$ at room temperature following heat treatments of (a) 600° C for 20 hrs in O_2, and (b) 960° C for 24 hrs in O_2. The source was Co^{57} in Cu (23° C); data are from [3.36]

splitting is associated with the d sites [3.41, 42]. The change in relative intensities of the absorption lines as a function of heat treatment is associated with the distribution of Fe^{3+} ions over the two inequivalent crystallographic sites; this subject will be discussed below. The curves shown through the data of Fig. 3.6 are least-squares-fits to four unconstrained Lorentz line shapes.

The temperature dependence of the quadrupole splitting for Fe^{3+} ions is usually small since the EFG arises only from lattice contributions. In Fig. 3.7 the temperature dependence of the quadrupole splitting for both Fe^{3+} sites is shown for three compositions of the $(Mn_{1-x}Fe_x)_2O_3$ system. The quadrupole splitting (peak separation) ΔE_Q is expressed as

$$\Delta E_Q = e^2 qQ/2. \tag{3.17}$$

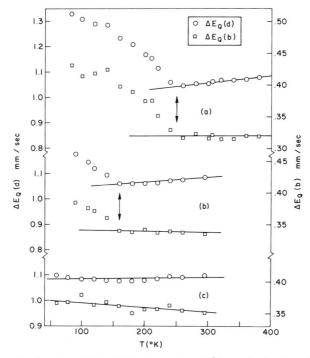

Fig. 3.7a–c. Quadrupole splitting (ΔE_Q) observed at Fe^{3+} ions in the 8b and 24d sites [$\Delta E_Q(b)$ and $\Delta E_Q(d)$, respectively] as a function of temperature for specimens in the $(Mn_{1-x}Fe_x)_2O_3$ system with (a) $x = 0.028$, (b) $x = 0.060$, and (c) $x = 0.082$. The crystallographic transition temperatures are indicated by arrows. Data are from [3.36]

In the high-temperature region ΔE_Q is observed to have little temperature dependence, as expected for Fe^{3+}-containing materials. However, for the specimens with $x = 0.028$ and 0.060, the variation of ΔE_Q with temperature increases markedly below specific temperatures (shown as bold arrows in Fig. 3.7). These temperatures correspond to the onset of the cubic-to-orthorhombic phase transition which is observed in this system. The sample with $x = 0.082$ remains cubic to below 55 K. The phase diagram, as determined by the above technique and by X-ray diffraction, may be found in [3.36].

3.3.4. Site Distribution Determination

The magnetic properties of materials which contain crystallographically-inequivalent cation sites often depend on the relative populations of the sites. In ferrimagnetic materials, for example, the saturation magnetization can be strongly affected by preferential substitution of cations into specific sites. Mössbauer spectroscopy offers a tool for studying relative site populations.

In the $(Mn_{1-x}Fe_x)_2O_3$ system it has been shown [3.41, 42] that Fe^{3+} preferentially occupies the 8b sites as opposed to the 24d sites. This is easily seen in Fig. 3.6a by noting that while there are three times as many d sites in the crystal, the absorption line intensities associated with the b sites are actually more intense. For the present discussion, small saturation corrections and possible differences in recoil-free fractions will be neglected. By integrating the absorption areas associated with the two Fe^{3+} sites, one can derive the cation site distribution. The d sites will be denoted by parentheses (d) and the b sites by square brackets [b]. The site distribution determined for the $(Mn_{0.9925}Fe_{0.0075})_2O_3$ specimen which was annealed at 600° C in O_2 (Fig. 3.6a) was determined to be $(Mn_{2.986}Fe_{0.014})[Mn_{0.984}Fe_{0.016}]O_6$. By annealing and quenching this specimen at a higher temperature, a more nearly random Fe^{3+} site distribution would be expected. This behavior was observed; the site distribution for the specimen annealed at 960° C in O_2 (Fig. 3.6b) was found to be $(Mn_{2.982}Fe_{0.018})[Mn_{0.988}Fe_{0.012}]O_6$.

Site distribution data can be used to estimate the energy difference (or, more appropriately, the enthalpy difference) associated with ions in crystallographically inequivalent sites by assuming a Boltzmann distribution of ions over the sites and considering the blocking of sites which results from preferential substitution: This information, in turn, can be used to estimate the effect of annealing temperature or compositional variation on relative site distribution. A general expression for the Boltzmann distribution is [3.43]

$$\frac{n_K}{n_t} = \frac{g_K \exp(-\varepsilon_K/k_B T)}{\sum_K g_K \exp(-\varepsilon_K/k_B T)}, \tag{3.18}$$

where n_K is the number of particles in the state with energy ε_K, n_t is the total number of particles, g_K is the statistical weight, k_B is Boltzmann's constant, and T is the absolute temperature. For the $(Mn_{1-x}Fe_x)_2O_3$ system where there are only two possible Fe^{3+} sites, (3.18) can be used to obtain an approximate expression for the site distribution which is

$$\exp(-\Delta\varepsilon_K/k_B T) = \frac{C_d(1-C_b)}{C_b(1-C_d)} = \frac{y(1+y-4x)}{3+y(3-4x)}, \tag{3.19}$$

where $(\Delta\varepsilon_K) = H_d - H_b$ is the site enthalpy difference, C_d and C_b are the fractions of d and b sites which are occupied by Fe^{3+} ions, $y = A_d/A_b = 3\,C_d/C_b$, and A_d and A_b are the total Mössbauer absorption areas associated with the d and b sites, respectively. The parameter x is the compositional parameter in $(Mn_{1-x}Fe_x)_2O_3$. In the $(Mn_{1-x}Fe_x)_2O_3$ system it was found [3.36] that $\Delta\varepsilon_K = +0.059 \pm 0.005$ eV adequately predicted the measured site distribution for $x \leqq 0.1$ and for $T \leqq 800°$ C.

3.4. Magnetic Structure Studies

As briefly noted in Subsection 3.3.1, Mössbauer spectroscopy can be used to investigate the nature of magnetic ordering in solids. When single crystals of magnetically-ordered compounds are available, considerable information regarding the spin orientations and magnetic structure can often be obtained. The determination of the microscopic arrangement of atomic magnetic moments in a crystal lattice is often of interest because the macroscopic magnetic properties are related to the magnetic structure in much the same way as other physical properties are related to the crystal structure. In those cases where the hyperfine field is parallel or antiparallel to the atomic magnetic moment, as, for example, in ionic Fe^{3+} where the hyperfine field primarily originates from H_c, Mössbauer spectroscopy can be used to determine the direction of H_{int} relative to the crystal axes and thus the spin directions.

The determination of spin directions in magnetically-ordered materials makes use of the angular dependence of absorption line intensities. To simplify the discussion in this section it will be assumed that the magnetic dipole interaction is much stronger than the electric quadrupole interaction so that the effect of the quadrupole interaction on the angular dependence of absorption lines can be ignored. This approximation is frequently adequate in practice. The case of a small H_{int}, large EFG and low site symmetry would have to be treated uniquely by using the general type of formulation, as outlined in Subsection 3.2.1.

For convenience, the hyperfine level diagram observed in magnetically-ordered Fe^{57} compounds in the absence of an EFG is reproduced in Fig. 3.8. As indicated in Chapter 1, the transitions involving $\Delta m_I = \pm 1$ have an angular dependence of $(1 + \cos^2\theta)$ while those involving $\Delta m_I = 0$ vary as $\sin^2\theta$. In favorable cases these angular dependences may be used to determine spin directions. For example, the spin direction of a simple colinear ferromagnetic or antiferromagnetic sublattice could be determined by using a single crystal absorber and determining the crystallographic orientation at which the $\Delta m_I = 0$ lines vanish. Experimentally, this usually means that single crystal absorbers with several orientations must be prepared or relative absorption line intensities must be measured as a function of absorber orientation. In the latter case, accurate saturation corrections must usually be applied to the data. Many crystals grow with habits which make it difficult or impossible to obtain single crystal absorbers with arbitrary orientation, or sufficient size to be useful for Mössbauer absorbers. In addition, some crystals have natural cleavage planes so that arbitrarily-oriented absorbers can be obtained only with difficulty. In many cases where spin directions are observed to be near or within the single crystal absorber plane, the use of polarized gamma-ray sources can be very advantageous. Because this approach has proved to be especially useful for magnetic structure studies, the technique and the angular dependence of absorption line intensities will be discussed here.

Several methods exist [3.44–46] to produce sources of polarized Fe^{57} gamma rays (see Chapt. 1). One simple approach is to embed the Co^{57} parent isotope in a ferromagnetic host (e.g., α-Fe) and to magnetically saturate the host material with an appropriate external magnetic field H_{ext}. FRAUENFELDER et al. [3.47] describe this arrangement in detail. Gamma-rays emitted parallel to the source internal magnetic field direction, H_S, will be circularly polarized, those emitted perpendicular to H_S will be linearly polarized. For all other orientations of k relative to H_S, the gamma rays will be elliptically polarized. The source of Co^{57} in α-Fe will emit six lines which when overlapping a simple six-line absorber hyperfine pattern will lead to 36 possible absorption lines. Some

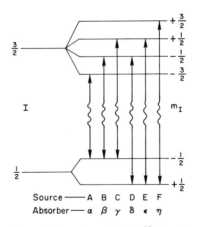

Fig. 3.8. Magnetic hyperfine splitting observed in Fe^{57}. The six allowed $M1$ transitions and notation used to designate source and absorber transitions are shown

notation is needed to identify the origin of these absorption lines. As indicated in Fig. 3.8, the source and absorber lines will be identified by roman (A, B, ..., F) and Greek characters ($\alpha, \beta, ..., \eta$), respectively, both in order of ascending energy.

The angular dependence of absorption line intensities for polarized sources has been discussed by FRAUENFELDER et al. [3.47] and by WEGENER and OBENSHAIN [3.48]. To derive expressions for these intensities, it is necessary to adopt a coordinate system which relates k to H_A and H_S; H_A is the internal magnetic field at the absorber nuclei. A convenient system for this purpose is shown in Fig. 3.9. The source coordinates and parameters are unprimed while those of the absorber are primed. The z axis common to both source and absorber is parallel to k. The projection of H_S onto a plane perpendicular to z defines x and the xyz and $x'y'z'$ coordinate systems are identical except for a shift of

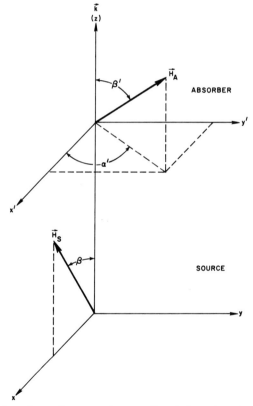

Fig. 3.9. Definition of coordinates used to specify relative orientations of H_S and H_A relative to k

the origin along z (z is perpendicular to both x and y). The angle α' is defined by the projection of $\boldsymbol{H}_A$ onto the $x'y'$ plane.

Following the formulation of [3.47] the relative intensity of source line i overlapping absorber line j can be expressed as

$$I_{ij} = \begin{pmatrix} 1/2 & 1 & 3/2 \\ m_1 & \Delta m_I & -m_3 \end{pmatrix}^2 \begin{pmatrix} 1/2 & 1 & 3/2 \\ -m'_1 & \Delta m'_I & m'_3 \end{pmatrix}^2$$
$$\cdot J_{\Delta m_I}(\beta)\, J_{\Delta m'_i}(\beta')\, K_{\Delta m_I, \Delta m'_i}(\beta, \alpha', \beta')\,. \tag{3.20}$$

For Fe^{57} the necessary $3j$ symbols are [3.47]

$$\begin{pmatrix} 1/2 & 1 & 3/2 \\ -1/2 & \pm 1 & 3/2 \end{pmatrix}^2 = \begin{pmatrix} 1/2 & 1 & 3/2 \\ 1/2 & \pm 1 & -3/2 \end{pmatrix}^2 = 1/4$$

$$\begin{pmatrix} 1/2 & 1 & 3/2 \\ -1/2 & 0 & 1/2 \end{pmatrix}^2 = \begin{pmatrix} 1/2 & 1 & 3/2 \\ 1/2 & 0 & -1/2 \end{pmatrix}^2 = 1/6 \tag{3.21}$$

$$\begin{pmatrix} 1/2 & 1 & 3/2 \\ -1/2 & \pm 1 & -1/2 \end{pmatrix}^2 = \begin{pmatrix} 1/2 & 1 & 3/2 \\ 1/2 & \pm 1 & 1/2 \end{pmatrix}^2 = 1/12\,.$$

As in Subsection 3.2.1, $\Delta m_I = m_3 - m_1$ and transitions involving $\Delta m_I = 2$ are forbidden ($3j$ symbols with $\Delta m_I = 2$ are zero). The expressions defining K in (3.20) are

$$K_{1, \pm 1} = K_{-1, \mp 1} = [(\cos \beta \pm \cos \beta')^2 + \sin^2 \beta \sin^2 \beta' \cos^2 \alpha']/(1 + \cos^2 \beta)(1 + \cos^2 \beta')$$
$$K_{\pm 1, 0} = (1 - \sin^2 \beta \cos^2 \alpha')/(1 + \cos^2 \beta) \tag{3.22}$$
$$K_{0, 0} = \cos^2 \alpha'$$

and the J terms of (3.20) are

$$J_{\pm 1}(\xi) = (1 + \cos^2 \xi)/2$$
$$J_0(\xi) = \sin^2 \xi\,, \tag{3.23}$$

where ξ is β or β'.

With some algebra, (3.20) can be used to derive expressions for the absorption intensities of the 36 possible absorption lines. These intensities can be expressed as the product of an intensity and an angular factor. The relative intensity factors are

	α, η	β, ε	γ, δ
A, F	9	12	3
B, E	12	16	4
C, D	3	4	1

(3.24)

and the angular factors are

	α, δ	β, ε	γ, η
A, D	S_1	S_3	S_2
B, E	S_4	S_5	S_4
C, F	S_2	S_3	S_1

(3.25)

where the S_i are given by

$$S_1 = (\cos\beta + \cos\beta')^2 + \sin^2\beta \sin^2\beta' \cos^2\alpha'$$
$$S_2 = (\cos\beta - \cos\beta')^2 + \sin^2\beta \sin^2\beta' \cos^2\alpha'$$
$$S_3 = \sin^2\beta'(1 - \sin^2\beta \cos^2\alpha')$$
$$S_4 = \sin^2\beta(1 - \sin^2\beta' \cos^2\alpha')$$
$$S_5 = \sin^2\beta \sin^2\beta' \cos^2\alpha'.$$

(3.26)

As an example of the use of the above expressions, the relative absorption intensity of line $C\eta$ would be $I_{C\eta} \sim 3[(\cos\beta + \cos\beta')^2 + \sin^2\beta \sin^2\beta' \cos^2\alpha']$. The I_{ij} given by (3.24)–(3.26) strictly apply only in the thin source, thin absorber approximation and the quadrupole interaction is assumed to be negligible. In practice, these assumptions are often good enough to permit the direct use of the expressions in data analysis. It can be seen from (3.26) that for a simple ferromagnetic sublattice, values of α' and β' can always be found for each absorption line where the absorption intensity will vanish. These angles can be used to directly determine the spin direction.

To illustrate applications of the use of polarized gamma-rays for magnetic structure studies, in the following sections three experimental investigations will be reviewed. The first example involves the determination of the colinear antiferromagnetic structure of $Ca_2Fe_2O_5$. Subsection 3.4.2 discusses the determination of the spin reorientation mechanism in $ErFeO_3$, and in Subsection 3.4.3 studies of a noncolinear antiferromagnetic structure are described.

3.4.1. $Ca_2Fe_2O_5$ — A Colinear Antiferromagnetic Structure

The crystal structure of $Ca_2Fe_2O_5$ was determined several years ago by BERTAUT et al. [3.49] and has recently been refined by COLVILLE [3.50]. The material crystallizes in the orthorhombic space group Pcmn and contains alternating layers of octahedral $[Fe^{3+}]$ and tetrahedral (Fe^{3+}) ferric ions perpendicular to the crystallographic b axis. Equal numbers of $[Fe^{3+}]$ and (Fe^{3+}) exist in the structure. The Mössbauer spectra of $Ca_2Fe_2O_5$ and of isostructural materials in which some of the Fe^{3+} has been replaced by Ga^{3+} or Sc^{3+} are shown in Fig. 3.10; these spectra were obtained by GELLER et al. [3.51]. It is well known from studies of garnet systems, that Sc^{3+} ions strongly prefer octahedral sites, while Ga^{3+} prefers tetrahedral coordination; see, for example, the review of the garnet crystal chemistry by GELLER [3.52]. This information can be used to easily identify the hyperfine lines associated with $[Fe^{3+}]$ and (Fe^{3+}) by noting that in Fig. 3.10b one set of hyperfine transitions is reduced in intensity while in Fig. 3.10c the other set has reduced intensity. The positions of the hyperfine transitions associated with the crystallographically inequivalent sublattices is noted in Fig. 3.10a. Two of the expected 12 transition lines in $Ca_2Fe_2O_5$ overlap at about -4.6 mm/sec. The magnetic susceptibility of the three specimens indicated in Fig. 3.10 was low which led GELLER et al. [3.51] to conclude that both magnetic sublattices were antiferromagnetically coupled; an antiferromagnetic intersublattice superexchange interaction was also predicted.

GONSER et al. [3.53] determined the spin directions of Fe^{3+} in $Ca_2Fe_2O_5$ by making use of linearly polarized gamma-rays. A single crystal absorber of $Ca_2Fe_2O_5$ was used which was polished into a thin slab parallel to the crystallographic ac plane. Analysis of this absorber by using an unpolarized source with k parallel to the b axis showed that the spins on both sublattices were within the absorber ac plane to within experimental error. Mössbauer spectra obtained with a source of Co^{57} in α-Fe and a single crystal absorber of $Ca_2Fe_2O_5$ are shown in Fig. 3.11 for two different source polarization angles. Referring to Fig. 3.9, the experimental arrangement corresponded to $\beta = \beta' = 90°$. The spectrum shown in Fig. 3.11a is for H_S parallel to the a axis; in

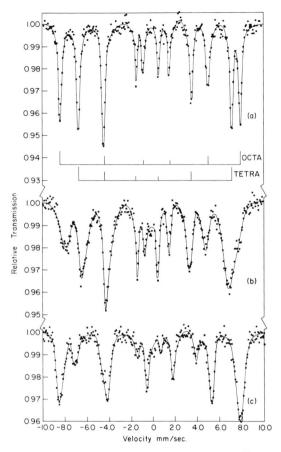

Fig. 3.10a–c. Mössbauer spectra obtained with a source of Co^{57} in Pt ($\approx 22°$ C) and polycrystalline absorbers of (a) $Ca_2Fe_2O_5$ ($\approx 22°$ C), (b) $Ca_2Sc_{0.5}Fe_{1.5}O_5$ ($\approx 22°$ C), and (c) Ca_2FeGaO_5 (5 K). Data are from [3.51]

Fig. 3.11b H_S is parallel to c. The expected absorption line positions and intensities for H_S parallel and perpendicular to the [Fe^{3+}] and (Fe^{3+}) spin directions are shown at the top of Fig. 3.11. The line positions are obtained directly by overlapping a Mössbauer spectrum of α-Fe and the spectrum of $Ca_2Fe_2O_5$ shown in Fig. 3.10. The expected line intensities are calculated from (3.24)–(3.26). By comparing the calculated and observed spectra, it is determined that the Fe^{3+} ion spins on both magnetic sublattices are parallel to c and thus the magnetic structure is as shown in Fig. 3.12. This same structure has been obtained from three independent neutron diffraction investigations [3.54–56].

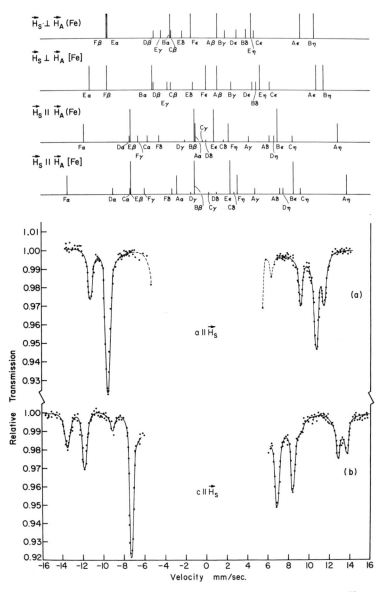

Fig. 3.11a and b. Calculated and experimental Mössbauer spectra for a Co^{57} in α-Fe source (magnetized in the source foil plane by an external field of ≈1 kOe) and a single crystal absorber of $Ca_2Fe_2O_5$; both source and absorber were at room temperature. At the top of the figure the positions and intensities of the absorption lines are given for the $[Fe^{3+}]$ and (Fe^{3+}) sites for H_S both perpendicular and parallel to H_A (in all cases k was perpendicular to both H_S and H_A). In (a) H_S was parallel to a; in (b) H_S was parallel to c [in both (a) and (b) k was parallel to b]. Data are from [3.53]

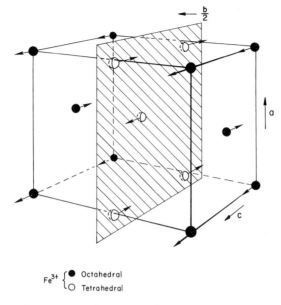

$Fe^{3+} \begin{cases} \bullet & \text{Octahedral} \\ \circ & \text{Tetrahedral} \end{cases}$

Fig. 3.12. Magnetic structure of $Ca_2Fe_2O_5$

3.4.2. Spin Reorientation in $ErFeO_3$

As discussed in Subsection 3.3.3, Mössbauer spectroscopy is a useful tool to study phase transitions in magnetic materials. Magnetic phase transitions may or may not be accompanied by a change in the crystallographic space group. A particularly interesting magnetic structure transition occurs in several of the rare earth orthoferrites (for a review of the literature on this subject, see [3.57]). Most rare earth orthoferrites have a canted antiferromagnetic structure. The very small canting angle of the atomic spins produces a weak ferromagnetic moment, and it is this weak moment that is responsible for much of the technological interest in this class of materials.

The rare earth orthoferrites have chemical formula $RFeO_3$ (R is a rare earth ion) and crystallize with an orthorhombic distortion of the perovskite structure [3.58, 59]. The structure belongs to the space group Pbnm ($a < b < c$); all Fe^{3+} sites are crystallographically equivalent and are located on the 4b sites with point symmetry $\bar{1}$. Several of the rare earth orthoferrites exhibit a spin reorientation transition in which the weak ferromagnetic moment rotates from the crystallographic a to c axis with increasing temperature [3.60, 61]. The transition occurs over a temperature range of typically 10–50 K; in $ErFeO_3$ this transition

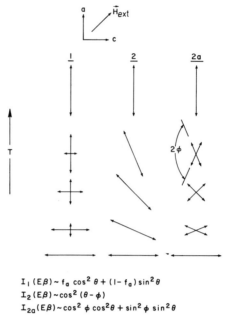

$$I_1(E\beta) \sim f_a \cos^2\theta + (1-f_a)\sin^2\theta$$
$$I_2(E\beta) \sim \cos^2(\theta - \phi)$$
$$I_{2a}(E\beta) \sim \cos^2\phi \cos^2\theta + \sin^2\phi \sin^2\theta$$

Fig. 3.13. Schematic description of the two most probable mechanisms for the *ac* spin reorientation in rare earth orthoferrites

range is centered at about 100 K. It is well established that the weak ferromagnetic moment rotates continually from the *a* to *c* axis during the reorientation transition. However, it was recognized that the spin reorientation could occur by at least two different mechanisms. These two most probable mechanisms for reorientation are shown schematically in Fig. 3.13. In this figure the arrows represent spin directions and the small canting angle which produces the weak ferromagnetic moment is ignored. The first mechanism involves a discontinuous spin flip from *c* to *a* as the temperature is raised where the fraction of spins parallel to *a*, f_a, is a temperature-dependent function. The second mechanism involves a continuous coherent rotation of spins. The mechanism indicated as 2a in Fig. 3.13, considers the possibility that in a large demagnetized crystal which contains several magnetic domains, continuous spin rotation in domains of opposite magnetization may occur in opposite directions. The polarized gamma-ray technique has been used [3.62] to distinguish between these two mechanisms; this investigation is described below.

In Fig. 3.14 Mössbauer spectra of a 1.5-mil-thick ErFeO$_3$ single crystal absorber, oriented so that **k** was along the *b* axis, are shown at

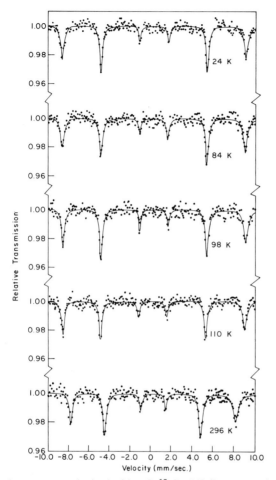

Fig. 3.14. Mössbauer spectra obtained with a Co^{57}-Cu (23° C) source and a single crystal $ErFeO_3$ absorber at several temperatures. The absorber was oriented so that **k** was parallel to *b*

various absorber temperatures. These spectra were obtained with a single line unpolarized source. The strong intensity of the $\Delta m_I = 0$ lines confirms that at all temperatures, including 98 K which is near the spin reorientation mid-point, the spins lie within the absorber *ac* plane. The curves through the data of Fig. 3.14 are least-squares fits to six Lorentzian line shapes. To determine the spin orientation within the *ac* plane, linearly polarized gamma-rays ($\beta = 90°$) were used.

The positions of the 36 possible absorption lines expected with a Co^{57} in α-Fe source and a $ErFeO_3$ absorber are determined by over-

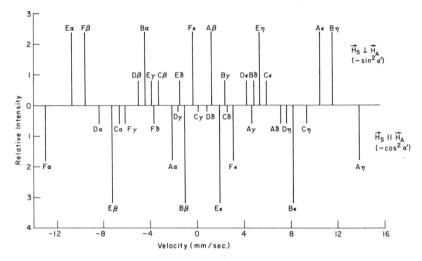

Fig. 3.15. Expected absorption line positions for a linearly polarized Co^{57}-α-Fe source (23° C) and a single crystal absorber of $ErFeO_3$ (23° C) oriented with k parallel to b. The relative intensities and angular dependence of the absorption lines are indicated for H_S both parallel and perpendicular to H_A (in both cases H_S and H_A are perpendicular to k)

lapping the six source emission energies with the absorption line positions shown in Fig. 3.14. The expected line positions and relative intensities, assuming a single crystal absorber oriented so that k is parallel to b are shown in Fig. 3.15 for both source and absorber at room temperature. Since the absorber spin directions are within the ac plane and linearly polarized radiation is being used, $\beta = \beta' = 90°$. The angular dependence of the 36 transitions can be derived from (3.25), (3.26) and is proportional to either $\sin^2 \alpha'$ or $\cos^2 \alpha'$. The relative absorption line intensities shown in Fig. 3.15 were calculated from (3.24)–(3.26). As indicated in the figure, 16 lines will be observed for H_S perpendicular to H_A while 20 lines will be observed for H_S parallel to H_A. The $E\beta$ absorption line is a major intensity line and since it is relatively free from complications due to overlapping transitions, the angular dependence of this line was studied as described below.

The temperature range over which the spin reorientation occurs was determined by measuring the absorption intensity of the $E\beta$ line with H_S parallel to c; below the reorientation region the spins are known to be parallel to this axis. The intensity of the $E\beta$ transition as a function of temperature is shown in Fig. 3.16 (at ≈ 100 K the position of this transition is ≈ -7.65 mm/sec). At about 88 K the absorption intensity of the $E\beta$ line starts to decrease and it reaches zero at ≈ 105 K (where

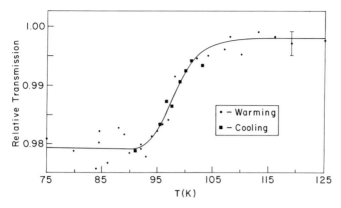

Fig. 3.16. Absorption intensity of the $E\beta$ line (-7.65 mm/sec) as a function of temperature obtained with a Co^{57}-α-Fe foil source (23° C) and a single crystal (38 µm thick) $ErFeO_3$ absorber (k was parallel to b). The source was polarized in the foil plane by an external magnetic field $H_{ext} = 0.5$ kOe which was parallel to c and perpendicular to k

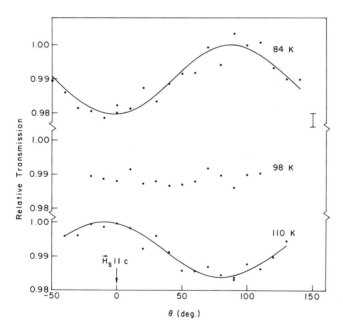

Fig. 3.17. Angular dependence of the $E\beta$ absorption line intensity (-7.65 mm/sec) at three absorber temperatures. The source was a Co^{57}-α-Fe (23° C) foil polarized in the foil plane by an external magnetic field of 0.5 kOe (H_{ext} (source) was perpendicular to k); the absorber was a 38 µm thick single crystal of $ErFeO_3$ with k parallel to b. The angle θ is between H_{ext} (source) and c

the absorber spins are parallel to a); the spin reorientation transition mid-point in $ErFeO_3$ is ≈ 98 K.

The dependence of the $E\beta$ absorption intensity on α' was determined above, below, and at the transition mid-point. These data are shown in Fig. 3.17 together with a least-squares fit to a $1 - A\cos^2(\theta - \phi)$ curve through the 84 and 110 K data (A is a constant). The angle θ is defined so that $\theta = 0°$ for H_{ext} (source) parallel to c. The angle ϕ (defined in Fig. 3.13), therefore, describes the spin orientation direction in the ac plane. The maximum resonance parallel to c and a at 84 and 110 K, respectively, confirms that the spins are parallel to c and a, respectively, at these two temperatures. At the transition mid-point, (≈ 98 K), an essentially angular invariant transition is observed. At the bottom of Fig. 3.13, the expected $E\beta$ absorption lines intensities for the reorientation mechanisms

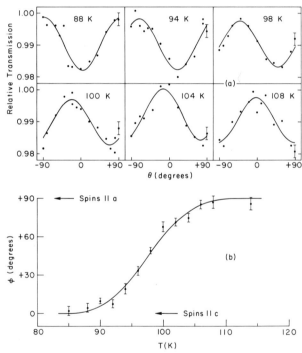

Fig. 3.18a and b. (a) Angular dependence of the $E\beta$ absorption line intensity (-7.65 mm/sec) for a Co^{57}-α-Fe source ($23°$ C) and single crystal $ErFeO_3$ absorber at several absorber temperatures. Polarizing magnetic fields of 0.5 and 1.1 kOe were applied to the source and absorber, respectively. k was perpendicular to both H_{ext} (source) and H_{ext} (absorber) and parallel to b; H_{ext} (absorber) was at $\theta = -45°$ where θ is the angle between H_{ext} (source) and c for H_{ext} (source) projected onto the absorber ac plane. (b) Fe^{3+} ion spin direction in $ErFeO_3$ vs. T. Data are from [3.62]

are shown. Both mechanism 1 and 2a lead to an angular invariant absorption intensity at the transition mid-point ($\cos^2 \phi = \sin^2 \phi = f_a = 1/2$). In fact, by choosing $f_a = \cos^2 \phi$, one can see that these two mechanisms are indistinguishable by the measurements shown in Fig. 3.17. To distinguish between the spin reorientation mechanisms, it was necessary to magnetically saturate the absorber.

To produce a single magnetic domain absorber, a polarizing magnetic field of H_{ext} (absorber) = 1.1 kOe was applied at an angle of 45° relative to a and c, as shown in Fig. 3.13. The angular dependence of the $E\beta$ absorption line was determined at several temperatures throughout the spin reorientation region. Some of these data are shown in Fig. 3.18a; a least-squares fit to a $B - A \cos^2(\theta - \phi)$ function is shown through the data (A and B are constants). As can be seen from the figure, the position of the $E\beta$ absorption maximum shifts continuously with temperature which establishes that the spin rotation is continuous, as described schematically by mechanism 2 of Fig. 3.13. The results of several determinations of ϕ as a function of temperature are collected in Fig. 3.18b. The sense of the spin rotation relative to H_{ext} (absorber) is shown in Fig. 3.13 (mechanism 2). The spins rotate away from H_{ext} (absorber) thus allowing the weak ferromagnetic moment to rotate toward H_{ext} (absorber).

3.4.3. FeOCl — A Noncolinear Antiferromagnetic Structure

As a final example of magnetic structure investigations with Mössbauer spectroscopy, measurements on the antiferromagnetic compound FeOCl will be discussed here. While both of the previous examples considered essentially colinear spin arrangements, the measurements on FeOCl [3.63] show that the Fe^{3+} spins of this compound order with a non-colinear magnetic structure.

The room temperature crystal structure of FeOCl was first determined by GOLDSZTAUB [3.64, 65] and has more recently been refined by LIND [3.66]. Crystals of FeOCl belong to the orthorhombic space group Pmnm (with $c < a < b$). At room temperature, all Fe^{3+} ions are crystallographically equivalent and have point symmetry mm. The Néel temperature has been determined as 92 K [3.63].

Mössbauer spectra obtained with an unpolarized source and a single crystal absorber of FeOCl in the magnetically-ordered state are shown in Fig. 3.19. The spectra in Fig. 3.19a was obtained with k parallel to the crystallographic b axis and with the absorber at 6 K. The width of the highest and lowest energy absorption lines in this spectrum indicates that more than one set of crystallographically in-

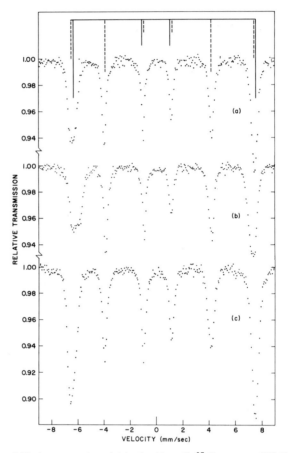

Fig. 3.19a–c. Mössbauer spectra obtained with a Co^{57}-Cu source (23° C) and a single crystal FeOCl absorber. (a) Absorber at 6 K and **k** parallel to *b*; (b) absorber at 21 K and **k** parallel to *b*; (c) absorber at 6 K and **k** at 45° from both *b* and *c*

equivalent Fe^{3+} sites is present at low temperatures. The broadening of these outer lines is even more pronounced in the spectrum obtained at 21 K which is shown in Fig. 3.19b. This observation implies that a crystallographic phase transition occurs between room temperature and low temperature. The exact nature of this transition has not been completely established [3.63]. By analyzing the relative absorption line intensities observed in Fig. 3.19a and b one can rule out the possibility of a colinear magnetic structure with all spins parallel to either *a*, *b* or *c*; additional measurements are needed, however, to rule out other possible colinear structures.

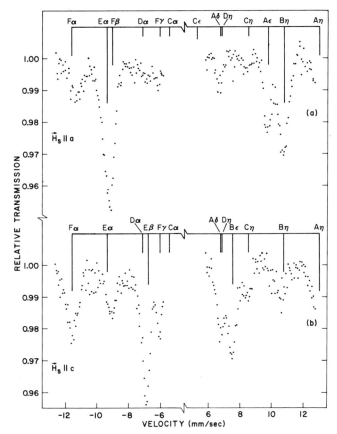

Fig. 3.20a and b. Mössbauer spectra obtained with a Co^{57}-α-Fe foil source (23° C) and a single crystal FeOCl absorber (6 K). The source was polarized by an external magnetic field of 0.5 kOe in the foil plane; k was parallel to b and perpendicular to H_{ext} (source). (a) H_{ext} (source) parallel to a; (b) H_{ext} (source) parallel to c. Data are from [3.63]

In Fig. 3.20, spectra obtained with a linearly-polarized source of Co^{57} in α-Fe for two source polarization directions are shown; the single crystal FeOCl absorber was at 6 K and had k parallel to b. The expected absorption line positions determined as before are indicated in the figure (in determining these line positions the presence of more than one six-line hyperfine pattern in FeOCl was ignored). An analysis of the relative absorption line intensities observed in these spectra by using (3.24)–(3.26) indicates that all absorber spins are confined to the absorber bc plane. This is most easily seen from the $B\varepsilon$ and $A\varepsilon$ absorption line intensities; for example, the $B\varepsilon$ line at ≈ 7.5 mm/sec strongly absorbs for H_{ext} (source) parallel to c but does not absorb for H_{ext} (source) parallel to a.

The relative absorption line intensities observed in the spectra shown in Fig. 3.19a and b would be consistent with a colinear spin arrangement in which the spins were oriented at $\approx 45°$ with respect to b and c. This possibility is ruled out by analyzing the absorption line intensities obtained with a single-line unpolarized source and a single-crystal absorber of FeOCl oriented so that k was 45° from both b and c; this spectrum is shown in Fig. 3.19c. To within experimental error, the relative absorption line intensities observed in all three spectra shown in Fig. 3.19 are the same; this rules out the possibility of a colinear spin arrangement. The simplest spin arrangement consistent with the results of Figs. 3.19 and 3.20 requires two antiferromagnetically-coupled sublattices oriented at 90° relative to each other.

The relative absorption line widths observed in the spectra shown in Fig. 3.19a and b are most easily explained by requiring two antiferromagnetic sublattices with spins parallel to b and c, respectively. An important feature of these spectra is that although the outer absorption lines are significantly broadened, the $\Delta m_I = 0$ resonance lines remain very narrow. The EFG parameters at the Fe^{3+} sites in FeOCl at room temperature have been accurately determined [3.67]. The absorption line positions shown at the top of Fig. 3.19 (and those in Fig. 3.20) were calculated [3.63] by assuming that the Fe^{3+} EFG parameters at low temperature were the same as observed at room

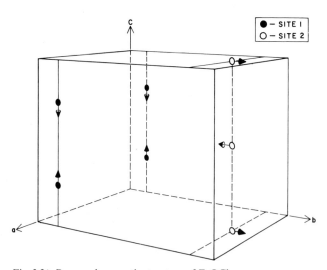

Fig. 3.21. Proposed magnetic structure of FeOCl

temperature and that the only difference in the hyperfine parameters at the inequivalent Fe^{3+} sites involved the two different orientations of H_{int} relative to the EFG parameters. For FeOCl the electric quadrupole interaction is much smaller than the magnetic dipole interaction so that the small effect of the non-zero quadrupole interaction on absorption line intensities was ignored.

For a spin arrangement with half of the spins parallel to b and c, respectively, the $\Delta m_I = 0$ absorption lines should be narrow for k parallel to b because only the sublattice with H_{int} parallel to c would contribute significantly to these absorption line intensities. Line broadening of the $\Delta m_I = 0$ transition would be expected and is observed for k at 45° relative to b and c (Fig. 3.19c) because in this case both sublattices contribute to the absorption intensity. The simplest possible magnetic structure of FeOCl consistent with the above observations is shown in Fig. 3.21. Further details concerning this structure and the analysis of the FeOCl Mössbauer data may be found in [3.2, 63, and 67].

Acknowledgements

Much of the work used in this chapter to illustrate various applications of Mössbauer spectroscopy in magnetism was carried out in collaboration with my colleagues Professor S. GELLER, Professor U. GONSER, Dr. R. M. HOUSLEY, and Dr. H. WIEDERSICH.

References

3.1. R. W. GRANT: IEEE Trans. Magnetics MAG-8, 637 (1972).
3.2. R. W. GRANT: AIP Conference Proceedings No. 5, *Magnetism and Magnetic Materials 1971*, ed. by C. D. GRAHAM, JR., and J. J. RHYNE (Amer. Inst. of Phys., New York, 1972), pp. 1395—1414.
3.3. E. MATTHIAS, W. SCHNEIDER, R. M. STEFFEN: Arkiv. För Fysik **24**, 97 (1963).
3.4. E. MATTHIAS, W. SCHNEIDER, R. M. STEFFEN: Phys. Rev. **125**, 261 (1962).
3.5. J. R. GABRIEL, D. OLSON: Nucl. Instr. and Methods **70**, 209 (1969).
3.6. K. A. HARDY, D. C. RUSSELL, R. M. WILENZICK, R. D. PURRINGTON: Nucl. Instr. and Methods **82**, 72 (1970).
3.7. G. R. HOY, S. CHANDRA: J. Chem. Phys. **47**, 961 (1967).
3.8. P. G. L. WILLIAMS, G. M. BANCROFT: Chem. Phys. Letters **3**, 110 (1969).
3.9. W. KÜNDIG: Nucl. Instr. and Methods **48**, 219 (1967).
3.10. G. G. HALL: *Matrices and Tensors* (Pergamon Press, Oxford, 1963).
3.11. G. T. EWAN, R. L. GRAHAM, J. S. GEIGER: Nucl. Phys. **19**, 221 (1960).
3.12. M. F. THOMAS, M. A. GRACE: Phys. Letters **10**, 306 (1964).
3.13. R. M. HOUSLEY, R. W. GRANT, U. GONSER: Phys. Rev. **178**, 514 (1969).
3.14. J. M. BLATT, V. F. WEISSKOPF: *Theoretical Nuclear Physics* (John Wiley & Sons, Inc., New York, 1952), Chapter 12 and Appendices A and B.
3.15. K. ÔNO, A. ITO: J. Phys. Soc. Japan **19**, 899 (1964).
3.16. L. R. WALKER, G. K. WERTHEIM, V. JACCARINO: Phys. Rev. Letters **6**, 98 (1961).

3.17. G. K. WERTHEIM: Phys. Letters **30**A, 237 (1969).
3.18. R. W. GRANT, H. WIEDERSICH: Unpublished.
3.19. R. E. WATSON, A. J. FREEMAN: Phys. Rev. **123**, 2027 (1961).
3.20. W. MARSHALL, C. E. JOHNSON: J. Phys. Radium **23**, 733 (1962).
3.21. A. OKIJI, J. KANAMORI: J. Phys. Soc. Japan **19**, 908 (1964).
3.22. C. E. JOHNSON, M. S. RIDOUT, T. E. CRANSHAW: Proc. Phys. Soc. **81**, 1079 (1963).
3.23. S. S. HANNA, J. HEBERLE, G. J. PERLOW, R. S. PRESTON, D. H. VINCENT: Phys. Rev. Letters **4**, 513 (1960).
3.24. N. BLUM, L. GRODZINS: Phys. Rev. **136**, A 133 (1964).
3.25. U. GONSER, R. M. HOUSLEY: Phys. Letters **26**A, 157 (1968).
3.26. R. W. GRANT, R. M. HOUSLEY, S. GELLER: Phys. Rev. **5**B, 1700 (1972).
3.27. T. F. N. BARTH, E. POSNJAK: Z. Krist. **88**, 265 (1934).
3.28. A. H. MUIR, JR., K. J. ANDO, H. M. COOGAN: *Mössbauer Effect Data Index 1958 to 1965* (Interscience Publishers, New York, 1966).
3.29. J. G. STEVENS, V. E. STEVENS: *Mössbauer Effect Data Index 1969* (Plenum, New York, 1970), and three subsequent volumes covering the years 1970, 1971, and 1972 by the same authors and publishers. A new volume covering the years 1966—1968 is in preparation.
3.30. A. J. FREEMAN, R. E. WATSON: In *Magnetism*, ed. by G. T. RADO and H. SUHL, Vol. II A (Academic Press, New York, 1965), pp. 167—305.
3.31. N. N. GREENWOOD, T. C. GIBB: *Mössbauer Spectroscopy* (Chapman & Hall, London, 1971).
3.32. S. FREIER, M. GREENSHPAN, P. HILLMAN, H. SHECHTER: Phys. Letters **2**, 191 (1962).
3.33. R. S. PRESTON, S. S. HANNA, J. HEBERLE: Phys. Rev. **128**, 2207 (1962).
3.34. S. GELLER, H. J. WILLIAMS, R. C. SHERWOOD: J. Chem. Phys. **35**, 1908 (1961).
3.35. U. GONSER, C. J. MEECHAN, A. H. MUIR, H. WIEDERSICH: J. Appl. Phys. **34**, 2373 (1963).
3.36. R. W. GRANT, S. GELLER, J. A. CAPE, G. P. ESPINOSA: Phys. Rev. **175**, 686 (1968).
3.37. R. M. HOUSLEY, M. BLANDER, M. ABDEL-GAWAD, R. W. GRANT, A. H. MUIR, JR.: Geochim. Cosmochim. Acta Suppl. **1**, 2251 (1970).
3.38. R. M. HOUSLEY, R. W. GRANT, A. H. MUIR, JR., M. BLANDER, M. ABDEL-GAWAD: *Proceedings of the Second Lunar Science Conference*, Vol. 3 (The MIT Press, 1971), pp. 2125—2136.
3.39. A. H. WEBSTER, N. F. H. BRIGHT: J. Am. Ceramic Soc. **44**, 110 (1961).
3.40. S. GELLER: Acta Cryst. B **27**, 821 (1971).
3.41. E. BANKS, E. KOSTINER, G. K. WERTHEIM: J. Chem. Phys. **45**, 1189 (1966).
3.42. W. HASE, W. MEISEL: Phys. Stat. Solidi **18**, K 41 (1966).
3.43. W. J. MOORE: *Physical Chemistry*, 2nd ed. (Prentice-Hall, Englewood Cliffs, N.J., 1955), p. 351.
3.44. S. S. HANNA, J. HEBERLE, C. LITTLEJOHN, G. J. PERLOW, R. S. PRESTON, D. H. VINCENT: Phys. Rev. Letters **4**, 177 (1960).
3.45. R. M. HOUSLEY: Nucl. Instr. and Methods **62**, 321 (1968).
3.46. J. P. STAMPFEL, P. A. FLINN: In *Mössbauer Effect Methodology*, Vol. 6, ed. by I. J. GRUVERMAN (Plenum Press, New York, 1971), pp. 95—107.
3.47. H. FRAUENFELDER, D. E. NAGLE, R. D. TAYLOR, D. R. F. COCHRAN, W. M. VISSCHER: Phys. Rev. **126**, 1065 (1962).
3.48. H. H. F. WEGENER, F. E. OBENSHAIN: Z. Physik **163**, 17 (1961).
3.49. E. F. BERTAUT, P. BLUM, A. SAGNIÈRES: Acta Cryst. **12**, 149 (1959).
3.50. A. A. COLVILLE: Acta Cryst. B **26**, 1469 (1970).
3.51. S. GELLER, R. W. GRANT, U. GONSER, H. WIEDERSICH, G. P. ESPINOSA: Phys. Letters **20**, 115 (1966).
3.52. S. GELLER: Z. Krist. **125**, 1 (1967).

3.53. U. GONSER, R. W. GRANT, H. WIEDERSICH, S. GELLER: Appl. Phys. Letters **9**, 18 (1966).
3.54. L. M. CORLISS, J. M. HASTINGS, W. KUNNMANN, E. BANKS: Acta Cryst. Suppl. **21**, A95 (1966).
3.55. Z. FRIEDMAN, H. SHAKAD, S. SHTRIKMAN: Phys. Letters **25**A, 9 (1967).
3.56. T. TAKEDA, Y. YAMAGUCHI, S. TOMIYOSHI, M. FUKASE, M. SUGIMOTO, H. WATANABE: J. Phys. Soc. Japan **24**, 446 (1968).
3.57. R. L. WHITE: J. Appl. Phys. **40**, 1061 (1969).
3.58. S. GELLER: J. Chem. Phys. **24**, 1236 (1956).
3.59. S. GELLER, E. A. WOOD: Acta Cryst. **9**, 563 (1956).
3.60. R. M. BOZORTH, V. KRAMER, J. P. REMEIKA: Phys. Rev. Letters **1**, 3 (1958).
3.61. R. C. SHERWOOD, J. P. REMEIKA, H. J. WILLIAMS: J. Appl. Phys. **30**, 217 (1959).
3.62. R. W. GRANT, S. GELLER: Solid State Commun. **7**, 1291 (1969).
3.63. R. W. GRANT: J. Appl. Phys. **42**, 1619 (1971).
3.64. S. GOLDSZTAUB: Compt. Rend. **198**, 667 (1934).
3.65. S. GOLDSZTAUB: Bull. Soc. France Mineral Crist. **58**, 6 (1935).
3.66. M. D. LIND: Acta Cryst. B **26**, 1058 (1970).
3.67. R. W. GRANT, H. WIEDERSICH, R. M. HOUSLEY, G. P. ESPINOSA, J. O. ARTMAN: Phys. Rev. 3B, 678 (1971).

4. Mössbauer Spectroscopy in Biology

C. E. JOHNSON

With 16 Figures

4.1. Biological Molecules

Many biological molecules contain iron. Since the Mössbauer effect provides a powerful probe of the chemical state and the environment of iron atoms, it is clear that it can be a useful tool to be applied to the study of proteins and enzymes. Indeed the first measurements of the Mössbauer spectrum of Fe^{57} in hemin were reported by GONSER [4.1] at the International Conference on the Mössbauer effect in Paris in 1961, only four years after the appearance of Mössbauer's papers on the discovery of the effect.

Proteins are large molecules, with molecular weights typically between 10^4 and 10^6. They contain a large number of amino-acids joined together by polypeptide bonds and coiled around to form a helix. One of the triumphs of X-ray diffraction has been the determination of the structure of several of them. This is a long and difficult process and has been successful in proteins which can be crystallized and in which heavy atoms can be substituted in order to determine the phase of the diffracted X-rays. The complexity of these molecules can be seen from Fig. 4.1, which shows the structure of myoglobin (molecular weight $= 17000$). This protein like many others contains a transition metal atom (iron) which plays a central role in the biological activity of the molecule. The changes which occur in a biochemical reaction are localized near this atom and a knowledge of the state of the iron as well as the overall molecular structure might enable one to understand the mechanism by which the molecule works.

The measurement of the magnetic properties of transition metal elements in biological molecules has for many years been recognized as an important way of finding the electronic state of the metal ion, and hence of providing a clue to the structure and function of the molecule. The experimental techniques used in the study of magnetic properties of biological materials include nuclear magnetic resonance (NMR), electron paramagnetic resonance (EPR) and most recently the Mössbauer effect, as well as conventional magnetic susceptibility measurements. NMR in biochemistry is mainly applied to determining the

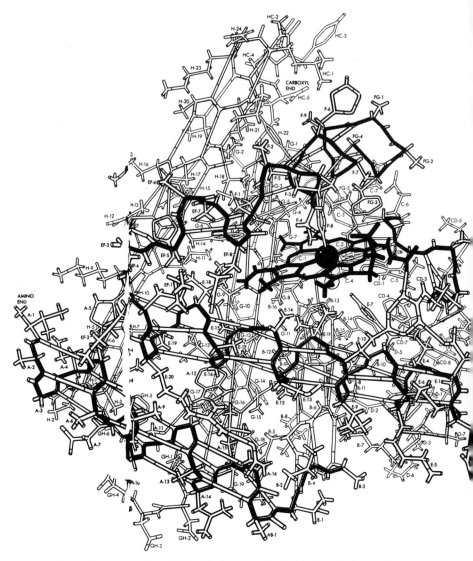

Fig. 4.1. Structure of myoglobin. The iron atom is the black circle close to the centre. The heme group and the main amino-acid chain are shown in heavy black

detailed structure of protein molecules, and may provide information on a magnetic ion by measuring the field it produces at neighboring protons. EPR and the Mössbauer effect are similar to each other in that they measure the paramagnetic transition metal ions themselves and

Table 4.1. Some proteins which contain iron

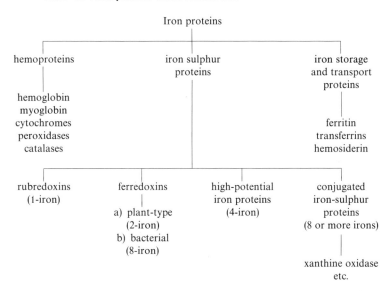

may be used a) to study their chemical state and bonding and b) to obtain qualitative data on the local structure and symmetry in their neighborhood.

The main groups of biological molecules which contain iron at their active centers are shown in Table 4.1.

The heme proteins are the best understood of these molecules, and the first systematic study of biological molecules using the Mössbauer effect was done on hemoglobin and its derivatives by LANG and MARSHALL [4.2]. Since then a great deal of work has been done on the iron-sulphur proteins and on iron storage proteins. In principal useful biological information could be obtained with other Mössbauer isotopes (e.g. I^{127}, I^{129}) but so far no data have been reported on proteins containing them.

4.2. Mössbauer Spectroscopy

Information on electronic structure and bonding in biological molecules has been obtained over many years using spectroscopic techniques (NMR, EPR, optical and infra-red spectroscopy, ESCA, etc.). These methods were first applied to problems in physics and chemistry, and as understanding of the spectra and confidence in their interpretation developed, their extension to applications in biology eventually followed. To these techniques Mössbauer spectroscopy has now been added.

The Mössbauer spectrum is essentially a property of the Mössbauer nuclei (i.e. the Fe^{57}) and so gives information local to the iron atoms in the protein. Conventional physical and chemical methods for studying the state of iron atoms are often difficult to apply because of the small number of these atoms compared with the total number of atoms in a biological molecule.

Each of the three main features of the Mössbauer spectrum
a) The isomer (chemical) shift.
b) The quadrupole splitting.
c) The magnetic hyperfine splitting
gives different and independent information about the electrons of the iron, and is sensitive (especially the magnetic hyperfine structure) to small details of the electron wave functions.

The Mössbauer effect has become well established as a powerful tool for probing the electronic charge and spin densities in solids. Its use for studying iron in biological molecules is, of course, no different in principle to its application to iron in other solids. However, there are some differences in detail and we shall now describe them.

4.2.1. Preparation of Specimen

The measurements are usually made on frozen aqueous solutions of the proteins, as this is usually the simplest solid form which is stable and easily obtainable. Some measurements have been made on concentrated proteins which have been precipitated and separated in solid form using a high speed centrifuge.

The molecules are generally enriched in Fe^{57}, since natural iron contains only 2 % of the Mössbauer isotope, although some measurements have been done using naturally occurring iron. The Fe^{57} may be incorporated in the molecule in either of two ways; either by growing the organism from which the protein is extracted on the separated isotope Fe^{57}, or by incorporating it by chemical exchange. The growing method requires more Fe^{57}, but it is more reliable and more generally applicable than exchange, which must be tested carefully to ensure that the protein is not modified by this process.

4.2.2. The Isomer (Chemical) Shift (δ)

Because of the effects of covalency the shifts and splittings observed in the Mössbauer spectrum may be different in biological molecules compared with inorganic complexes and we compare first some ex-

Table 4.2. Effect of ligands and co-ordination number on isomer shift of some inorganic compounds (in mm/sec measured at 77 K, relative to iron metal at 290 K)

Ion	Co-ordination	Compound	Ligands	Isomer shift [mm/s]
Fe^{2+} (high spin)	octahedral	$FeSiF_6 \cdot 6\,H_2O$	$6\,H_2O$	1.42
		$FeCl_2 \cdot 4\,H_2O$	$4\,H_2O, 2\,Cl^-$	1.34
		$FeCl_2 \cdot 2\,H_2O$	$2\,H_2O, 4\,Cl^-$	1.24
		$FeCl_2$	$6\,Cl^-$	1.20
	tetrahedral	$(NMe_4)_2FeCl_4$	$4\,Cl^-$	1.05
		$FeBaSi_4O_{10}$	$4\,O^{2-}$	0.87
Fe^{3+} (high spin)	octahedral	$FeCl_3$	$6\,Cl^-$	0.53
		Fe_2O_3	$6\,O^{2-}$	0.50
		Fe-tris-dtc	$6\,S^{2-}$	0.50
	tetrahedral	$(NMe_4)FeCl_4$	$4\,Cl^-$	0.30
Fe^{2+} (low spin)	octahedral	$K_4Fe(CN)_6$	$6\,CN^-$	0.06
Fe^{3+} (low spin)	octahedral	$K_3Fe(CN)_6$	$6\,CN^-$	-0.03

perimental data typical of the different type of compounds. Although the isomer shift depends upon the oxidation state and degree of covalency of the iron, it is not always possible to use them unambiguously to measure the oxidation state in proteins. There is no general theory of the isomer shift, and an empirical calibration of it is not always easy. However, in many cases the shift does give a good guide to the state of iron, as may be seen from the data listed in Table 4.2.

It is seen that the shift decreases as the degree of covalency of the ligands increases, i.e. in the order $-H_2O$, $-Cl^-$, $-O^{2-}$, $-S^{2-}$, $-CN^-$ etc. Also it is systematically less by about 0.2 mm/sec for tetrahedral co-ordination compared with octahedral co-ordination to the same ligands. It is clear that the chemical state cannot be inferred from the value of the isomer shift alone. A possible exception might be high spin Fe^{2+} which normally has a large positive shift value, but in biological compounds with tetrahedral sulphur co-ordination (e.g. reduced rubredoxin) it can be as low as 0.6 mm/sec which overlaps with the values found for Fe^{3+} in other compounds.

4.2.3. Quadrupole Splitting (ΔE_Q)

This is mainly a measure of the local structure and symmetry in the region of the iron atom. It may also sometimes help to confirm the oxidation state of the atom. The sign of the splitting may be determined by the application of an external magnetic field. This enables the orbital wave function of the d-electrons to be determined. This in turn may be used to deduce the nature of the distortion of the neighboring atoms from cubic symmetry, i.e. it provides qualitative data on the local molecular structure close to the iron atom.

4.2.4. Magnetic Hyperfine Splitting

This is most sensitive to the state of the iron atom and hence can be very powerful. It may be observed at low temperatures even in zero applied field for Fe^{3+} atoms where the electron spin relaxation times are long. For Fe^{2+} atoms the electron spin—lattice relaxation time is short and it is necessary to apply a strong magnetic field at low temperatures in order to observe magnetic splittings. The magnetic hyperfine interaction is a tensor quantity, and when its anisotropy can be measured it enables (as does the sign of the quadrupole splitting) the orbital wave function of the iron d-electrons to be determined.

While the isomer shift may provide a valuable clue to the state of the iron, measurements of magnetic hyperfine coupling are especially valuable for providing information in biological compounds since they are generally more sensitive to the finer details of the electronic state of the iron atoms. For slowly relaxing paramagnetic ions the application of an external magnetic field usually produces a simpler Mössbauer spectrum, which is easier to interpret than the zero-field spectrum. To illustrate this consider the simple example of an iron with spin 1/2 with isotropic g-value and hyperfine coupling A. This describes approximately the behaviour of low spin ferric in some of the hemoglobin compounds and high spin ferric when antiferromagnetically coupled to high spin ferrous in iron-sulphur proteins. This also shows the relation between magnetic hyperfine interactions measured by EPR and Mössbauer spectra. The energy levels of the ion are given by the spin-hamiltonian

$$\mathscr{H} = g\beta \mathbf{H} \cdot \mathbf{S} + A\mathbf{S} \cdot \mathbf{I} - g_N \beta_N \mathbf{H}_{ext} \cdot \mathbf{I} ; \tag{4.1}$$

β and β_N are the Bohr and nuclear magnetons, and g and g_N the electronic and nuclear g-factors, respectively. The energies are shown in Fig. 4.2 as a function of the magnetic field $\mathbf{H}$ for nuclei with spin $I_g = 1/2$ (coupling constant A_g) and $I_e = 3/2$ (coupling constant $A_e = 0.562\ A_g$). The subscripts g and e refer to the ground and excited states of Fe^{57}. The Mössbauer effect involves transitions between these states with the selection rules $\Delta m = 0, \pm 1, \Delta M_a = 0$. The EPR spectrum involves transi-

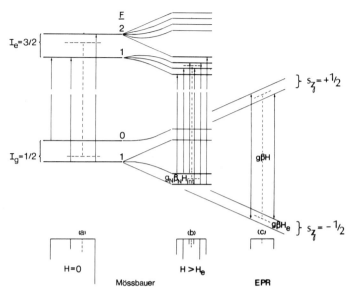

Fig. 4.2a–c. Energy levels of a paramagnetic ion in an applied magnetic field H. The ion, with electron spin $S = 1/2$ and nuclear spin $I = 1/2$, $3/2$, is assumed to have a simplified spin Hamiltonian $\mathscr{H} = A S \cdot I + g\beta H_{\text{ext}} \cdot S$. Mössbauer spectrum shows coupling between S and I in zero magnetic field (a) and decoupling in higher magnetic fields (b). EPR spectrum (c) shows transitions within the ground nuclear state only

tions within the ground state only, and with selection rules $\Delta m = 0$, $\Delta M_a = \pm 1$; m and M_a are the projections of the nuclear and electron spins, respectively, on the axis of quantization.

The condition for observing hyperfine interactions in the spectra measured by the two techniques is the same, and is that the electron spin relaxation time τ_s should be greater than $\hbar/A$. When $\tau_s \ll \hbar/A$ no magnetic effects are seen in the Mössbauer spectrum, which then looks similar to that of a diamagnetic ion. When $\tau_s \ll \hbar/g\beta H$ no EPR signal is obtainable, although the Mössbauer spectrum may still be observed so long as the sample is still in the solid state. The electron spin relaxation times may be made long by cooling the specimen to low temperatures, which increases the spin-lattice relaxation time T_1, and by using magnetically dilute samples, which increases the spin-spin relaxation time T_2. Biological materials are, almost by definition, magnetically dilute so that hyperfine interactions will usually be observed in their Fe^{57} Mössbauer spectra at low temperatures.

In zero magnetic field the hyperfine interaction couples S and I to give a total angular momentum $F = S + I$, similar to the situation in a free atom. For slow electron-spin relaxation the Mössbauer spectrum shows the asymmetrical three-line pattern of Fig. 4.2a.

When the applied magnetic field is larger than $A/g\beta$, the fluctuating components $A(S_+ I_- + S_- I_+)/2$ of the hyperfine interaction tensor are suppressed, and the splitting of the hyperfine levels is $A/2$. The Mössbauer spectrum becomes symmetrical and shows a six-line Zeeman pattern (Fig. 4.2b), with an effective field at the nuclei $H_{int} = A/2g_N\beta_N$. Effectively the nuclear and electron spins have become decoupled from each other and precess independently about the external field. In the EPR spectrum the line is split by $2H_e$, where $H_e = A/2g\beta$ is the field at the electrons produced by the nuclei (Fig. 4.2c). For Fe^{57}, $g_N = 0.18$ and since $\beta/\beta_N = 1840$, H_{int} is about 10^4 times $A/g\beta$ (or $2H_e$). Typical values for $A/g\beta$ from EPR measurements on iron-sulphur proteins are about 20 Oe, and for H_{int} from Mössbauer data are 200 kOe.

When the external field H_{ext} is large (> 10 kOe) the magnitude of the Zeeman splitting changes, since the term $-g_N\beta_N H_{ext} \cdot I$ in the Hamiltonian becomes important and the effective field at the nuclei is $H_{int} + H_{ext}$.

If the ligand nuclei have a spin I_L there will be a transferred hyperfine interaction term of the form $\Sigma_L S \cdot A_L \cdot I_L$ in the Hamiltonian. This will complicate the zero field spectrum since the energy of the system will depend upon the relative orientations of the iron nuclei and the ligand nuclei. LANG [4.3] has interpreted the very broad spectrum found for hemoglobin fluoride in terms of the hyperfine interactions with the fluorine and nitrogen ligands. When a small magnetic field is applied, however, the ligand nuclear spins precess independently of the electron

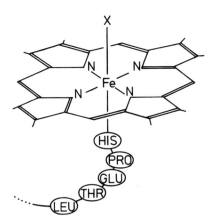

Fig. 4.3. The heme group

spin S and so do not affect the Fe^{57} Mössbauer spectrum which again has the appearance of Fig. 4.2b or c.

For ions with anisotropic g-values and hyperfine interaction tensor, the lines of the zero field Mössbauer spectrum become split. When in addition the quadrupole interaction is taken into account the lines are further shifted. The splittings in the presence of an applied field then become a function of the angle between the field and the axis of the ion, and in a specimen where these axes are randomly oriented the lines will become broadened. In general, the spectra are weighted to accentuate the spectrum for a field at right angles to the symmetry direction (usually taken to be z), since the probability $p(\theta)$ that the field makes an angle θ with this direction is proportional to $\sin\theta$, which is a maximum for $\theta = 90°$. However, the effect of the external field is similar in that a simpler and more symmetrical spectrum is generally produced.

4.3. Heme Proteins

Hemoglobin is the pigment in red blood cells; it and its derivatives were the first biological molecules for which extensive studies of their magnetic properties were made. It was also one of the first biological molecules to have its molecular structure determined from X-ray diffraction measurements. The structure of myoglobin, which has one iron atom per molecule is shown in Fig. 4.1. The iron has a fixed and characteristic environment known as the heme group (Fig. 4.3) which is a relatively small planar molecule in which the iron is co-ordinated to four nitrogen ligands in the plane, and two further ligands above and below the plane may also be joined to the iron. In hemoglobin there are four heme groups in each of which one of the non-planar ligands is attached via a nitrogen atom to a protein molecule (a chain of amino-acids). The sixth ligand may be varied, and the state of the iron atom varies with it. The heme group is very stable, and can exist even when the protein is removed, and it also occurs in other biological molecules as well as hemoglobin and myoglobin e.g. cytochromes. Previous studies of the iron had been made by magnetic susceptibility and EPR techniques. Magnetic susceptibility data [4.4] showed that the chemical state of the iron atom and its spin state were very sensitive to the nature of the sixth ligand. In healthy blood the iron is ferrous, being low spin ($S = 0$) when oxygenated and high spin ($S = 2$) when de-oxygenated. Abnormal blood may contain ferric iron, which may be high spin ($S = 5/2$) as in methemoglobin (where the sixth ligand is a water molecule) or low spin ($S = 1/2$) in hemoglobin cyanide. The application of EPR [4.5] confirmed all these conclusions and enabled the orientation of the heme planes in

Table 4.3. Isomer shifts δ and quadrupole splittings ΔE_Q for hemoglobin at 195 K

Material	δ	ΔE_Q
HiF	(0.43)	(0.67)
HiH$_2$O	0.20	2.00
HiCN	0.17	1.39
HiN$_3$	0.15	2.30
HiOH	0.18	1.57
Hb	0.90	2.40
HbNO[a]	—	—
HbO$_2$	0.20	1.89
HbCO	0.18	0.36

[a] Spectrum very broad.

the molecule to be determined. The Mössbauer spectra of these molecules have been valuable in confirming these earlier conclusions, and have yielded quantitative data on the way that the energy levels and wave-functions of the iron atoms are affected by the ligand field and spin-orbit coupling in the protein. They have also been valuable in providing standard spectra for each of the four common states of iron, and hence in establishing on a firm basis the use of Mössbauer spectroscopy as a way of obtaining information about iron in a biological (e.g. heme) environment. More recent work has been directed towards the study of new heme derivatives, and measurements on single crystals [4.7].

A review of work on heme proteins has been given by LANG [4.8]. A summary of the chemical shifts and quadrupole splittings measured at 195 K are shown in Table 4.3. The symbol Hi is used for ferric hemoglobin and Hb for ferrous hemoglobin. Each of the four possible spin states of iron from the work of LANG [4.2, 8, 9] will now be discussed briefly, and examples of their Mössbauer spectra will be given. It will be seen that the magnetic hyperfine splitting distinguishes easily between the spin states.

4.3.1. Low Spin Ferrous

This is the state of iron in oxygenated hemoglobin, HbO$_2$, which occurs in arterial blood, and in hemoglobin carbon monoxide HbCO.

Since $S = 0$ no magnetic hyperfine interaction would be expected and the Mössbauer spectrum in zero field is a quadrupole doublet at all temperatures. The chemical shift is about 0.20 mm/sec at 195 K. Figure 4.4a shows the spectrum of HbO$_2$ at 4.2 K. The quadrupole

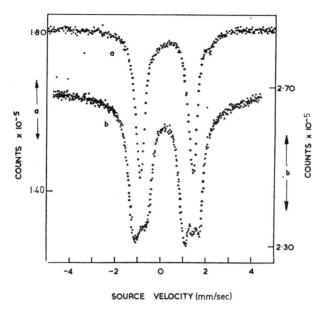

Fig. 4.4a and b. Mössbauer spectrum of a low spin ferrous hemoglobin, HbO₂ as red cells. (a) at 4.2 K in zero field (b) at 4.2 K in an applied field of 30 kOe. No internal field is produced as $S = 0$, so the splitting in (b) is that due to the applied field only [4.2]

splitting is 2.24 mm/sec, and decreases to 1.89 mm/sec on warming to 195 K. Application of a magnetic field (Fig. 4.4b) shows a total field at the nuclei equal to the applied field, i.e. as expected there is no magnetic hyperfine field.

4.3.2. High Spin Ferrous

When hemoglobin carries oxygen the iron atom lies in the heme plane. When it becomes de-oxygenated (i.e. Hb) the iron becomes high spin ferrous, and has been shown to lie out of the plane. The isomer shift shows a marked increase to 0.90 mm/sec, measured at 195 K, as expected for a high spin ferrous compound, though not surprisingly this value is lower than those found in ionic ferrous compounds. The quadrupole splitting is 2.4 mm/sec (Fig. 4.5a).

Again no magnetic hyperfine splitting is observed in the spectra in zero field. This is because the electron spin-lattice relaxation for ferrous is rapid even at low temperatures, so that the effective magnetic field at the iron nuclei averages to zero. When a strong magnetic field is applied at

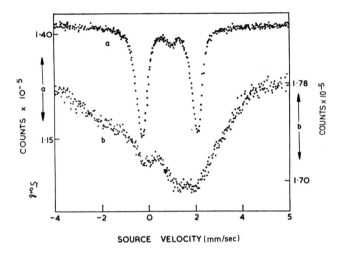

Fig. 4.5a and b. Mössbauer spectrum of a high spin hemoglobin, Hb (de-oxyhemoglobin) (a) at 4.2 K in zero field (b) at 4.2 K in an applied field of 30 kOe. The field in (b) produces a large internal field which is different for each of the random orientations of the heme plane and which broadens the spectrum [4.2]

low temperatures the spectrum becomes broadened due to magnetic hyperfine interaction (Fig. 4.5b). Sharp resolved lines are not observed partly because of the anisotropy of the ferrous ion; since the external field makes varying angles with the ligand field axes the resulting spectrum is the superposition of a large number of spectra, and so appears broad.

4.3.3. Low Spin Ferric

When diseased, hemoglobin may become ferric, and usually low spin, e.g., hemoglobin cyanide Hi CN, azide HiN_3 or hydroxide HiOH. The observation of an EPR spectrum arising from these forms is a possible way of early diagnosis of blood diseases.

The most noticeable feature of the Mössbauer spectra is the appearance of magnetic hyperfine structure at 77 K and below. Spectra of HiCN at these temperatures are shown in Fig. 4.6. At 195 K a quadrupole splitting of 1.39 mm/sec is observed, with an isomer shift of about 0.17 mm/sec. At 77 K the lines are beginning to show broadening. At 4.2 K the magnetic hyperfine spectrum is well resolved, but complex and asymmetrical owing to the anisotropy of the hyperfine interaction tensor.

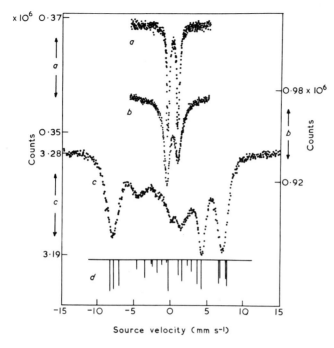

Fig. 4.6a–d. Mössbauer spectra of a low spin ferric hemoglobin HiCN: (a) at 195 K (b) at 77 K and (c) at 4.2 K. Note the broadening at 77 K relative to 195 K due to the slower electron spin relaxation rate. At 4 K the relaxation is so slow that the hyperfine pattern is resolved, but complex (d) shows the predicted spectrum [4.2]

4.3.4. High Spin Ferric

In hemoglobin fluoride, HiF, and methemoglobin, HiH_2O the iron is high spin ferric.

The ferric ion is in a ^6S state and so has zero orbital magnetic moment. This gives rise to very slow spin-lattice relaxation rates and isotropic magnetic properties. Even at high temperatures (195 K) magnetic hyperfine interaction strongly broadens the Mössbauer spectrum of HiF, so that it is not possible to obtain accurate values of the quadrupole splitting (which is small) or the isomer shift. The spectrum is still unresolved at low temperatures, owing to the coupling (transferred hyperfine interaction) with the magnetic moment of the neighboring fluorine nucleus and to a lesser extent with the nitrogen nuclei in the heme group. On applying a small magnetic field (100 Oe is enough) a remarkable change occurs to the spectrum, and an almost symmetrical 6-line pattern appears as shown in Fig. 4.7a. The

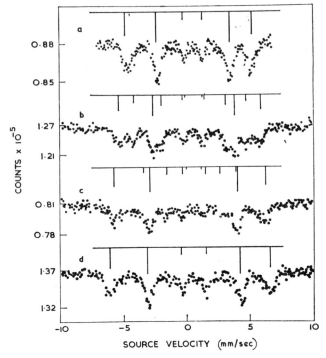

Fig. 4.7a–d. Mössbauer spectrum of a high spin ferric hemoglobin HiF at 4.2 K in fields of (a) 0.5 kOe, (b) 7.5 kOe, (c) 15 kOe, and (d) 30 kOe. Each is composed of two six-line patterns caused by the effective fields of the upper and lower members of the magnetically split $|S_z = \pm 1/2\rangle$ doublet. In (a) the effective fields are very nearly equal, while in (d) the Boltzmann factor of one of the spin states is very small [4.2]

small quadrupole splitting and six sharp lines (observed because the hyperfine interaction is isotropic) is characteristic of high spin ferric. The change in the spectrum is produced by the de-coupling by the external magnetic field of the electron spin from the nuclear spins of the Fe^{57}, F^{19}, and N^{14} nuclei.

The value of the effective field observed is governed by the ligand field. The very strong ligand field at the ferric atom splits the ^6S state into three doublets according to the hamiltonian

$$\mathcal{H} = D[S_z^2 - \tfrac{1}{3}S(S+1)], \tag{4.2}$$

D is large and positive ($\sim +7\,cm^{-1}$). This means that the ground state is a doublet with $S_z = \pm 1/2$ and is $2D$ in energy below the next excited state, so it is effectively the only state populated at 4.2 K. Since the external field has a larger probability of being perpendicular to the ligand field axis, the effective field of the nuclei in small external fields is proportional to $\langle S_x \rangle$ i.e. to $(1/2) [(5/2)(7/2) - (-1/2)(1/2)]^{1/2} = 3/2$. So the observed value of about 300 kOe is consistent with that of 500 kOe usually found when $S_z = 5/2$.

On applying larger magnetic fields the higher ligand field states may be mixed in to the ground state, so that the effective fields of the $|S_z = \pm 1/2\rangle$ states become different, increasing for the $|S_z = -1/2\rangle$ state and decreasing for the $|S_z = +1/2\rangle$ state, as seen in Fig. 4.7b–d.

Methemoglobin HiH_2O shows a similar behaviour, though the relaxation times are faster and the quadrupole splitting is larger. Both these point to a considerable mixing in of orbital moment into the ferric states by the ligand field.

4.4. Iron-Sulphur Proteins

The iron-sulphur proteins are a group of molecules which are found in many diverse organisms, in plants, animals and bacteria. They are involved in oxidative electron transfer processes in many different kinds of function, e.g. photosynthesis, nitrogen fixation, digestion, respiration, vision etc. Their widespread occurrence in nature is only just becoming recognised and their importance in biochemistry may well be comparable to that of the hemoglobins [4.10].

Structural information has only recently become available for the iron-sulphur proteins. Unlike the hemoglobins, however, the iron is not bound in a stable basic structural unit. Instead it is held rather loosely in the chain of amino acids via sulphur atoms. Any attempt to remove the iron chemically causes the whole molecule to break up, and hence the valuable clue of knowing the heme structure which helped in unravelling the structure of hemoglobin, does not have an analogue in the iron-sulphur proteins. The structure has only recently been determined for three of them. These are a rubredoxin [4.11], a bacterial ferredoxin [4.12] – both from *Clostridium Pasteurianum* – and a high potential iron protein (HIPIP) [4.13] from *Chromatium*. Although these molecules are different in size, structure and function, they all contain iron atoms in similar environments with the iron at the center of four sulphur atoms which form an approximate tetrahedron. The simplest of these molecules are the rubredoxins, as they contain only one iron-sulphur group per molecule (Fig. 4.8). Next in order of complexity are the plant ferredoxins and hydroxylase proteins (adrenodoxin and putidaredoxin), which contain two iron atoms per molecule. Their structure has not yet been determined, and a good deal of spectroscopic work

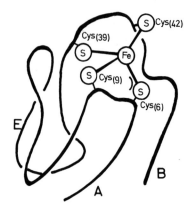

Fig. 4.8. The structure of the one-iron
rubredoxin of *C. pasteurianum* [4.11]

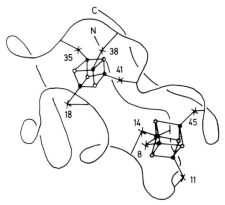

Fig. 4.9. The structure of the *P. aerogenes* eight-iron ferredoxin from X-ray analysis [4.12]
● Fe; ○ S (inorganic); × S (cysteine); C Carboxy terminal; N Amino terminal

has been focussed on them. More complex still are the bacterial ferredoxins (Fig. 4.9) and HIPIP's; in both of these the iron appears to be in
units containing four iron atoms, each surrounded by a tetrahedron of
sulphurs (Fig. 4.10).

The many-iron proteins were first classified because of their magnetic
properties, and not because of any similarity in their molecular structure
or biochemical properties. In the reduced state they all gave similar and
rather unusual EPR signals with g-values all below 2, with an average
value of $g \sim 1.94$ [4.14]. When oxidized, these proteins do not give an
EPR signal. Recent measurements [4.15] of the susceptibility have

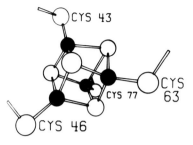

CYS 43

CYS 77

CYS 63

CYS 46

Fig. 4.10. The structure of the four-iron centre of *Chromatium* HIPIP [4.13]. Black circles are iron; open circles are sulphur atoms

Table 4.4. Isomer shifts δ and quadrupole splittings ΔE_Q for Fe^{57} in oxidized and reduced iron-sulphur proteins at 195 K

Material	Oxidized		Reduced	
	δ	ΔE_Q	δ	ΔE_Q
Rubredoxin	0.25	—	0.65	3.10
Ferredoxin (plant)	0.22	0.59	0.56[a]	2.75[a]
Adrenodoxin	0.22	0.61	—	—
HIPIP	0.28[b]	0.77[b]	0.38[b]	1.01[b]
Ferredoxin (bacterial)	0.39[b]	0.75[b]	0.52[b]	1.07[b]

[a] Value for ferrous atom.
[b] Average value.

shown that it follows a Curie law $\chi \propto 1/T$ for reduced proteins, while it is practically independent of temperature for oxidized proteins, confirming that the latter are non-magnetic. The $g \sim 1.94$ is unusual for iron since spin-orbit interaction generally couples spin and orbit parallel to each other. By enriching the proteins in Fe^{57} and S^{33} hyperfine broadening has been observed in the EPR signal establishing that the unpaired electron is localized in the region of the iron and sulphur atoms. It has been proposed that these properties arise from anti-ferromagnetic coupling between groups of iron atoms. The Mössbauer effect, in view of its success with the hemoglobins, offers an obvious chance to determine the chemical and magnetic state of the iron atoms and measurements on the iron-sulphur proteins have been made in several laboratories. TSIBRIS and WOODY [4.16] and HALL et al. [4.10] have reviewed the physical data, including Mössbauer spectra, which have been obtained on the iron-sulphur proteins.

The Mössbauer effect has been widely used in the study of the iron-sulphur proteins. From measurements of the 1-iron protein rubredoxin in the oxidized and reduced states, the isomer shifts and magnetic hyperfine interaction of Fe^{2+} and Fe^{3+} in tetrahedral sulphur co-ordination have been measured. This effectively calibrates these quantities, i.e. it allows for the effects of covalency of the irons in this environment. These single-iron data can then be used in the interpretation of the data on the two-iron proteins. Here the magnetic moments of the two iron atoms in the molecule have been shown to be antiferromagnetically coupled together, and the resulting hyperfine spectrum is very different from that usually observed for a single iron atom. This is a situation unlike that found in inorganic complexes of iron, and it is not easy by any other method to observe directly the antiferromagnetic coupling between the pairs of iron atoms. Thus the Mössbauer effect has been able to make a very real contribution to our knowledge of the iron-sulphur proteins.

The Mössbauer spectra of each of the iron-sulphur proteins will now be described, both in the oxidized and reduced states.

4.4.1. 1-Iron Proteins (Rubredoxins)

The Mössbauer spectrum of oxidized rubredoxin at 4.2 K is shown in Fig. 4.11 and is a six-line Fe^{3+} pattern with an effective field of -370 kOe [4.17, 18]. The hyperfine splitting is observed because the electron spin relaxation times are long, and the single field arises because the distorted tetrahedral ligand field is roughly of the form

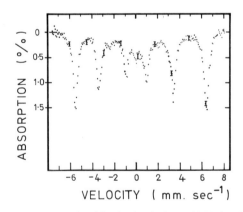

Fig. 4.11. Mössbauer spectrum of oxidized rubredoxin at 4.2 K showing that the iron is high spin Fe^{3+}

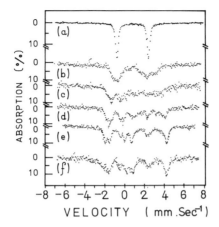

Fig. 4.12a–f. Mössbauer spectra of reduced rubredoxin at 4.2 K in fields of (a) 0 kOe, (b) 5 kOe, (c) 15 kOe, (d) 30 kOe, (e) 60 kOe, and (f) 60 kOe at 1.5 K

$D(S_z^2 - 35/12)$ (compare with hemoglobin fluoride) which splits the energy levels of the ion so that the ground state $|S_z = \pm 5/2\rangle$ is the only one populated at liquid helium temperatures. Since $g_\parallel$ for this state is 9.4, the hyperfine field $H_{int}(Fe^{3+})$ is -395 kOe. In Fe_2O_3 it is -550 kOe, in ferric trispyrrolidyldithiocarbamate, which has octahedral sulphur co-ordination, it is -475 kOe. The low value in rubredoxin is partly a result of the covalent bonds between the iron and the sulphur ligands and partly due to the tetrahedral co-ordination. The quadrupole splitting is positive. It arises from the asymmetry of the charges of the sulphur ligands, and shows that they are distorted by a compression along the symmetry (z) axis.

The Mössbauer spectra of reduced rubredoxin at 4.2 K for several values of applied magnetic field are shown in Fig. 4.12. They are characteristic of high spin Fe^{2+}. In zero field there is a large quadrupole splitting (3.3 mm/sec) and a shift (0.65 mm/sec) which is low for Fe^{2+} but which is entirely consistent with tetrahedral sulphur ligands. Magnetic hyperfine splitting is observed when large fields (up to 60 kOe) are applied and the effective field at the nuclei is predominantly per-pendicular to the symmetry axis of the ligand field, so that

$$H_{eff} = H_{ext} + H_{int\,x}.\tag{4.3}$$

The internal field $H_{int\,x}$ is plotted as a function of the applied field H_{ext} in Fig. 4.13. The saturated value of the hyperfine field $H_{int\,x}$ (Fe^{2+}) is estimated to be -210 kOe.

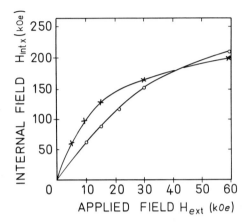

Fig. 4.13. Comparison of internal fields at Fe^{57} as a function of applied field for reduced rubredoxin (X) (from Fig. 4.12) and ferrous fluosilicate (0)

These spectra are qualitatively similar to these observed [4.19] for polycrystals of ferrous fluosilicate. This is a well understood salt, with $H_{int\,x}(0) = -248\,\text{kOe}$, and an axial ligand field splitting given by $D(S_z^2 - 2)$, where $D = +10.9\,\text{cm}^{-1}$. The values of the internal field are compared with those in rubredoxin in Fig. 4.13. It may be seen that although the saturated value of the hyperfine field is smaller for the rubredoxin, the values for small applied fields are larger than for ferrous fluosilicate. This is because D is smaller in rubredoxin. Assuming axial symmetry the internal field for small applied fields ($g_\perp \beta H_{ext} \ll D$) is given by

$$H_{int\,x}(\text{Fe}^{2+}) = \frac{3g_\perp \beta H_{ext}}{D}. \tag{4.4}$$

A comparison with the fluorsilicate data shows that in reduced rubredoxin, $D \simeq +4.4\,\text{cm}^{-1}$. This is an approximate value, of course, as non-axial ligand field splittings have been neglected.

The sign of the quadrupole coupling is seen to be negative. It arises from the asymmetrical charge distribution of the electron of the Fe^{2+} ion and shows that the ground state of the Fe^{2+} ion is d_z^2, and hence that the sulphur tetrahedron is distorted by a compression along the z-axis. The observed value for the hyperfine field may be understood using the approach of MARSHALL and JOHNSON [4.20]. The core polarization field for Fe^{2+} ($S = 2$) may be estimated to be 4/5 of the Fe^{3+} ($S = 5/2$) field, i.e. $H_c = -315\,\text{kOe}$. The dipolar field $H_{dip\,x}$ is about

$+ 64\,kOe$. From the value of D, $g_\perp$ is estimated to be 2.04, and hence the orbital field $H_{orb\,x} = + 36\,kOe$. Adding these values

$$H_c = - 315\,kOe$$
$$H_{dip\,x} = +\ \ 64\,kOe$$
$$H_{orb\,x} = +\ \ 36\,kOe$$

together gives an expected total for $H_{int\,x}$ (Fe^{2+}) of $- 215\,kOe$, which agrees well with the measured value of $- 210\,kOe$.

4.4.2. 2-Iron Proteins (Plant-Type Ferredoxins)

At 195 K the Mössbauer spectrum of the oxidized proteins consists of a doublet, while on reduction two doublets are observed [4.21] one due to Fe^{2+} and one due to Fe^{3+} (Fig. 4.14). In both forms of the protein the iron atoms are believed to be coupled together antiferromagnetically. When oxidized there are two Fe^{3+} atoms and their total spin is zero, which agrees with their observed temperature independent susceptibility.

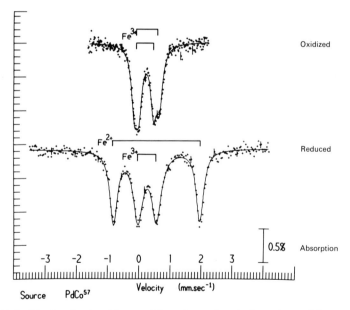

Fig. 4.14. Oxidized and reduced forms of *Scenedesmus* ferredoxin, an iron-sulphur protein involved in plant photosynthesis. Spectrum of reduced form appears to be a superposition of two doublets, indicating that the two iron atoms are inequivalent

By observing quantitavely the growth of the intensity of the EPR signal as the proteins are titrated with a reducing agent (as well as by more conventional chemical techniques) the number of electrons transferred per molecule on reduction has been measured. It is found that one electron is transferred to the molecule. The atom with the larger quadrupole splitting has a positive chemical shift compared with the other atom, i.e. the electron transferred on reduction is localized on it, so that one Fe^{3+} is converted to Fe^{2+} while the other remains unchanged.

In the reduced protein the coupling between the Fe^{3+} atom (with $S_1 = 5/2$) and the Fe^{2+} atom (with $S_2 = 2$) results in a ground state with total spin $S = S_1 + S_2 = 1/2$. This model was proposed to account for the unusual g-values centered around 1.94 found from the EPR spectra of these molecules [4.22]. Figure 4.15 shows that way the spins S_1 and S_2 couple together to give the resultant S.

At low temperatures (e.g. 4K) the Mössbauer spectrum of the reduced protein shows magnetic hyperfine splitting because the electron spin-lattice relaxation time has become long compared with $\hbar/A$, A being the hyperfine coupling. The spins S_1 and S_2 precess about their resultant S, and the observed spectrum is asymmetrical and has broad and partly resolved lines. When a small magnetic field $H_{ext} > AS/g\beta$ is applied a more symmetrical spectrum with sharper lines results. The effect of the field is to cause S_1 and S_2 to precess about it and this results in two separate effective magnetic fields at the nuclei. The resulting spectrum is a superposition of two contributions, one from Fe^{3+} and one from Fe^{2+} and the lines from each are strongly overlapping.

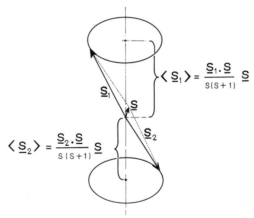

Fig. 4.15. Coupling of the spins $S_1 (= 5/2)$ and $S_2 (= 2)$ of the ferric and ferrous atoms in the reduced two-iron proteins

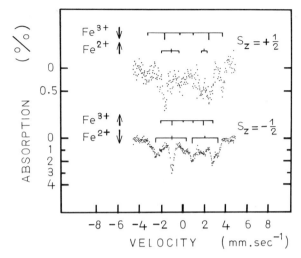

Fig. 4.16. Derived Mössbauer spectra of the higher ($S_z = +1/2$) and ground ($S_z = -1/2$) states of the $S = 1/2$ doublet of reduced *Scenedesmus* ferredoxin, in an external magnetic field of 30 kOe at 4.2 K

On increasing the size of the applied field the spectrum splits into two components, showing that H_{1z} and H_{2z} have different signs owing to the antiferromagnetic coupling between the two iron atoms. At 1.7 K the population of the $|S_z = +1/2\rangle$ state is small (9%) and the lines due to Fe^{3+} and Fe^{2+} can be separated out as shown. On warming the samples to 4.2 K the $|S_z = +1/2\rangle$ state becomes appreciably populated (28%) and contributes extra lines to the spectrum.

The separation of the spectrum due to the ground state $|S_z = -1/2\rangle$ from the excited state $|S_z = +1/2\rangle$ is carried out by subtracting the 1.7 K spectrum ($S_{1.7}$) from that measured at 4.2 K ($S_{4.2}$), suitably weighting each according to their populations at these temperatures. Thus the upper spectrum of Fig. 4.16 is the contribution from the excited state, and is constructed by taking $4.82 S_{4.2} - 3.82 S_{1.7}$ while the lower spectrum is that due to the ground state which is given by $1.45 S_{1.7} - 0.45 S_{4.2}$.

The Mössbauer spectrum therefore allows the antiferromagnetic coupling between the Fe^{2+} and Fe^{3+} atoms in reduced 2-iron proteins to be confirmed. Atoms with spins pointing "up" (i.e. parallel to the resultant spin S) have the effective field at the nucleus reduced by the external field (since the hyperfine field is negative), so that their spectrum is compressed by the field. On the other hand, atoms with spins "down" have their effective field increased, i.e. the spectrum appears to expand in the external field. However, it is not easy to identify all the lines, especially those due to Fe^{2+}, from the Mössbauer spectrum alone. The hyperfine interaction tensor for the Fe^{2+} atoms has been measured [4.23] in some of these proteins using ENDOR, and from these data the Mössbauer spectra of spinach ferredoxin [4.24] and putidaredoxin [4.25] have been interpreted in detail. Another technique which has shown the presence of antiferromagnetic coupling both in oxidized and reduced iron-sulphur proteins is NMR on protons [4.26].

Because of the coupling between the two atoms the effective field at their nuclei is reduced from the values in the free atoms, and is about $(-)$ 180 kOe for Fe^{3+} and very roughly $(-)$ 120 kOe for Fe^{2+}. This may be understood as follows. The fields are proportional to the projections $\langle S_1 \rangle$ and $\langle S_2 \rangle$ of their spins along the total spin S, i.e.

$$H_{1z} = \frac{\langle S_1 \rangle}{S_1} H_{\text{int } z}(Fe^{3+}) \quad \text{and} \quad H_{2z} = \frac{\langle S_2 \rangle}{S_2} H_{\text{int } z}(Fe^{2+}), \quad (4.5)$$

where $H_{\text{int } z}(Fe^{3+})$ and $H_{\text{int } z}(Fe^{2+})$ are components of the hyperfine field tensor for the uncoupled ferric and ferrous ions, respectively. The projections of the S_1 and S_2 upon S are (see Fig. 4.15)

$$\langle S_1 \rangle = \frac{S_1 \cdot S}{S} = \frac{S_1 \cdot S}{S(S+1)} \langle S \rangle = 7/3 \langle S \rangle$$

and   (4.6)

$$\langle S_2 \rangle = \frac{S_2 \cdot S}{S} = \frac{S_2 \cdot S}{S(S+1)} \langle S \rangle = -4/3 \langle S \rangle,$$

so

$$H_{1z} = 7/3 \frac{\langle S \rangle}{S_1} H_{\text{int } z}(Fe^{3+}) = 7/15 H_{\text{int } z}(Fe^{3+}),$$

and   (4.7)

$$H_{2z} = -4/3 \frac{\langle S \rangle}{S_2} H_{\text{int } z}(Fe^{2+}) = -1/3 H_{\text{int } z}(Fe^{2+})$$

since $\langle S \rangle = S = 1/2$.

For the Fe^{3+} atom H_{int} will be approximately isotropic, and taking the value found in oxidized rubredoxin, one would expect $H_{1z} = -185$ kOe, in good agreement with the observed value of about -180 kOe. For the Fe^{2+} ion the hyperfine field is anisotropic and we need to estimate $H_{\text{int } z}(Fe^{2+})$ using the value of $H_{\text{int } x}(Fe^{2+})$ measured in reduced rubredoxin. Taking the value for H_c found in reduced rubredoxin, and estimating $H_{orb\,z}$ ($+40\,kOe$) from the value of g_z and $H_{dip\,z}$ ($-128\,kOe$ for the d_z^2 orbital ground state), we have

$$H_c = -315\,kOe$$
$$H_{dip\,z} = -128\,kOe$$
$$H_{orb\,z} = +40\,kOe$$
so that
$$H_{int\,z}\,(Fe^{2+}) = -403\,kOe$$

Thus H_{2z} should be $+135\,kOe$, again agreeing with the measured value of about $120\,kOe$.

4.4.3. 4- and 8-Iron Proteins

As well as in the two-iron proteins, magnetic coupling has been found between iron atoms in iron-sulphur proteins containing more than two iron atoms. These proteins include the bacterial ferredoxins, which may contain four iron atoms per molecule (e.g. *Bacillus* ferredoxin) or eight iron atoms (e.g. from *Clostridium Pasteuranium* or *Chromatium*), as well as the high potential iron proteins (HIPIP's) (four iron atoms per molecule) and the conjugated iron-sulphur proteins (flavoproteins, iron-molybdenum proteins etc.) which contain 8 or more iron atoms per molecule.

The bacterial ferredoxins have many features in common with the simpler plant-type ferredoxins; they are non-magnetic when oxidized and have negative redox potentials, and become magnetic with an average g-value less than 2 when reduced. Their Mössbauer spectra [4.27] show a considerably more complex behaviour than the two-iron proteins. This, of course, is hardly surprising as there is a large number of ways that more than two atoms can be magnetically coupled together. The molecular structure of one of the eight-iron ferredoxins (that from *Peptococcus aerogenes*) has been determined [4.12] and shows that the iron is in units containing four iron atoms close together (see Fig. 4.9). Distinct quadrupole doublets corresponding to Fe^{3+} and Fe^{2+} states are not observed in their high temperature Mössbauer spectra. At high temperatures (77 K and above) the spectra of both oxidized and reduced states consist essentially of the superposition of two or more closely similar doublets. The average isomer shift for the oxidized protein suggests that each of the two four-iron active centres consists formally of two Fe^{3+} and two Fe^{3+} atoms. Both the average isomer shift and the quadrupole splitting increase on reduction, consistent with there being one Fe^{3+} and three Fe^{2+} atoms per sub-unit in the reduced molecule.

The marked change in isomer shift and quadrupole splitting which is observed on reduction, shows that all the iron atoms are affected when one electron is added to each four iron centre. The fact that separate Fe^{3+} and Fe^{2+} spectra were not observed (as they were, for instance, in the reduced two-iron plant ferredoxins) suggested that the d-electrons are not localized on particular atoms but are shared approximately equally by all four atoms in the four-iron centres. At low temperatures (4 K and below) no magnetic hyperfine interaction was observed in the oxidized protein even in an applied magnetic field, confirming the non-magnetic nature of the molecule in the oxidized state, and suggesting that the four iron atoms in each sub-unit are antiferromagnetically coupled together to give zero spin. For the reduced protein, however, magnetic hyperfine interaction was observed at low temperatures, and showed that all iron atoms were magnetic. This demonstrates that one electron goes to each center on reduction. On applying a large magnetic field to the reduced protein at low temperatures, both positive and negative hyperfine fields were shown to be present. Thus Mössbauer data provides direct evidence for antiferromagnetic coupling between the iron atoms in bacterial as well as plant-type ferredoxins.

The HIPIPs have 4 iron atoms per molecule all close together in a cluster (see Fig. 4.10). They have positive redox potentials and are non-magnetic in the reduced state, but they lose one electron per molecule when oxidized and then become magnetic with an average g-value greater than 2. Mössbauer measurements [4.28] on the reduced protein confirm that it is non-magnetic. Spectra of the oxidized protein in applied magnetic fields clearly indicate that some iron atoms have a positive while others have a negative hyperfine field, which is evidence for antiferromagnetic coupling between them. The spectra can be interpreted in terms of two types of iron atom with fields of $+90$ and -120 kOe, respectively. A consideration of the isomer shifts and other evidence suggests formal valences of two Fe^{3+} and two Fe^{2+} atoms in the non-magnetic reduced state, and three Fe^{3+} atoms and one Fe^{2+} atom in the oxidized state. However, separate Fe^{3+} and Fe^{2+} spectra are not seen, suggesting that the d-electrons are not localized on particular iron atoms.

Thus the 4-iron centres in HIPIP in the reduced form and *Clostridium* ferredoxin in the oxidized form are similar to each other, and appear to contain two Fe^{3+} and two Fe^{2+} atoms. In reduced *Clostridium* ferredoxin there are one Fe^{3+} and three Fe^{2+}, while in oxidized HIPIP there are three Fe^{3+} and one Fe^{2+}.

Xanthine oxidase is a flavoprotein which contains eight iron atoms and one molybdenum in a molecule of molecular weight about 275000. Its redox potential is negative, and it is non-magnetic in the oxidized state and magnetic when reduced with an average g-value below 2. This was the first iron-sulphur protein in which magnetic hyperfine splitting was observed [4.29] by Mössbauer spectroscopy, and the behaviour seemed most closely to resemble the plant-type ferredoxins, i.e. in the reduced state separate Fe^{3+} and Fe^{2+} spectra were observed at high temperatures. Presumably the 8 iron atoms in the molecule are in four pairs, each pair being in a unit which resembles the active centre in the plant-type ferredoxins.

4.5. Possible Applications in Medical Research

The Mössbauer effect is potentially important for its practical applications, e.g. in medicine. The main difficulties to be overcome in order for the technique to become widely used concern the form of the sample, which must be a "solid" and which usually must be cooled in order to get a large effect. For iron the small amount present in biological tissue and the low abundance of the Mössbauer isotope Fe^{57} makes the technique insensitive and slow compared with EPR for example. However, if these difficulties can be overcome the Mössbauer effect could become a powerful tool for determining the state of iron in a clinical specimen.

It has been shown that measurements on human blood and tissue samples are quite feasible. Whether these will result in any advances in medical diagnosis is not yet clear. However, Mössbauer spectroscopy has been shown in many cases to yield information which had not been obtained previously by any other method. It is quite likely, therefore, that it could become a valuable tool for qualitative and quantitative analysis in medical research, just as it has become a powerful and detailed probe for the study of biological molecules and biochemical reactions.

References

4.1. U. Gonser: Proc. 2nd Int. Conf. Mössbauer effect, Paris (Wiley Interscience, London, 1962), p. 280
4.2. G. Lang, W. Marshall: Proc. Phys. Soc. **87**, 3 (1966)
4.3. G. Lang: Phys. Letters **26** A, 223 (1968)
4.4. E. F. Hartree: Ann. Rept. Prog. Chem. **43**, 287 (1946)
4.5. J. E. Bennett, J. F. Gibson, D. J. E. Ingram: Proc. Roy. Soc. A **240**, (1957)
4.6. M. R. C. Winter, C. E. Johnson, G. Lang, R. J. P. Williams: Biochim. Biophys. Acta **263**, 515 (1972)
4.7. U. Gonser, Y. Maeda, A. Trautwein, F. Parak, H. Formanek: Z. Naturforsch. **29** b 241 (1974)

4.8. G. LANG: Quart. Rev. Biophys. **3**, 1 (1970)

4.9. G. LANG: J. Appl. Phys. **38**, 915 (1967)

4.10. D. O. HALL, R. CAMMACK, K. K. RAO: In *Iron in Biochemistry and Medicine*, ed. A. JACOBS (Academic Press, New York, 1974), Chapter 8

4.11. J. R. HERRIOTT, L. C. SIEKER, L. H. JENSEN, W. LOVENBERG: J. Mol. Biol. **50**, 391, (1970)

4.12. L. H. JENSEN, L. C. SIEKER, K. D. WATENPAUGH, S. T. ADMAN, J. R. HERRIOTT: Biochem. Soc. Trans. **1**, 27 (1973)

4.13. C. W. CARTER, J. KRAUT, S. T. FREER, R. A. ALDEN, L. C. SIEKER, E. ADMAN, L. H. JENSEN: Proc. Nat. Acad. Sci. USA **69**, 3526 (1972)

4.14. H. BEINERT, G. PALMER: Advan. Enzymology **27**, 105 (1965)

4.15. T. H. MOSS, D. PETERING, G. PALMER: J. Biol. Chem. **244**, 6143 (1969)

4.16. J. C. M. TSIBRIS, R. W. WOODY: Co-ordination Chemistry Reviews (Elsevier, 1969)

4.17. W. D. PHILLIPS, M. POE, J. F. WEIHER, C. C. MCDONALD, W. LOVENBERG: Nature **227**, 574 (1970)

4.18. K. K. RAO, M. C. W. EVANS, R. CAMMACK, D. O. HALL, C. L. THOMPSON, P. J. JACKSON C. E. JOHNSON: Biochem. J. **129**, 1063 (1972)

4.19. C. E. JOHNSON: Proc. Phys. Soc. **92**, 748 (1967)

4.20. W. MARSHALL, C. E. JOHNSON: J. Phys. Radium. **23**, 733 (1962).

4.21. K. K. RAO, R. CAMMACK, D. O. HALL, C. E. JOHNSON: Biochem. J. **122**, 257 (1971).

4.22. J. F. GIBSON, D. O. HALL, J. H. M. THORNLEY, F. R. WHATLEY: Proc. Nat. Acad. Sci. USA **56**, 987 (1966).

4.23. J. FRITZ, R. ANDERSON, J. FEE, G. PALMER, R. H. SANDS, J. C. M. TSIBRIS, I. C. GUNSALUS, W. H. ORME-JOHNSON, H. BEINERT: Biochim. Biophys. Acta **253**, 110 (1971).

4.24. W. R. DUNHAM, A. J. BEARDEN, I. T. SALMEEN, G. PALMER, R. H. SANDS, W. H. ORME-JOHNSON, H. BEINERT: Biochim. Biophys. Acta **253**, 134 (1971).

4.25. E. MUNCK, P. G. DEBRUNNER, J. C. M. TSIBRIS, I. C. GUNSALUS: Biochem. **11**, 855 (1972).

4.26. M. POE, W. D. PHILLIPS, J. D. GLICKSON, C. C. MACDONALD, A. SAN PIETRO: Proc. Nat. Acad. Sci. USA **68**, 68 (1971).

4.27. C. L. THOMPSON, C. E. JOHNSON, D. P. E. DICKSON, R. CAMMACK, D. O. HALL, U. WESTER, K. K. RAO: Biochem. J. **139**, 97 (1974).

4.28. D. P. E. DICKSON, C. E. JOHNSON, R. CAMMACK, M. C. W. EVANS, D. O. HALL, K. K. RAO: Biochem. J. **139**, 105 (1974).

4.29. C. E. JOHNSON, P. F. KNOWLES, R. C. BRAY: Biochem. J. **103**, 10C (1967).

5. Mössbauer Spectroscopy in Lunar Geology and Mineralogy

S. S. HAFNER

With 11 Figures

5.1. Introduction

The first studies of geologically important minerals using γ-ray resonant absorption were performed shortly after Mössbauer's discovery. They concerned the quadrupole perturbed magnetic hyperfine interaction of Fe^{57} in hematite (α-Fe_2O_3) by KISTNER and SUNYAR in 1960 [5.1], and the effect of the Verwey transition (Fe^{2+}/Fe^{3+} order-disorder) on the internal magnetic fields in magnetite (Fe_3O_4) by BAUMINGER et al. in 1961 [5.2]. Of course, the aims in that early period were primarily directed toward the properties of nuclear states, i.e. problems of low-energy nuclear physics. General interest in its application to crystallography, mineralogy, and geology developed a few years later. Among the early attempts to tackle problems in earth and planetary science were the work of DE COSTER et al. in 1962–1963 [5.3, 4] on iron in natural silicates, and of SPRENKEL-SEGEL and HANNA in 1964 [5.5] on the distribution of iron in stone meteorites. A large number of investigations were subsequently carried out with a considerable divergence of interests to collect data of geological significance. In view of the great importance of iron in the earth's crust and the widespread occurrence of this element in rock-forming minerals, earth scientists naturally focussed their attention on applications of Fe^{57} resonance. Little work has been performed so far on other Mössbauer nuclei in minerals.

One of the most important groups of rock-forming minerals are the silicates which generally have large unit cells with low lattice symmetries and complex crystal structures. Silicates frequently crystallize as solid solutions at elevated temperatures. In the course of subsequent natural cooling processes in the subsolidus region, they are subjected to atomic exchange reactions among lattice sites within the crystals, exsolution phenomena, atomic exchange between crystals of coexisting phases etc. Natural crystals of rock-forming minerals commonly represent complex metastable states which depend on the conditions of crystallization and subsequent thermal history.

In the past two decades, an impressive amount of data has been published on crystal structure refinements of silicate minerals using

X-ray and neutron diffraction. The positional parameters and inter-atomic distances of a large number of rock-forming silicates have been determined in the past few years with considerable accuracy. However, a particular lattice position is occupied often by more than two atomic species. In these cases, accurate site occupancy numbers for each species cannot be obtained by diffraction alone. Mössbauer spectroscopy has been an useful tool for investigating the local properties of iron sites in complex crystal structures, particularly when employed on minerals with carefully refined positional parameters. In these cases, the determined hyperfine fields and resonant absorption intensities of Fe^{57} yield valuable complementary data.

Typical applications of Mössbauer spectroscopy to mineralogy and geology have been the analysis of the oxidation state of iron at iron sites in minerals. In certain crystal structures, e.g. in oxides of the spinel type, or in chain silicates, a lattice position may be occupied by ferric and ferrous iron in various proportions. In such cases the ferric to ferrous iron ratio reveals important information on the partial pressure of oxygen during crystallization which is a parameter of geological significance.

The assignment of distinct hyperfine patterns in a Mössbauer spectrum to non-equivalent lattice positions has allowed site preferences of Fe^{2+} or Fe^{3+} ions in minerals to be determined. The assignment may be deduced from the observed isomer shifts, nuclear quadrupole splittings, and internal magnetic fields using crystal chemical arguments (coordination number, interatomic distances, polyhedral distortion, crystal field, etc.).

The study of area ratios of distinct hyperfine patterns has led to thermodynamical analyses of order-disorder phenomena in minerals. Thermodynamical parameters like the exchange energies of atomic reactions between non-equivalent lattice positions, rate constants for the disordering and ordering processes, activation energies, etc. have been determined.

Application of the Mössbauer effect of Fe^{57} to poorly crystallized materials of geological relevance may be fruitful. Studies have been made on hydrolysis and absorption in clay minerals or coordination polyhedra of iron in glasses.

As an example of recent applications of Mössbauer spectroscopy to mineralogy and geology the results from the studies of lunar samples, which have been reported during the past five years in the course of the six manned Apollo missions, are reviewed.

Since the first landing on the moon in July 1969, a large number of physical techniques have been employed to study lunar samples returned in the course of the Apollo and Luna missions. Information on major, minor, and trace elements, radiometric ages, solar-wind effects and radiation damage, thermal, magnetic, electrical, and optical properties, thermoluminescence, seismic velocities, mineralogy, etc. have led to comprehensive characterizations of the lunar surface. The large body of data collected on a rather limited number of samples has initiated an exceedingly rapid and successful development in the understanding of the origin and history of the moon.

The Mössbauer effect has made a modest, more or less descriptive contribution to the study of composite samples and separated mineral phases from the moon. The data should not, of course, be interpreted in an isolated form, but when correlated with the results of other techniques employed on the same samples they allow a number of interesting conclusions to be drawn.

Table 5.1. Chemical analysis of lunar landing sites (after [5.7])

Mission	Date	Geographical area	Location	Type of area	Type of analysis
Surveyor 5	1967, Sept. 11	Mare Tranquillitatis	23.20° E 1.42° N	mare	*in situ* α-particle
Surveyor 6	1967, Nov. 10	Sinus Medii	1.37° W 0.46° N	mare	*in situ* α-particle
Surveyor 7	1968, Jan. 10	Outside Crater Tycho	11.44° W 40.97° S	terra	*in situ* α-particle
Apollo 11	1969, July 20	Mare Tranquillitatis	23.49° E 0.67° N	mare	returned samples
Apollo 12	1969, Nov. 19	Oceanus Procellarum	23.40° W 3.20° S	mare	returned samples
Apollo 14	1971, Feb. 5	Frau Mauro Formation	17.47° W 3.67° S	mare	returned samples
Apollo 15	1971, July 30	Hadley Rille, Palus Putredinus	3.65° E 26.10° N	mare	returned samples
Apollo 16	1972, April 21	North of Crater Descartes	15.51° E 8.99° S	terra	returned samples
Apollo 17	1972, Dec. 11	Taurus mountains-Littrow region	30.77° E 20.17° N	mare	returned samples
Luna 16	1970, Sept. 19	Mare Fecunditatis	56.18° E 0.41° S	mare	returned samples
Luna 17	1970, Nov. 17	NW of Mare Imbrium	35° W 38° N	mare	*in situ* X-ray fluorescence
Luna 20	1972, Feb. 23	South of Mare Crisium	56.55° E 3.53° N	terra	returned samples

Technical data from the surveyor Project Final Report Part II, Science Results (Technical Report 32-1265 Jet Propulsion Laboratory 1968) and Preliminary Science Reports of the Apollo Missions (NASA SP-214, SP-235, SP-272, SP-289, SP-315, SP-330); cf. also [5.7].

At present, data on the chemical composition of the lunar surface are available from nine mare and three terra regions. Samples have been returned to earth from eight sites whereas data have been collected *in situ* from the other sites using α-particle and X-ray fluorescence techniques. In addition, orbital measurements of the X-rays excited by solar radiation and of γ-rays from the lunar surface were carried out on the Apollo 15 and 16 missions. The number of landing sites on the moon is still very small, and the sites are restricted to one hemisphere. However, the body of data studied so far indicates that the lunar surface is chemically rather homogeneous, except for small but significant differences between mare and terra regions. For this reason, the chemical composition of the lunar surface is fairly well known; it may be considered as at least as well known as that of the solid part of the earth's surface. The locations, geographical areas of the landing sites and the type of chemical analysis carried out are given in Table 5.1 (cf. also [5.6, 7]). The landing sites are shown in Fig. 5.1.

The principal elements which form more than 99 % of the lunar surface are, in order of decreasing abundance: oxygen, silicon, aluminum, iron, calcium, titanium, sodium, and potassium. The aluminum and calcium contents are somewhat higher in the terra regions or highlands, whereas iron and titanium show higher concentrations in the mare regions. The significant difference in the iron and titanium contents appears to be the principal reason for the darker albedo of the maria compared to the lighter albedo of the terrae.

In view of the chemical composition of the lunar surface, applications of the Mössbauer effect have naturally been restricted to iron which is one of the four most abundant elements.

5.2. The Lunar Regolith

The uppermost layer of the lunar surface consists almost entirely of *regolith*, which is composed of weakly coherent fragmental material with an increasing porosity towards the surface. Large areas of exposed coherent rock, as commonly found in terrestrial mountains, have not yet been detected on the moon. The thickness of the regolith at the Apollo 11 landing site was estimated to be about 4 m, but it is almost certainly thicker at many other places on the moon by several orders

Fig. 5.1. Composite photograph of first and last quarters of the moon, showing the landing sites of the Surveyor, Apollo, and Luna missions. (USAF Lunar Reference Mosaic, scale 1 : 10000000, orthographic projection, LEM-1A, Lunar earthside hemisphere, 3rd ed. July 1967)

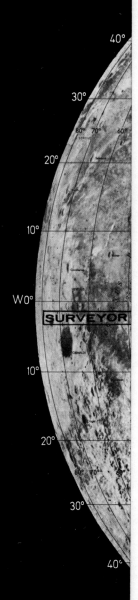

of magnitude. Some of the physical and mechanical properties of the regolith such as density, porosity, strength, compressibility, and stress-strain characteristics were predicted long before the first landing on the moon. Estimates were obtained from telescopic studies and from crater analysis using satellite photography. They were generally confirmed later by measurements on the returned samples.

The samples collected and returned to earth from the regolith may be divided into two distinct groups: coherent rock fragments between one cm and several dm in size, and fines, or "soil", which comprize loose material with a grain size smaller than one cm. A substantial fraction of the soil is of a remarkably small grain size. In typical samples collected with a scoop at the landing sites of the Apollo missions, approximately half of the fragments have diameters between 1 μm and 0.1 mm. The size frequency may be compared with terrestrial silty fine sands found in glacial tills.

5.3. The Lunar "Soil"

Origin and history of the fines are closely related to crater formation by impacting bodies on the lunar surface. Photographic studies of the size and distribution of primary and secondary craters in certain regions of the moon showed [5.8, 9] that the soil was stirred, turned, and mixed over within an area of several square miles by the continual impact of bodies in later lunar history. The soil constituents include a wealth of information on the overall mineralogical and chemical characteristics of the larger environment at each landing site. They are probably more representative for a certain region than the few large rocks and boulders which may be of more local significance. An example is provided by the chemical compositions of soil and rocks at the Apollo 11 landing site in Mare Tranquillitatis. All the rocks analyzed had a higher titanium content than the soil returned from that site. Thus, the soil must include an "exotic" component which modifies its average chemical composition.

The constituents of the lunar soil are of a highly complex nature. Since 1969 a large number of correlated techniques have been used on returned samples to study the physical and chemical processes that led to the present composition of the lunar surface. The main constituents include glassy agglomerates which consist of composite particles agglutinated by inhomogeneous vesicular glass, and isolated homogeneous or inhomogeneous glass fragments with a wide range of color and transparency and with angular, ellipsoidal, or spherical shapes, or formed like dumbbells. Some glass particles show devitrification or inclusions of partially molten crystals. Additional components of the soil are isolated mineral particles of plagioclase ((Na, Ca)(Al, Si)$_4$O$_8$), pyroxene ((Ca, Mg, Fe)SiO$_3$), ilmenite (FeTiO$_3$), and olivine ((Mg, Fe)$_2$SiO$_4$), or fragments of mineral composites which are considered to be parts from crystalline rocks. The soil also includes small amounts of alloys with compositions close to metallic iron.

5.3.1. The Mössbauer Spectrum of the Soil

Mössbauer spectroscopy of Fe^{57} has been used mainly as a complement to various other techniques to characterize the soil fraction with a grain size smaller than one mm. The primary aim has been to study the amount of iron in the soil, the distribution of iron over the soil constituents, and the particular valence states. Of special interest are, of course, the amount and properties of iron in the smallest particles of the soil since analytical data on grain sizes smaller than about 1 μm are not easily obtainable with other techniques such as X-ray emission microprobe analysis.

The resonant absorption spectra of the bulk fines represent remarkable "fingerprints" of the landing sites. For example, the spectra of the soils from Mare Tranquillitatis (Apollo 11) and from Oceanus Procellarum (Apollo 12) are significantly different [5.10, 11]. The difference is primarily due to the higher concentration of ilmenite in the soil of Mare Tranquillitatis. However, virtually no distinction was observed in spectra from soil samples collected at different locations of the Apollo 12 site or at different depths from the surface at that site. The data suggest that the regolith has been fairly well mixed within the area of the site which is in agreement with the conclusions drawn from the abundance of impact craters. Moreover, it was found that the resonant absorption of the bulk fines cannot be interpreted in terms of the bed rock (mare basalt) at the base of the regolith as the only source for the soil particles. The soils at the landing sites do not represent averages of the collected rocks. The soil spectrum includes contributions from exotic constituents which must have been transported over large distances.

The spectrum of the soil (Fig. 5.2) consists primarily of the superimposed resonant absorption patterns of Fe^{57} in the silicate minerals, silicate glasses, ilmenite (FeTiO$_3$), metallic iron, and troilite (stoichiometric FeS). Minerals of iron-bearing oxides of the spinel type and iron titanites have been detected under the microscope by mineralogists, but their concentrations are too small for a positive identification in the Mössbauer spectrum [5.10–14].

Resonant absorption patterns of the different phases exhibit, of course, considerable overlap. However, the absorption areas of the individual

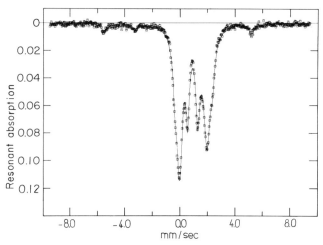

Fig. 5.2. Resonant absorption spectrum of Fe^{57} (295 K) in lunar soil from the Apollo 11 landing site at Mare Tranquillitatis. The absorption in the range between 0 and 0.3 mm/sec results primarily from iron in silicate glass, pyroxene, and olivine; the peaks at lower and higher velocities are due to metallic iron. (After [5.14])

patterns may be determined, for example, with the stripping technique [5.15]. This technique uses fixed standard values for line positions and widths obtained from single-phase spectra of the corresponding minerals.

The identification of the magnetic patterns of metallic iron and FeS and the quadrupole-split pattern of paramagnetic $FeTiO_3$, is generally no problem in spectra from soil absorbers kept at room temperature (Fig. 5.2). Yet the paramagnetic silicates in the soil cannot be identified easily because of the substantial overlap of their quadrupole-split patterns. Moreover, the analysis is hampered since the particles of pyroxene $((Ca, Mg, Fe)SiO_3)$, olivine $((Mg, Fe)_2SiO_4)$, and glass in the lunar soil are generally solid solutions with exceedingly inhomogeneous chemical compositions on a very fine scale. In addition, the absorption pattern of "pyroxene" is complicated by the coexistence of distinct clinopyroxene [monoclinic $(Ca, Mg, Fe) SiO_3$], orthopyroxene [ortho-rhombic $(Mg, Fe) SiO_3$], and pyroxferroite $((Fe, Ca) SiO_3)$ phases, and by exsolution phenomena in the crystals. The isomer shifts and quadru-pole splittings at the iron sites depend to some extent on the chemical composition of the solid solution. Therefore, broad lines are expected and the average positions of the lines cannot be predicted easily.

The total iron content in the bulk fines of the Apollo 11 and 12 soils was roughly estimated from the total resonant absorption to be about

Table 5.2. [57]Fe spectra of bulk fines from lunar regolith. Ratios of absorption area or iron in ilmenite (FeTiO$_3$) to iron in silicates

Soil (< 1 mm)		Area ratio Fe(ilmenite)/ Fe(silicates + ilmenite)	Ref.
Number	Location		
Mare Tranquillitatis			
10084		0.21	[5.12]
10084		0.21	[5.19]
Oceanus Procellarum			
12001	NW of lunar module[a]	0.051	[5.20]
12032	N of Head Crater	0.067	[5.10]
12033	N of Head Crater	0.062	[5.10]
12037	NW of Bench Crater	0.068	[5.10]
12042	SW of Surveyor Crater	0.04 ± 0.02	[5.11]
12057	SW of lunar module[b]	0.096	[5.20]
12070	Contingency sample[c]	0.064	[5.20]
Fra Mauro			
14003	Contingency sample[d]	0.08	[5.21]
14162	EVA-1[e]	0.08	[5.21]
14163	EVA-1[e]	0.11	[5.21]
14259	Comprehensive sample[f]	0.11	[5.21]
Taurus-Littrow			
4220	Shorty Crater (orange soil)	0.06	[5.18]
Mare Fecunditatis			
Luna 16	Average of 7 samples	0.066 ± 0.013	[5.22]

[a] Fines from the sample return container of the first extravehicular activity traverse (up to 300 m from the lunar module); for details cf. NASA Report MSC-01512.

[b] Fines from sample return container of the second ectravehicular activity traverse (1.5 km); for details cf. NASA Report MSC-01512.

[c] The contingency sample was collected 10 m northwest of the lunar module; for details cf. NASA Report MSC-01512.

[d] The contingency sample was collected 10 m northwest of the lunar module; for details cf. NASA Report SP-272.

[e] First extravehicular activity (up to 550 m west of the lunar module); for details cf. NASA Report SP-272.

[f] The comprehensive sample was collected 150 m west of the lunar module; for details cf. NASA Report SP-272.

10–12 weight percent [5.12]. This figure may be determined more accurately using wet chemical analysis. More significant information is obtained on the distribution of iron over the individual phases from the relative absorption areas of the corresponding patterns in the spectrum. An example is shown in Table 5.2. Data on the area ratios are certainly more easily obtainable than data on absolute areas. Reliable determinations of relative abundances of iron-bearing phases from area ratios require appropriate corrections for the different recoilless fractions at each lattice position of iron, for saturation effects due to finite absorber thickness, and for preferred orientations of the particles in the absorber.

5.3.2. The Oxidation State of the Soil

An interesting problem is the oxidation state of iron in the constituents of the soil. In view of the lack of a visual atmosphere it was assumed long before launching the Apollo missions that the oxidation state of the lunar regolith would be very low, and that hydrate minerals in the regolith would be very rare. The resonant absorption spectrum of Fe^{57} in the soil shows that iron is primarily in the ferrous and metallic states. Other valence states have not yet been positively identified in the spectra. Ferric iron would be expected to occur predominantly in clinopyroxene, ilmenite, various spinels including magnetite (Fe_3O_4), or pyrrhotite ($Fe_{1-x}S$). However, in view of the strong absorptions of Fe^{2+} the sensitivity to Fe^{3+} in the spectra is limited. The amount of Fe^{3+} which could be present without being detected depends on the kind and number of the superimposed patterns. HOUSLEY et al. [5.13] estimated the limit of detectability in composite soil spectra to be approximately 1% for Fe^{3+} in the form of magnetite (Fe_3O_4) or other magnetic phases and approximately 3% for Fe^{3+} in the paramagnetic phases.

In a sample of Apollo 11 soil, HOUSLEY et al. [5.13, 16] investigated the stoichiometry of ilmenite ($FeTiO_3$) using Mössbauer spectroscopy. Fe^{2+} in ilmenite is known to become magnetically ordered at temperatures below 57 K. The transition temperature was found to be clearly discernable. Within a temperature accuracy of ± 2 K, it corresponds to the value of synthetic $FeTiO_3$. It is known that Fe_2O_3 in solution with $FeTiO_3$ lowers the transition temperature of ilmenite at a rate of about 2.8 K per 0.01 mole. It was concluded that ilmenite in the Apollo 11 soil must contain less than 0.5% Fe_2O_3. The slight broadening of the transition noted towards the low temperature side is probably due to the presence of magnesium in some of the ilmenite crystals, as was observed by several investigators using X-ray emission microprobe analysis. Although the effect of magnesium on the transition temperature of ilmenite is not known in detail it is assumed to be less than the effect of Fe^{3+}. This is concluded from a comparison with other oxide systems.

In absorbers of pyroxene and glass separated from Apollo 11 soil with grain size smaller than 1 mm [5.14] no Fe^{3+} could be discovered with a detectability limit of ± 0.01. The two spectra are shown in Figs. 5.3 and 5.4.

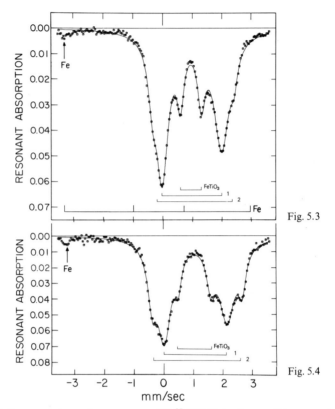

Fig. 5.3. Resonant absorption spectrum of Fe^{57} (295 K) in glass particles separated from Apollo 11 soil. The doublets 1 and 2 are due to Fe^{2+} ions in two distinct positions similar to $M1$ and $M2$ in pyroxene, suggesting a high degree of devitrification. The doublet due to ilmenite (FeTiO$_3$) results from inclusions. (After [5.14])

Fig. 5.4. Resonant absorption spectrum of the glass particles (cf. Fig. 5.3) at 77 K. The temperature dependence of the doublets 1 and 2 is similar to $M1$ and $M2$ doublets in pyroxene. (After [5.14])

At the Apollo 17 landing site in the Taurus Mountains-Littrow Region, on the rim of *Shorty Crater*, a soil with an unique color was collected: the "*orange soil*". Shorty Crater is a fresh impact crater 110 m in diameter which penetrated the regolith and probably the top of the subfloor basalt. Before the Apollo 17 mission, it was thought that Shorty Crater might be a volcanic vent. Unexpectedly, the astronauts discovered a band of soil with an intense orange color at the rim of the crater. The band exhibits a sharp boundary to gray soil layers. In an early speculation, it was suggested that the orange color might be a sign of alteration by water or fumarolic activity.

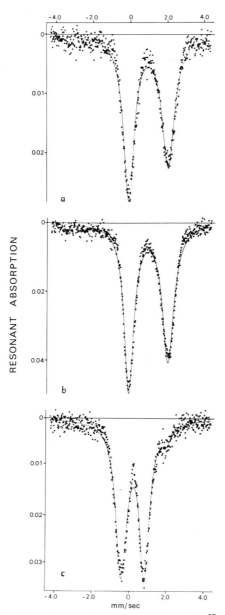

Fig. 5.5a–c. Upper spectrum Resonant absorption spectrum of Fe^{57} in orange glass from the Apollo 17 landing site at the Taurus-Littrow Region. The absorption is due principally to Fe^{2+} ions. The amount of Fe^{3+} ions is estimated to be less than 10%. Medium spectrum: Resonant absorption spectrum of Fe^{57} in synthetic glass prepared at 1330° C ($f_{O_2} = 10^{-10.5}$ atm). The absorption is due principally to Fe^{2+} ions. Lower spectrum: Resonant absorption spectrum of Fe^{57} in a synthetic glass prepared at 1500° C, atmospheric pressure. The most intense absorption is due to Fe^{3+} ions, with a less intense peak at 1.8 mm/sec due to Fe^{2+}. (After [5.18])

The orange soil consists primarily of nonvesicular yellow to ruby-red glass sperules and glass fragments which are partly devitrified. Additional particles are clinopyroxene, olivine, and ilmenite. MAO et al. [5.17, 18] studied the Mössbauer effect of Fe^{57} in the orange soil and in two synthetic glasses of similar chemical composition which were prepared under different oxygen fugacities (f_{O_2}). Three spectra are shown in Fig. 5.5. The upper spectrum is from a separate of orange glass which was purified from crystalline particles to 99% by hand-picking. The medium spectrum is from a synthetic glass prepared at $f_{O_2} \sim 10^{-11}$. The glass of the lower spectrum was synthesized at 1500° C in air.

The upper and medium spectra in Fig. 5.5 are similar. They consist of apparently two broad Fe^{2+} absorption peaks of unequal intensity which result from a superposition of a large number of somewhat different quadrupole-split doublets due to Fe^{2+} in predominantly pseudo-octahedral coordination. The apparent line widths and the average isomer shifts and nuclear quadrupole splittings are shown in Table 5.3; they may be compared with the values of a glass separate from the soil of Mare Tranquillitatis. The Mössbauer spectra indicate (cf. Figs. 5.4 and 5.5) that the glass from the orange soil of Shorty Crater is more homogeneous and less devitrified than that from the Apollo 11 soil. Fe^{2+} peaks due to ilmenite are absent in the orange glass separate.

The position of the Fe^{3+} peaks in glass spectra can be inferred from the sample synthesized at 1500° C in air which exhibits iron primarily in the

Table 5.3. Isomer shifts, quadrupole splittings, and line widths in glasses from lunar soils and synthetic glasses at room temperature

Sample	State of iron	Average isomer shifts [a] mm/sec	Average quadrupole splitting mm/sec	Line width lower position mm/sec	Line width upper position mm/sec	Ref.
Apollo 11 glass doublet 1 [b]	2+	1.16	2.72	0.27	0.37	[5.14]
doublet 2 [b]	2+	1.17	1.87	0.49	0.64	
Apollo 17 orange glass	2+	1.05	1.99	0.64	0.78	[5.18]
synthetic glass prepared at 1335° C	2+	1.04	1.97	0.57	0.72	[5.18]
synthetic glass prepared at 1500° C	3+	0.32	1.15	0.66	0.58	[5.18]

[a] Referred to a metallic iron absorber.

[b] Area ratio $1/(1 + 2) = 0.15$. Additional peaks due to ilmenite inclusions are not tabulated.

ferric state. Fe^{3+} peaks cannot be observed in the spectrum of the lunar orange glass. MAO et al. [5.18] estimated the Fe^{3+}/Fe^{2+} ratio to be clearly less than 0.1. Studies of optical absorption spectra of a series of synthetic glasses showed [5.18] that the lunar orange glass formed under relatively oxidized conditions at oxygen fugacitites (f_{O_2}) between 10^{-8} and 10^{-9}. This does not mean that the glass is grossly oxidized. On the contrary, ferric iron is present in an amount less than 1 wt-% which is the detection limit of the Mössbauer technique. The relatively oxidized conditions are consistent with the observation that metallic iron, in contrast to the glass from the Apollo 11 soil, apparently is not observed in the Mössbauer spectrum (cf. Figs. 5.4 and 5.5).

5.3.3. Metallic Iron in the Soil

Immediately after the first samples were returned from the moon, it was noted that the bulk fines contained significant amounts of metallic iron. Indeed, the Mössbauer spectra of lunar soil generally include the typical magnetic six-line pattern of metallic iron (cf. Fig. 5.2). In the Apollo 11 soil, that pattern comprises about 5–7% of the total resonant absorption area. About the same amount was observed in the Luna 16 soil. In the Apollo 12 soil, the area of the iron pattern was 2–3 times less.

An interesting question concerns the occurrence and location of metallic iron in the soil. A minor fraction of iron occurs in the form of irregular shapes up to a few mm across or as spherical or lensiod droplets. Yet the majority of metallic iron is associated with the glass. It is attached to or included in the glass fragments as minute particles or thin films. Mössbauer spectra of soil fractions with different specific gravities which were separated with heavy liquids showed that the most intense six-line patterns of metallic iron are obtained from the *light* separates ($\varrho < 3.3$) which include most of the glass [5.13, 14]. The heavy separates consist predominantly of ilmenite ($FeTiO_3$) and contain virtually no iron. HERZENBERG et al. [5.10] noted from Mössbauer spectra that the ratio of Fe^{2+} in the glass phase to total Fe^{2+} in the crystalline silicate fragments, as well as the ratio of the magnetic iron pattern to the total resonant absorption, is smaller in the Apollo 12 soil than in the Apollo 11 soil. If it is assumed that the mean distribution coefficient for Fe^{2+} between glass and crystalline silicates is about the same in both soils, the observation by HERZENBERG et al. [5.10] also indicates that metallic iron in the lunar regolith is primarily associated with glass particles.

HOUSLEY et al. [5.11] showed that the intensity of the magnetic six-line pattern of iron in the bulk fines from Mare Tranquillitatis was in excess of the expected increase due to the change in recoil-free fraction when the absorber was cooled to lower temperatures. This was interpreted in terms of a transformation of superparamagnetic particles to ferromagnets at lower temperatures. In this connection, it should be noted that the room temperature spectra of the bulk fines generally exhibit excess resonant absorption in the range of ~ 0 mm/sec Doppler velocity which was ascribed to superparamagnetic particles [5.10, 11, 14]. To appear completely ferromagnetic in an Fe^{57} Mössbauer experiment, the reorientation times for the magnetic moments of the iron particles must be longer than 10^{-7} sec. The reorientation rate τ_r of spherical particles may be approximated by

$$\frac{1}{\tau_r} = \frac{g_r^{K_a}}{M_{sat}} C^{1/2} e^{-C}. \tag{5.1}$$

Here g_r is the gyromagnetic ratio, K_a the magnetocrystalline anisotropy, M_{sat} the saturation magnetization and

$$C = \frac{K_a V}{k_B T}, \tag{5.2}$$

where V is the particle volume, and $k_B T$ the temperature in energy units. Using constants measured for pure Fe in the above expressions one finds that the transition between ferromagnetic and superparamagnetic behavior starts at a diameter of ~ 40 Å for spherical particles at room temperature and at a somewhat smaller size at 77 K (cf. [5.11] and additional references cited therein).

In Table 5.4, estimates of the amount of ferromagnetic and superparamagnetic iron particles are tabulated for samples from the double core tube collected at the Apollo 12 landing site in Oceanus Procellarum. The errors indicated in Table 5.4 are standard deviations. They do not include systematic errors, which may be significant. The values given in Table 4.5 may underestimate the actual amount of superparamagnetic iron up to 0.1 wt-%. In summary, it is concluded that significant amounts of metallic iron are present in the lunar soil in form of very small particles, probably not larger than ~ 40 Å. Similar conclusions were made by NAGATA et al. [5.23] and RUNCORN et al. [5.24] from magnetic properties of the bulk fines. The dispersion of very small superparamagnetic particles probably plays an important role in the degree of darkening (albedo) of the lunar regolith.

The iron particles in the soil are generally α-phase nickel-iron alloys (kamacite) of rather heterogeneous composition. The nickel content varies from about 0.5 to more than 30%. Minor amounts of cobalt (up to 1–2%) are also present. It is well-known that some nickel or cobalt diluted in iron increases the local magnetic field H_{int} at the Fe^{57} nucleus

Table 5.4. ^{57}Fe spectra of bulk fines from lunar regolith. Metallic iron and troilite (FeS) content

Sample	Absorber temperature K	Specific gravity	Ferromagnetic iron wt-%	Superparamagnetic iron wt-%	FeS wt-%
Mare Tranquillitatis					
10084	~295	<3.3	0.51±0.04	0.39±0.02	—
10084	77	<3.3	0.61±0.04	0.29±0.02	—
Oceanus Procellarum					
12042	~295	<3.3	0.34±0.05	0.17±0.02	0.36±0.06
12042	~295	>3.3	0.04±0.07	—	0.10±0.08
12025 double core tube 0.5 cm[a]	~295		0.38±0.06	0.35±0.02	0.23±0.07
12025 double core tube 5 cm[a]	~295		0.37±0.06	0.35±0.02	0.42±0.06
12028 double core tube 19 cm[a]	~295		0.39±0.08	0.22±0.02	0.36±0.08
12028 double core tube 30 cm[a]	~295		0.31±0.05	0.43±0.01	0.29±0.06

[a] Approximate distance from top.

[5.25], whereas most of the other metals reduce the splitting. An increase of the total magnetic splitting is indeed observed in the Mössbauer spectra of certain lunar soils. Values reported for Apollo 11 and 14 soils are 1.005 times [5.14] and 1.01 times [5.21] the splitting of pure iron, respectively. This corresponds to an average nickel content of about 2–3 at-%. The fairly broad line widths of the six-line pattern (~ 0.40–0.60 mm/sec full width at half height) are indicative of chemically inhomogeneous alloys. MALYSHEVA [5.22] studied the magnetic hyperfine splitting in the soil returned by Luna 16 from Mare Fecunditatis as well as in meteoritic iron. While H_{int} values corresponding to typical nickel-iron alloys were observed in the meteoritic samples as expected, a value close to that of pure iron was determined for the Luna 16 soil.

There are several possible explanations for the presence of metallic iron in the soil:

1. Small amounts of metallic iron are generally present in mare basalts because of the reducing conditions during crystallization from the magma. It is assumed that the oxygen fugacities during crystallization are several orders of magnitude less than those of common terrestrial basalts. Metallic iron occurs in blebs coexisting with troilite (FeS); it is evidently separated from an immiscible sulfur-iron melt close to the eutectic of the Fe-FeS system. The proportion of Fe:FeS is about 1:6. This iron is essentially pure, with very little nickel. However, the amount of iron in mare basalts is much too small to fully account for the total metallic iron in the regolith. In the Mössbauer spectra of lunar basalts, it is close to, or even below the limit of detectability.

2. It might be expected that the nickel-iron particles are original fragments from meteorites. However, this is rather unlikely. Meteorites hit the lunar surface with unattenuated velocity because of the absence of an atmosphere. Their kinetic energy is generally high enough to melt both the meteorite and a considerable amount of the rock at the impact position. While original meteorite fragments are unlikely to survive, the chemical composition of the regolith will be significantly affected.

3. Metallic iron may result from dissociation of iron-bearing compounds in connection with glass formation at the high temperatures produced by impacts. The widely distributed minute iron particles in the glasses are certainly formed in this way. HOUSLEY et al. [5.26] suggested a model which is primarily based on micrometeorite impacts. The fines in the lunar regolith are generally saturated with solar wind gases which produce H_2O and CO, the agents for the reduction processes during the impacts. Of course, the coexistence of fine-grained metallic iron and silicate glass is thermodynamically unstable, and the preservation of the two phases implies that the reduction process was followed by a rapid quench.

5.4. The Minerals from Lunar Rocks

The three most important groups of lunar rocks are basalts, anorthosites, and microbreccias. The *basalts* are relatively young dark-colored igneous rocks with approximately 15–20 wt-% FeO. They are quite similar to certain terrestrial volcanic rocks. The major minerals are clinopyroxene $((Ca, Fe, Mg) SiO_3)$, plagioclase $(Na_xCa_{1-x}Al_{2-x}Si_{2+x}O_8$ $(\sim 0.6 < x < 1))$, olivine $((Mg, Fe)_2 SiO_4)$, and ilmenite $(FeTiO_3)$. Generally the basalts form the basis of the lunar maria as lava flows or lava lakes. They are assumed to be shallow, near-surface crystallizations from a completely molten phase which came from the lunar interior. Some of the basaltic rocks may be crystallized from locally molten areas in hot ejecta blankets which comprise deposits from impacts of gigantic meteorites. The *anorthosites* are light-colored rocks which consist predominantly of calcium-rich plagioclase (often more than 90%; $\sim 0.9 < x < 1)$. Minor minerals are olivine, clino- and orthopyroxene. Anorthosites may contain less than one wt-% FeO, that is more than 10 times less than mare basalts. They are believed to be the major component of the terra regions. The anorthosites are considered to be early crystallizations of the lunar crust and now represent relatively old rocks with a complex history. The *microbreccias* are an abundant group of rocks with complex composition which were generated by impact events. They are accumulates of crystalline and glassy debris cemented together by glassy matrices.

Mössbauer spectroscopy of Fe^{57} has been employed particularly in the transition mode on mineral concentrates separated from basalts and anorthosites in combination with studies using diffraction techniques and X-ray emission microanalysis. Some Mössbauer work on total rock samples, including surface investigations of rock surfaces with scattering techniques, has also been attempted. The interpretation of the spectra from total rock spectra is, of course, complicated by the limited resolution due to superimposed mineral patterns. In view of the complex crystal structures of the individual phases in the rock, unambiguous conclusions cannot be reached easily.

Problems of interest have been the oxidation of iron in the rock-forming minerals and total rocks, the distribution of iron over non-equivalent lattice sites in pyroxene, olivine, and plagioclase obtained from intensity measurements (determination of thermodynamical data for conclusions on the thermal history of the crystals), and the crystalline fields at the iron positions. Complementary applications of the Mössbauer effect correlated with X-ray diffraction, electron microscopy, and X-ray emission microanalysis techniques have been particularly fruitful.

In this article, some results obtained from mineral concentrates of pyroxene and plagioclase which have been separated from lunar basalts and anorthosites are reviewed briefly.

5.5. Pyroxene

5.5.1. Crystal Structure

The lunar minerals of the pyroxene group are *augite* ($\sim Ca_{0.15-0.4}$ $(Mg, Fe)_{0.85-0.6} SiO_3$), *pigeonite* ($\sim Ca_{0.05-0.15}(Mg, Fe)_{0.95-0.85} SiO_3$), and *orthopyroxene* $((Mg, Fe) SiO_3)$. Augite and pigeonite are *clinopyroxenes* with the monoclinic space groups $C2/c$ and $P2/c$, respectively. Orthopyroxene is orthorhomic with space group $Pbca$. The pyroxenes are a special group of chain silicates with well-known topology. Their characteristic structural feature is SiO_4 tetrahedra linked to chains of infinite length via shared apices. The chains are held together by cations M in six- or eightfold oxygen coordination. The M cations are located in two distinct M polyhedra, both with triclinic point symmetries, labelled $M1$ and $M2$. The oxygen coordination of $M1$ is generally close to octahedral, whereas that of $M2$ is eightfold in space group $C2/c$, and approximately octahedral in space groups $P2_1/c$ and $Pbca$. Projections of two typical crystal structures of pyroxene are shown in Figs. 5.6 and 5.7.

An interesting problem is the location of the individual cations at the M positions. The Ca^{2+} ions are located exclusively at $M2$ while Mg^{2+} and Fe^{2+} may be distributed over $M1$ and $M2$ in various proportions. There is, however, preference of Mg^{2+} and Fe^{2+} for $M1$ and $M2$, respectively. The effective distribution depends on the thermal history of the crystal. In natural crystals of augite, pigeonite, and orthopyroxene, small amounts of Ca^{2+}, Mg^{2+}, and Fe^{2+} are generally substituted by Fe^{3+} and Al^{3+}. Charge balance is achieved with coupled substitutions either of Si^{4+} by Al^{3+}, or of bivalent cations at the $M2$ position by Na^+. In addition, small amounts of titanium, chromium, and manganese may also be present at the M positions and may participate in coupled substitutions.

Lunar pyroxene crystals generally exhibit exceedingly inhomogeneous chemical compositions which alter from spot to spot over distances of only a few μm. Their chemical variability is considerably greater than that of typical pyroxenes from most terrestrial rocks. Additional complexities are epitaxis and exsolution associated with the cooling of the crystals from a magmatic liquid. The pyroxenes crystallized from the magma as solid solutions which subsequently exsolved into augite and

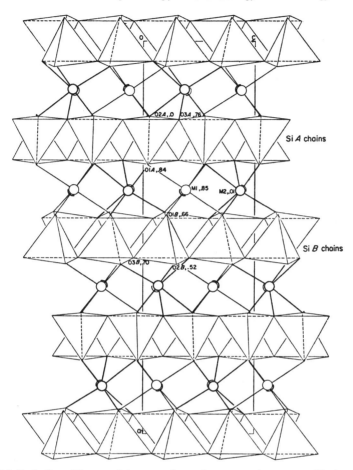

Fig. 5.6. Projection of the crystal structure of an orthopyroxene (space group *Pbca*) on (010). (After [5.50])

pigeonite phases intergrown with complex textural relationships. Initially intergrown exsolution lamellae have been found to be as small as 50 Å. The chemical and structural details of the intergrown phases reflect the crystallization processes in the original liquid and the subsequent subsolidus history. The chemical trends of the major cations and exsolution into chemically different augite and pigeonite phases are commonly described by plots in the $Ca_{0.5}Mg_{0.5}SiO_3 - MgSiO_3 - Ca_{0.5}Fe_{0.5}SiO_3$ quadrilateral. A typical example of crystallization trends in a mare basalt from the Hadley Rille at Palus Putredinus (Apollo 15) is shown in Fig. 5.8.

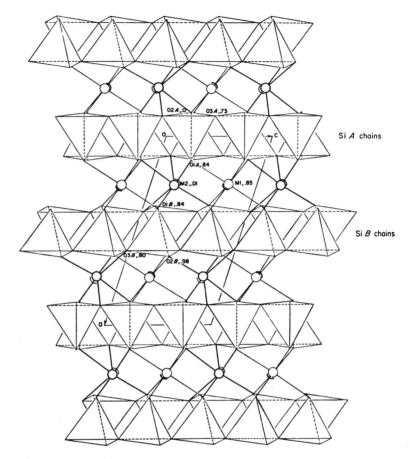

Fig. 5.7. Projection of the crystal structure of clinopyroxene (space group $P2_1/c$) on (010). (After [5.50])

5.5.2. The Hyperfine Spectrum of Fe^{57}

The Mössbauer spectrum of Fe^{57} in pyroxene consists of two superimposed quadrupole-split doublets which can be assigned to the Fe^{2+} ions at the two nonequivalent $M1$ and $M2$ positions. The observed isomer shifts and nuclear quadrupole splittings are indicative of Fe^{2+} in high spin configuration, as expected from the chemical composition and structure type. Accordingly, the quadrupole splitting is primarily due to the state of the 6th electron in the 3d valence shell of the ion. Typical values of shifts and splittings in pyroxene are shown in Table 5.5. Although in

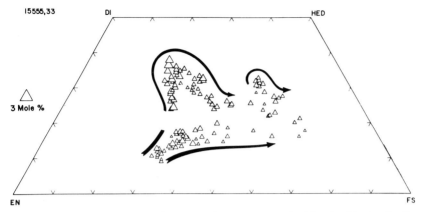

Fig. 5.8. Chemical compositions of pyroxenes from a coarse-grained basalt of the Apollo 15 landing site at Hadley Rille (Palus Putredinus). The compositions are plotted in the pyroxene quadrilateral showing the crystallization trends from the magma (EN: $MgSiO_3$; DI; $Ca_{0.5}Mg_{0.5}SiO_3$; HED: $Ca_{0.5}Fe_{0.5}SiO_3$; FS: $FeSiO_3$). (After [5.51])

Table 5.5. Nuclear hyperfine parameters of ^{57}Fe and coordination polyhedra in ortho-pyroxene $Mg_{0.13}Fe_{0.87}SiO_3$ [a]

Temperature K	Isomer shift [b, d] mm/sec		Quadrupole splitting [c, d] mm/sec		Coordination octahedron Å	
	M1	M2	M1	M2	M1	M2
295	1.17	1.13	2.48	1.96	2.186	2.576
					2.178	2.444
					2.123	2.224
					2.106	2.161
					2.106	2.130
					2.086	2.035
77	1.29	1.26	3.11	2.04	e	e

[a] Data from [5.31].
[b] Referred to a metallic iron absorber at 295 K.
[c] $1/2\ e^2qQ$.
[d] Total error: ± 0.01 mm/sec.
[e] Not determined.

the space groups *Pbca* and *P2₁/c* the $M1$ and $M2$ polyhedra possess the same coordination number, they are topologically distinct: each oxygen of the $M1$ polyhedron shares two Si tetrahedra (bridging atoms) whereas one of the oxygens of the $M2$ polyhedron is linked to only one tetrahedron (non-bridging atom). Thus, the nuclear quadrupole interactions of Fe^{2+} at the two positions are different.

Simple crystal field considerations predict that the octahedral site with the larger lattice contribution to the electric field gradient at the nucleus of the Fe^{2+} ion should yield the smaller quadrupole splitting [5.27]. The lattice contributions to the field gradient at $M1$ and $M2$ are not known. However, it may be assumed that the site with the stronger deviation from a regular coordination octahedron, i.e. $M2$ should yield the larger lattice field gradient. This assignment of the Fe^{57} doublets is in accord with the observed temperature dependence of the splittings, and it is confirmed by structure refinements of pyroxenes using X-ray diffraction. Diffraction and Mössbauer results reveal that Fe^{2+} in chain silicates generally prefers the more distorted $M2$ position. The observed trends in the isomer shifts and nuclear quadrupole splittings of Fe^{2+} in chain silicates may be correlated with differences in the geometry of the occupied coordination polyhedra, which perturb the chemical bonding [5.28, 29].

The quadrupole splittings in pyroxene exhibit different dependences on the temperature at the $M1$ and $M2$ positions because of the different distortions of the coordination polyhedra from regular octahedra (cf. Table 5.5). The strong temperature dependence of the quadrupole interaction at $M1$ reflects a smaller separation of the lowest crystalline field states [5.27]. The weak dependence at $M2$ suggests a large separation here. This interpretation is in accord with the aforementioned assignment of the doublets to the corresponding positions. It is also confirmed by crystal structure refinements using X-ray diffraction [5.30–32].

Iron-rich orthopyroxenes are magnetically ordered at very low temperatures [5.33]. The Neel point of $FeSiO_3$ (space group $Pbca$) determined to be 37 K using Mössbauer spectroscopy. The evaluation of the magnetically split patterns at 4.2 K yielded internal magnetic fields $H_{int} = 290 \pm 5\,kOe$ and a *negative* quadrupole interaction at $M1$, and $H_{int} = 113 \pm 5\,kOe$ and a *positive* quadrupole interaction at $M2$. The spectra of magnesium-rich pyroxenes at low temperatures show typical temperature dependent paramagnetic relaxation effects due to Fe^{2+} ions [5.33, 34].

5.5.3. Oxidation State of Iron

Mössbauer spectra of terrestrial pyroxenes generally exhibit, in addition to the Fe^{2+} peaks, a doublet which is assigned to Fe^{3+} at the M sites [5.35]. Its assignment follows from the smaller isomer shift and quadrupole splitting. That doublet can be used for a determination of the average oxidation state of iron in the pyroxene. Unfortunately, a precise analysis is hampered by the overlap of the low energy peaks of the Fe^{2+}

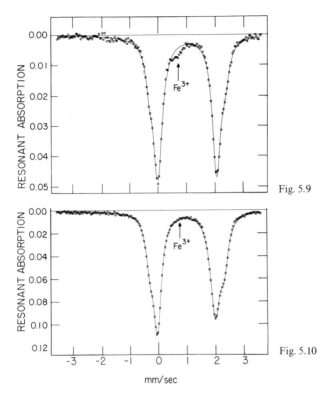

Fig. 5.9. Resonant absorption spectrum of Fe^{57} (295 K) in augite from a terrestrial volcanic rock. The intense absorption is due to Fe^{2+} ions. The weak Fe^{3+} peak is part of doublet which includes approximately 10% of the total resonant absorption. (After [5.14])

Fig. 5.10. Resonant absorption spectrum of Fe^{57} (295 K) in pigeonite separated from a coarse-grained basalt of the Apollo 11 landing site at Mare Tranquillitatis. No Fe^{3+} peak can be observed (cf. Fig. 5.9). The ratio Fe^{3+}/Fe_{tot} in this pyroxene is less than 0.003. (After [5.14], cf. also [5.36])

and Fe^{3+} doublets. The high energy peaks, however, are well resolved. A spectrum of a terrestrial augite is shown in Fig. 5.9.

So far no ferric iron has been positively identified in lunar pyroxenes (cf. Fig. 5.10). HAFNER et al. [5.36] estimated the upper limit of the ratio $r = Fe^{3+}/Fe_{tot}$ in a clinopyroxene separated from a lunar basalt to be $r < 0.003$. This ratio is consistent with the observation that blebs of metallic iron coexist with FeS in the rock. Metallic iron may be exsolved from immiscible sulfide liquids if the oxygen fugacity at the temperatures of magma crystallization is very low ($10^{-6} - 10^{-10}$ bar).

5.5.4. Doublet Intensity and Site Occupancy

The areas of the resonant absorption doublets may be used to obtain site occupancy numbers for iron at the $M1$ and $M2$ positions. Such data allow the study of the cation distribution in the crystal structures of solid solutions in detail. Particularly valuable are correlated crystal structure refinements using diffraction techniques and Mössbauer spectroscopical studies. For example, in solid solutions with crystallographic positions occupied by more than two different atoms, the site occupancy of each atomic species cannot be accurately determined with diffraction techniques alone. Moreover, the Mössbauer effect yields additional information on the vibrational properties of the sites of the atomic species in question.

Absolute site occupancy data from the Mössbauer spectra alone are not easy to obtain. For this, the recoilless fractions in source and absorber and the contributions to the background counting rate must be analyzed. However, if the total amount of iron in the sample is known, e.g. from chemical analysis, it is sufficient to determine the area ratios of the doublets which may be related to the total amount of iron in the crystal structure. The absolute areas are not needed. In this way, an extensive body of site occupancy data has been collected on terrestrial and lunar pyroxenes, using Mössbauer spectroscopy mainly in combination with X-ray emission microanalysis. For an accurate determination of the site occupancy from area ratios, the difference in the recoilless fractions of iron at the $M1$ and $M2$ positions and the saturation effects in the absorption peaks must be taken into account. Preferred orientation in polycrystalline absorbers is generally present because of anisotropic cleavage in the pyroxene crystals. However, its effect is small. In spectra with well resolved $M1$ and $M2$ doublets, preferred orientation may be neglected.

Studies of the site occupancy in lunar pyroxenes are complicated by the inhomogeneous chemical compositions of the crystals, by exsolution into different pyroxene phases with lamellae in the micrometer range or smaller, and by epitaxis. Superposition of somewhat different patterns in the spectra may significantly disturb the analysis. However, since the nuclear quadrupole splittings are not very sensitive to small changes in chemical composition or to a phase transformation within the pyroxene quadrilateral, the resolution of the $M1$ and $M2$ doublets is not substantially reduced. Independently obtained site occupancy numbers of orthopyroxenes and pigeonites using X-ray diffraction and Mössbauer spectroscopy, neglecting differences in recoilless fractions at $M1$ and $M2$, saturation effects, and paramagnetic relaxation, yield discrepancies of 0.01–0.05 atoms per site.

5.5.5. Mg^{2+}, Fe^{2+} Order-Disorder

From a thermodynamical point of view, the study of Mg^{2+}, Fe^{2+} order-disorder over the $M1$ and $M2$ positions in pyroxene is particularly attractive since the processes, in a first approximation, may be formulated by a simple, binary exchange reaction of the form [5.37, 38]

$$Mg^{2+}(M1) + Fe^{2+}(M2) \rightleftarrows Fe^{2+}(M1) + Mg^{2+}(M2). \tag{5.3}$$

The degree of Mg^{2+}, Fe^{2+} disorder in reaction (5.3) is uniquely described by the distribution coefficient k which may be defined as

$$k = \left(\frac{x_1^{Fe}}{x_1^{Mg}}\right) \Big/ \left(\frac{x_2^{Fe}}{x_2^{Mg}}\right). \tag{5.4}$$

Here, x_1^{Mg}, x_1^{Fe}, and x_2^{Mg}, x_2^{Fe} are the site occupancy numbers for Mg^{2+} and Fe^{2+}, at the $M1$ and $M2$ sites, respectively. Site occupancy studies of pyroxenes heated at various temperatures revealed that the Mg^{2+}, Fe^{2+} exchange is the predominant intracrystalline reaction. Other cations in pyroxenes either do not exchange between $M1$ and $M2$, even at temperatures close to the melting point (e.g. Ca^{2+}), or their exchange rates are so minor that they may be ignored. Of course, calcium, aluminum, titanium, etc. have an indirect effect on reaction (5.3) since the lattice constants and the atomic coordinates in the crystal structure depend on the chemical composition of the pyroxene. Yet they do not seem significantly to perturb the binary character of the Mg^{2+}, Fe^{2+} exchange.

Heat treatments of pyroxenes showed [5.37, 39, 40] that the exchange reaction (5.3) may be interpreted, in a first approximation, in terms of the *ideal solution model*: The Mg^{2+}, Fe^{2+} occupancy represents an ideal solution at each position $M1$ and $M2$. Observed small deviations from ideal solution have also been studied using regular solution models [5.41, 42] but the nature of those deviations has not yet been clarified in detail. It should be noted that in terms of the ideal solution model for a binary system, each metastable k value will correspond to a certain "equilibrium temperature" at which the cation distribution would be equilibrated.

Data on the Mg^{2+}, Fe^{2+} distribution as a function of temperature obtained from Mössbauer spectra of Fe^{57}, permit interesting conclusions. Below approximately $480°$ C the exchange reaction ceases. No cation exchange occurs even over geological times. Therefore, the observed Mg^{2+}, Fe^{2+} distribution in very slowly cooled pyroxenes, e.g. from metamorphic rocks, corresponds to an equilibrium temperature of $480°$ C, irrespective of the age of the rock. Rapidly cooled crystals which attained the barrier at $480°$ C without equilibration will exhibit metastable k coefficients which correspond to equilibrium temperatures higher than $480°$ C. The thermodynamical aspects of the limiting energy barrier at $480°$ C have been discussed by MUELLER [5.43].

At temperatures above $480°$ C the equilibrium conditions may be formulated by the relation

$$\Delta G_E^0 = -RT \ln k \tag{5.5}$$

based on the ideal solution model. Here ΔG_E^0 is the standard free Gibbs energy difference of the exchange reaction (5.3) and R is the gas constant. From (5.3) a simple rate equation may be derived [5.44] of the form

$$-dx_2^{Fe}/dt = -K_{12} x_1^{Fe} x_1^{Mg} + K_{21} x_2^{Fe} x_2^{Mg},$$
$$K_{21}/K_{12} = k \tag{5.6}$$

where K_{12} and K_{21} are the rate constants for the disordering reaction (from left to right) and for the ordering reaction (from right to left) in equilibrium relation (5.3). The rate constants K_{12} and K_{21} are functions of the temperature and may be determined by heating experiments at constant temperature over various periods of time. From K_{12} and K_{21}, the activation energies E_{dis} (disordering process) and E_{ord} (ordering process) may be obtained using the Arrhenius relationship

$$K_{21} = A \exp(-E_{dis}/RT). \tag{5.7}$$

Here, A is a constant that includes the entropy of activation and is independent of temperature, provided there is no change in mechanism of the exchange processes.

G_E^0, E_{dis} and E_{ord} are the basic thermodynamical parameters needed for a quantitative analysis of the thermal history of metastable cation distributions observed in natural pyroxenes. Approximate values have been obtained for a number of terrestrial and lunar pyroxenes from analyses of doublet intensities in Mössbauer spectra.

5.5.6. Cooling History of Lunar Basalts

The observed natural distribution coefficients $k = k_n$ may be used to study the cooling rate of rocks. The most critical range of temperatures for the intracrystalline Mg^{2+}, Fe^{2+} exchange in ortho- and clinopyroxenes is between 500 and $1000°$ C. It was found from heating experiments in the laboratory and from the study of well-documented samples from terrestrial lava flows [5.39] that the rate constants for the

Mg^{2+}, Fe^{2+} exchange at temperatures above $\sim 700°$ C are high compared to the heat flow in basaltic rocks. For this reason, metastable k_n values corresponding to equilibrium temperatures above $\sim 700°$ C can only be found in very rapidly cooled crystals located at the immediate surface of a lava flow, or in volcanic spills or spatters. Crystals located at some depth from the surface of a lava flow exhibit metastable distribution coefficients which correspond to equilibrium temperatures lower than 700° C.

The Mössbauer data of pyroxenes from lunar mare basalts yield site occupancies which correspond to equilibrium temperatures mainly between 600 and 700° C. This range of temperatures is higher than equilibrium temperatures found in slowly cooled, e.g. metamorphic rocks; but it is significantly lower than the equilibrium temperatures observed in crystals collected at the direct surface of rapidly cooled lava flows [5.39, 36, 40, 52].

X-ray diffraction studies of exsolution and epitaxial phenomena in pyroxene crystals from lunar mare basalts are indicative of exceedingly rapid cooling rates at temperatures of crystallization (1000–1100° C) and in the upper subsolidus region of the pyroxene phases. Yet the site occupancy in the individual pyroxene phases obtained from Mössbauer spectra is consistent with fairly slow cooling rates in the lower subsolidus region (500–900° C). These results are indicative of crystallizations in lava flows at depths of several meters from the surface.

An exceptionally high degree of cation disorder was found in clinopyroxene from a small basaltic rock fragment of the Fra Mauro Formation (Apollo 14). The observed high distribution coefficient k_n was interpreted to be due to a reheating process probably associated with impact and subsequent rapid quenching of the hot rock fragment in a cold regolith [5.40].

Accurate interpretations of the cooling history from intracrystalline cation distributions are based on subtle differences in site occupancy numbers and require precise knowledge of the cation exchange mechanisms, equilibrium conditions, and kinetics of the exchange reactions. A number of questions in the pyroxene system are not yet answered. In particular, the effect of chemical composition, trace elements, or lattice defects on the basic thermodynamic parameters are not yet understood completely. These rather serious difficulties can be bypassed by a determination of the thermodynamical parameters from *heating experiments* at various temperatures for each sample in question. An intensity analysis of the well-resolved quadrupole-split ^{57}Fe-doublets is a straightforward method to obtain additional information on such problems, particularly when combined with structure refinements using diffraction techniques.

5.6. Plagioclase

5.6.1. Crystal Structure

Plagioclases are solid solutions close to the system $Na_xCa_{1-x}Al_{2-x}Si_{2+x}O_8$ $(0 < x < 1)$. They possess framework crystal structures which consist of SiO_4 and AlO_4 tetrahedra linked via apices to eightfold rings. Each oxygen atom is shared by two tetrahedra. The calcium and sodium ions occupy seven-coordinated interstices. The crystal structures are triclinic with space groups $C\bar{1}$ or $P\bar{1}$.

Typical terrestrial and lunar plagioclases contain iron in concentrations of about 0.5 wt-%. This corresponds to approximately 0.025 iron atoms with reference to the formula $CaAl_2Si_2O_8$. Such small concentrations are just about at the limit of detectability in Mössbauer spectra recorded with conventional techniques. Iron is expected to occur predominantly in the form of Fe^{3+} ions replacing Al^{3+} at the tetrahedrally coordinated sites. This substitution is certainly most common in terrestrial plagioclases. In addition, small amounts of iron may possibly be located as Fe^{2+} at the Ca^{2+} position. However, this substitution is less favorable since the average interatomic distance of the CaO_7 coordination polyhedron in $CaAl_2Si_2O_8$ is more than 10% larger than typical Fe-O distances of ferrous iron in iron-bearing silicates. At any rate, in coexisting rock-forming silicates, plagioclase is expected to show comparatively high Fe^{3+}/Fe^{2+} ratios because of the favorable Fe^{3+}-Al^{3+} substitution at the tetrahedrally coordinated sites. Pyroxenes generally exhibit much smaller Fe^{3+}/Fe^{2+} ratios than plagioclase in terrestrial rocks. Yet it is anticipated that iron in lunar plagioclases will be predominantly in the ferrous state in view of the low partial pressure of oxygen during crystallization and subsequent subsolidus cooling in lunar rocks.

5.6.2. The Hyperfine Spectrum of Fe^{57}

In plagioclase, there are eight crystallographically non-equivalent Al^{3+} positions. Therefore, eight superimposed quadrupole-split Fe^{3+} doublets may be expected. However, since the oxygen coordination at the eight distinct positions is the same and the average Al-O distance of each coordination polyhedron is similar, the superimposed doublets are expected to exhibit considerable overlap. They may not be visually resolved. Electron paramagnetic resonance in oriented plagioclase crystals shows that Fe^{3+} ions strongly prefer three of the eight Al^{3+} positions [5.45, 46].

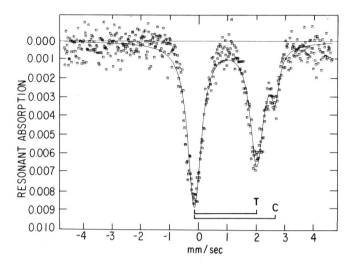

Fig. 5.11. Resonant absorption spectrum of Fe^{57} in plagioclase separated from a coarse-grained basalt of the Apollo 11 landing site at Mare Tranquillitatis. (C: doublet due to Fe^{2+} at Ca^{2+} sites; T: doublet due to Fe^{2+} ions at tetrahedrally coordinated Al^{3+} sites. The total amount of iron in the plagioclase was ~ 0.3 wt. %)

The isomer shift and nuclear quadrupole splitting of Fe^{2+} at the Ca^{2+} positiob should be significantly greater compared to the values of Fe^{3+} at the tetrahedral sites because of the large average Ca-O distance of the CaO_7 polyhedron and its strong asymmetry. The *smallest* Ca-O distance of that polyhedron in $CaAl_2Si_2O_8$ is 2.279 Å; it is distinctly larger than typical *average* Fe^{2+}-O distances in coordination octahedra of silicate structures.

The hyperfine spectrum of Fe^{57} in lunar plagioclases studied so far consists of an apparent three-line pattern which has been ascribed to two overlapping quadrupole-split doublets of *ferrous iron* at tetrahedrally coordinated Al^{3+} positions and at the Ca^{2+} position [5.47, 48]. A spectrum is shown in Fig. 5.11. The replacement of Al^{3+} ions at tetrahedral sites by Fe^{2+} ions is unusual; it has not yet been demonstrated in terrestrial plagioclases.

Unfortunately, the iron concentrations in plagioclases are low, and the observed Mössbauer effect in the samples is weak. The strongest peak of the resonance pattern referred to the background counting rate is commonly less than 1%. Therefore, precise values of the isomer shifts and quadrupole splittings have not been determined. The magnitudes of the isomer shifts as well as the dependence of the quadrupole splittings on temperature are indicative of ferrous iron in high-spin configuration. The isomer shift of Fe^{2+} at the CaO_7 polyhedron is approximately 10–15% larger than shifts observed at octahedrally coordinated sites in silicates. This is indicative of a comparatively ionic state, in agreement with the trends in the interatomic distances of the polyhedra determined in recent structure refinements using X-ray diffraction. The isomer shift of Fe^{2+} at the tetrahedral sites reveals a significant covalent participation in the Fe^{2+}-O bonding: This is expected because of the short interatomic distances in the AlO_4 tetrahedra.

An apparently anomalous dependence of the peak heights, widths, and thermal shifts of the doublets on temperature has been noted in the range of 77–295 K [5.29] although precise measurements are difficult to perform because of the small resonance absorption effect in the spectra. The anomalies have been interpreted in terms of lattice defects or oxygen vacancies close to the tetrahedral Fe^{2+} sites. In this connection, it should be noted that significant deviations of the chemical compositions of lunar plagioclases from the stoichiometric formula have been observed by a number of analysts as a unique and most striking feature of lunar plagioclase.

5.6.3. Oxidation State of Iron

Ferric iron, although commonly present in terrestrial plagioclase, has not been identified in the form of a resolved pattern in the Mössbauer spectra of lunar plagioclase. Yet it has been noted that the peak at approximately 0 mm/sec velocity (cf. Fig. 5.8) exhibits an anomalously high intensity. This may be interpreted to be due to a superimposed doublet of Fe^{3+} [5.47, 49]. Rough estimates of the Fe^{3+}- and Fe^{2+}-doublet intensities yield $Fe^{3+}/(Fe^{2+} + Fe^{3+})$ ratios of $r = 0.02$–0.1. The presence of Fe^{3+} ions in lunar plagioclase crystals has been confirmed recently by electron spin resonance [5.46]. Experiments of recrystallization and reequilibration of plagioclase crystals in a furnace at elevated temperatures under various partial oxygen pressures would be very interesting since they would allow the calibration of the ratio r in terms of the partial oxygen pressure using the Mössbauer effect. Such experiments have not yet been carried out.

The plagioclases studied until this time were separated from mare basalts of Mare Tranquillitatis (Apollo 11), Oceanus Procellarum (Apollo 12), Fra Mauro Formation (Apollo 14), and from an anorthosite of Hadley Rille (Apollo 15). In summary, it is concluded that the state of iron in these samples is significantly different from that in equivalent terrestrial rocks. While Al^{3+} in terrestrial crystals is generally replaced by ferric iron the substituting ions in lunar crystals are primarily in the bivalent state. The substitution at the tetrahedral sites in the lunar crystals seems to be associated with deformations or defects in the local environment of the Fe^{2+} sites.

Acknowledgement

I thank Mrs. FRANCES B. WARANIUS from the Lunar Science Institute, Houston, for supplying the requested data and for an updated modification of photograph of the lunar hemisphere (Fig. 5.1).

References

5.1. O. C. KISTNER, A. W. SUNYAR: Phys. Rev. Letters **4**, 412 (1960).
5.2. R. BAUMINGER, S. G. COHEN, A. MARINOV, S. OFER, E. SEGAL: Phys. Rev. **122**, 1447 (1961)
5.3. H. POLLAK, M. DE COSTER, S. AMELINCKX: Phys. Status Solidi **2**, 1653 (1962).
5.4. M. DE COSTER, H. POLLAK, S. AMELINCKX: Phys. Status Solidi **3**, 283 (1963).
5.5. E. L. SPRENKEL-SEGEL, S. S. HANNA: Geochim. Cosmochim. Acta **28**, 1913 (1964).
5.6. A. L. TURKEVICH: Proc. 4th Lunar Sci. Conf., Geochim. Cosmochim. Acta Suppl. 4, Vol. 2, 1159 (1973).
5.7. A. L. TURKEVICH: Acc. Chemical Research **6**, 81 (1973).
5.8. E. M. SHOEMAKER: In *The Nature of the Lunar Surface*, ed. by W. N. HESS, D. H. MENZEL, J. A. O'KEEFE (The Johns Hopkins Press, Baltimore, Md., 1966), p. 23.
5.9. E. M. SHOEMAKER, M. H. HAIT, G. A. SWANN, D. L. SCHLEICHER, D. H. DAHLEM, G. G. SCHABER, R. L. SUTTON: Science **167**, 452 (1970).
5.10. C. L. HERZENBERG, R. B. MOLER, D. L. RILEY: Proc. 2nd Lunar Sci. Conf., Geochim. Cosmochim. Acta Suppl. 2, Vol. 3, 2103 (1971).
5.11. R. M. HOUSLEY, R. W. GRANT, A. H. MUIR, M. BLANDER, M. ABDEL-GAWAD: Proc. 2nd Lunar Sci. Conf., Geochim. Cosmochim. Acta Suppl. 2, Vol. 3, 2125 (1971).
5.12. C. L. HERZENBERG, D. L. RILEY: Proc. Apollo 11 Lunar Sci. Conf., Geochim. Cosmochim. Acta Suppl. 1, Vol. 3, 2221 (1970).
5.13. R. M. HOUSLEY, M. BLANDER, M. ABDEL-GAWAD, R. W. GRANT, A. H. MUIR: Proc. Apollo 11 Lunar Sci. Conf., Geochim.Cosmochim. Acta Suppl. 1, Vol. 3, 2251 (1970).
5.14. S. S. HAFNER, B. JANIK, D. VIRGO: In *Mössbauer Effect Methodology*, ed. by I. J. GRUVERMAN, Vol. 6, 193 (1970).
5.15. A. H. MUIR: In *Mössbauer Effect Methodology*, Ed. by I. J. GRUVERMAN, Vol. 4, 75 (1968).
5.16. A. H. MUIR, R. M. HOUSLEY, R. W. GRANT, M. ABDEL-GAWAD, M. BLANDER: In *Mössbauer Effect Methodology*, ed. by I. J. GRUVERMAN, Vol. 6, 163 (1970).

5.17. H. K. MAO, D. VIRGO, P. M. BELL: Carnegie Inst. Washington Year Book **72**, 631 (1973).

5.18. H. K. MAO, D. VIRGO, P. M. BELL: Proc. 4th Lunar Sci. Conf., Geochim. Cosmochim. Acta Suppl. 4, Vol. 1, 397 (1973).

5.19. P. GAY, G. M. BANCROFT, M. G. BOWN: Proc. Apollo 11 Lunar Sci. Conf., Geochim. Cosmochim. Acta Suppl. 1, Vol. 1, 481 (1970).

5.20. P. GAY, M. G. BOWN, I. D. MUIR, G. M. BANCROFT, P. G. L. WILLIAMS: Proc. 2nd Lunar Sci. Conf., Geochim. Cosmochim. Acta. Suppl. 3, Vol. 1, 377 (1971).

5.21. T. C. GIBB, R. GREATREX, N. N. GREENWOOD: Proc. 3rd Lunar Sci. Conf. Geochim. Cosmochim. Acta Suppl. 3, Vol. 3, 2479 (1972).

5.22. T. V. MALYSHEVA: Proc. 3rd Lunar Sci. Conf., Geochim. Cosmochim. Acta Suppl. 3, Vol. 1, 105 (1972).

5.23. T. NAGATA, Y. ISHIKAWA, H. KINOSHITA, M. KONO, Y. SYONO: Proc. Apollo 11 Lunar Sci. Conf., Geochim. Cosmochim. Acta Suppl. 1, Vol. 3, 2325 (1970).

5.24. S. K. RUNCORN, D. W. COLLINSON, W. O'REILLY, M. H. BATTEY, A. STEPHENSON, J. M. JONES, A. J. MANSON, P. W. READMAN: Proc. Apollo 11 Lunar Sci. Conf., Geochim. Cosmochim. Acta Suppl. 1, Vol. 3, 2369 (1970).

5.25. C. E. JOHNSON, M. S. RIDOUT, T. E. CRANSHAW: Proc. Phys. Soc. **81**, 1079 (1963).

5.26. R. M. HOUSLEY, R. W. GRANT, N. E. PATON: Proc. 4th Lunar Sci. Conf., Geochim. Cosmochim. Acta Suppl. 4, Vol. 3, 2737 (1973).

5.27. R. INGALLS: Phys. Rev. **133**, A787 (1964).

5.28. S. S. HAFNER, S. GHOSE: Z. Kristallogr. **133**, 301 (1971).

5.29. G. M. BANCROFT, A. G. MADDOCK, R. G. BURNS: Geochim. Cosmochim. Acta **31**, 2219 (1967).

5.30. J. R. CLARK, D. E. APPLEMAN, J. J. PAPIKE: Mineral. Soc. Am. Spec. Pap. **2**, 31 (1969).

5.31. C. W. BURNHAM, Y. OHASHI, S. S. HAFNER, D. VIRGO: Am. Mineral. **56**, 850 (1971).

5.32. G. E. BROWN, C. T. PREWITT, J. J. PAPIKE, S. SUENO: J. Geophys. Res. **77**, 5778 (1972).

5.33. G. K. SHENOY, G. M. KALVIUS, S. S. HAFNER: J. Appl. Phys. **40**, 1314 (1969).

5.34. F. C. SCHWERER, G. P. HUFFMAN, R. M. FISCHER: Proc. 3rd Lunar Sci. Conf., Geochim. Cosmochim. Acta Suppl. 3, Vol. 3, 3173 (1972).

5.35. S. S. HAFNER, H. G. HUCKENHOLZ: Nature Phys. Science **233**, 9 (1971).

5.36. S. S. HAFNER, D. VIRGO, D. WARBURTON: Proc. 2nd Lunar Sci. Conf., Geochim. Cosmochim. Acta Suppl. 2, Vol. 1, 91 (1971).

5.37. R. F. MUELLER: Mineral. Soc. Amer. Spec. Pap. **2**, 83 (1969).

5.38. D. VIRGO, S. S. HAFNER: Mineral. Soc. Am. Spec. Pap. **2**, 67 (1969).

5.39. S. S. HAFNER, D. VIRGO: Proc. Apollo 11 Lunar Sci. Conf., Geochim. Cosmochim. Acta Suppl. 1, Vol. 3, 2183 (1970).

5.40. K. SCHÜRMANN, S. S. HAFNER: Proc. 3rd Lunar Sci. Conf., Geochim. Cosmochim. Acta Suppl. 3, Vol. 1, 493 (1972).

5.41. S. K. SAXENA, S. GHOSE: Am. Mineral. **56**, 532 (1971).

5.42. S. K. SAXENA: *Thermodynamics of Rock-Forming Crystalline Solutions* (Springer Berlin-Heidelberg-New York, 1973).

5.43. R. F. MUELLER: Am. Mineral. **55**, 1210 (1970).

5.44. R. F. MUELLER: J. Phys. Chem. Solids **28**, 2239 (1967).

5.45. J.-M. GAITE, J. MICHOULIER: Bull. Soc. Fr. Mineral. Cristallogr. **93**, 341 (1970).

5.46. H. H. NIEBUHR, S. ZEIRA, S. S. HAFNER: Proc. 4th Lunar Sci. Conf., Geochim. Cosmochim. Acta Suppl. 4, Vol. 1, 971 (1973).

5.47. S. S. HAFNER, D. VIRGO, D. WARBURTON: Earth Planetary Sci. Letters **12**, 159 (1971).

5.48. D. E. APPLEMAN, H.-U. NISSEN, D. B. STEWART, J. R. CLARK, F. DOWTY, J. S. HUEBNER: Proc. 2nd Lunar Sci. Conf., Geochim. Cosmochim. Acta Suppl. 2, Vol. 1, 117 (1971).

5.49. K. SCHÜRMANN, S. S. HAFNER: Proc. 3rd Lunar Sci. Conf., Geochim. Cosmochim. Acta Suppl. 3, Vol. 1, 615 (1972).

5.50. C. W. BURNHAM: Carnegie Inst. Wash. Year Book 65, 285 (1967).

5.51. A. E. BENCE, J. J. PAPIKE: Proc. 3rd Lunar Sci. Conf., Geochim. Cosmochim. Acta Suppl. 3, Vol. 1, 431 (1972).

5.52. T. YAJIMA, S. S. HAFNER: Proc. 5th Lunar Sci. Conf., Geochim. Cosmochim. Acta Suppl. 5 Vol. 1, 769 (1974).

6. Mössbauer Spectroscopy in Physical Metallurgy

F. E. FUJITA

With 19 Figures

6.1. Introduction

The recent development of the application of the Mössbauer effect to physical metallurgy can be readily observed. If any journal of physical metallurgy, published within the past few years, is opened, one will often find Mössbauer patterns with peculiar shapes. This directly shows how Mössbauer spectroscopy has become a useful tool in physical metallurgy. Four typical international magazines in physical metallurgy are: J. Phys. F (Metal Phys.), Acta Metallurgica, Z. Metallkunde, and Nippon-Kinzoku-Gakkaishi. Out of 829 papers published in these journals in 1972, 10 papers are concerned with the Mössbauer effect. In a few years, this number might be comparable to that of the X-ray diffraction papers (a total of 42 papers) which appeared in the same volumes.

In this respect, it may be worthy to compare the rapid development of the utilization of the Mössbauer effect in metallurgy with that of similar new tools which appeared in the same field during this century, e.g. X-ray diffraction and electron microscopy. The X-ray diffraction phenomenon was discovered in 1912 by VON LAUE, FRIEDRICH, and KNIPPING [6.1] while the first electron microscope was built in 1938 by BORRIES and RUSKA. Although, at present, the statistical data to trace the increase in the utilization of these two tools are not available to the author, it may not be unreasonable to assign the most rapid period of growth in the history of the application of X-ray diffraction method to about the time between the experiment by JOHANSSON and LINDE on the superlattice in 1925 [6.2) and KURDJUMOV and SACHS' work on the martensite lattice relation in 1930 [6.3]. On the other hand, electron microscopy seems to have grown into a powerful and useful method in physical metallurgy since the first direct observation of dislocations by transmission microscopy by BOLLMANN [6.4] and WHELAN et al. [6.5]. Today the basic principles and fundamental techniques of the two methods are well known among metallurgists, and their utilization is almost saturated except in some newer developments such as the synchrotron orbit radiation of X-rays and high voltage electron microscopy. In contrast, Mössbauer spectroscopy is still relatively unknown in the

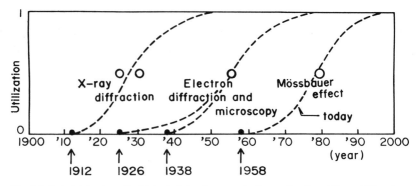

Fig. 6.1. A sketch to show the historical development in the application of X-ray diffraction, electron microscopy, and Mössbauer spectroscopy to physical metallurgy. Circles indicate the events mentioned in the text

field of physical metallurgy, so that the number of papers published during the past few years is low. The above three metallurgical tools are schematically compared in Fig. 6.1 with regard to their frequency of employment on a chronological scale. The degree of utilization is normalized on the coordinates between zero and one, and the curves are tentatively drawn so that similar shapes gradually appear as time elapses. The two white circles on the curves, corresponding to X-ray utilization, indicate the years in which the experiments concerning superlattice and martensite were made. The curve corresponding to electron diffraction starts at 1926 and connects to that of electron microscopy half way up, reflecting the fact that the completion of commercial electron microscopes enabled the full combination of the two methods in one apparatus. The circle on it indicates the year in which dislocations were observed.

Although the development of Mössbauer spectroscopy of metals and alloys is still at an early stage, many fundamental features and sophisticated experiments have already been carried out, as exemplified in an excellent review article on the application of the Mössbauer effect to physical metallurgy by GONSER [6.6]. By studying the last curve, one might be tempted to predict — in analogy to the other curves — a breakthrough around 1980 (perhaps Goldanskii's Gaser) and a saturation in the application in physical metallurgy around 1990.

In the present article, it is intended to describe work on the use of Mössbauer spectroscopy in physical metallurgy, particularly quantitative analyses which have enabled metallurgists to solve many old problems. For the above purpose, we will discuss first the fundamental concepts and principles of the quantitative analysis of Mössbauer spectroscopy and introduce the technique of deconvolution of a complex Mössbauer pattern. In contrast to other chemical and biological materials, metals are characterized by the formation of solid solution alloys, which naturally bring us a large number of different atomic and electronic configurations in one phase, and therefore necessitate a special technique of deconvolution of the complex spectra. Typical examples for the quantitative analysis of solid solutions will be given in almost every section which deals with solid solution alloys.

In the chapters following the introduction of the basic principles, metallurgical applications of Mössbauer spectroscopy, such as order-disorder alloys, interstitial alloys, ferromagnetic alloys, precipitation, diffusion, oxidation, lattice defects, etc. are discussed. Many other interesting topics have been omitted from the text, since complete coverage of the whole field of metallurgy was not intended. Nevertheless, the readers will see in this short article some examples of unsuccessful applications of the Mössbauer effect and the problems which still remain unsolved.

As GONSER already mentioned, metallurgical applications of the Mössbauer effect have been done mostly by utilizing the resonant absorption of Fe^{57} because of the ready availability of Co^{57} radiation sources, appropriate range of the energy of radiation and natural width, existence of ferro- and paramagnetic state of iron, and the natural abundance of Fe^{57}. So far, the applications of Mössbauer spectroscopy in physical metallurgy were mostly performed with Fe^{57} but the trend to use other isotopes is becoming more and more pronounced. The significant role of Fe^{57} is due to the fact that iron is the most important element in metallurgy and that the development of technology to enrich Fe^{57} isotope has enabled not only the investigation of iron and steel but also of the alloys with very small iron contents. Therefore, the present article will deal mainly with the metallurgical problems concerning iron.

6.2. Fundamental Concepts and Principles of Spectrum Analysis

In this chapter some basic concepts and principles necessary for the qualitative and quantitative analysis of the Mössbauer patterns from metals and alloys are discussed. At present, Mössbauer spectroscopy is insensitive to the non-resonance impurity and lattice defects in metals, if they are less than, for instance, 0.1 % in concentration. Therefore, the technique seems to be inadequate for the problems of pure metals except some special ones such as the phase transformations with temperature or pressure. This article is mainly confined to alloy problems. Alloys can be divided into two categories according to their structure, i.e. single-phase and multi-phase alloys. Each phase is characterized by the crystal structure and atomic arrangements in it. The Mössbauer pattern from a multi-phase alloy can be broken down into the components of individual phases, if any one of the Mössbauer parameters, internal magnetic field, isomer shift, or electric quadrupole splitting is different from phase to phase and each phase has a narrow range of chemical composition. An example is given in the following section regarding the analysis of plain carbon steel, which contains about one weight-% of carbon. The analysis becomes a difficult problem when the alloy has a wide range of composition in the order of 10% in concentration. In the solid solution with such a high alloy concentration, the atomic arrangements sur-rounding the probe isotope atoms, e.g. Fe^{57}, will be manifold and many components of absorption with continuously changing Mössbauer parameters will form a broad and rather smooth hybrid absorption spectrum. For a high concentration alloy with a closely packed structure thirteen different atomic configurations exist even if we assume that only the first neighbor interaction prevails and only the number of first neighboring atoms of one component determines the electronic configura-tion of the probe atom, and one has to take at least several components into account in the analysis of the Mössbauer spectrum. This problem becomes even more complex in considering the spatial arrangements of the neighbors. This sometimes leads us into trouble in finding a unique solution in the deconvolution of the spectrum even though computer calculations are applied. Some statistical calculations to classify the atomic configurations in various types of alloys are introduced in Subsection 6.2.2 and some examples of analysis of the complex Möss-bauer patterns of alloys are shown in the following subsections.

6.2.1. Four Important Mössbauer Parameters

Internal Magnetic Field (Hyperfine Field)

The internal magnetic field at the nuclear position inducing the nuclear Zeeman splitting is determined mostly by the magnetic moment rising from the incomplete shell of its own atom, the $3d$ moment in the case of iron. This moment is, in turn, largely affected by the interactions between the atom and its surroundings. The interactions appear roughly in two ways: by the chemical interaction of near neighbors determined by the electronic configuration in the incomplete shell and, therefore, the amount and direction of the magnetic moment of the atom, and secondly by the thermal and lattice defect disturbance which allow fluctuations in time and space of the moments accompanying the atoms in the alloy. As a result of the competition between the exchange energy among the atoms and the thermal energy, an alloy or a compound appears as a ferro- (or antiferro-) or paramagnetic substance at a certain temperature and it can be observed either as a hyperfine pattern (six lines in the case of iron) or as a single-line Mössbauer spectrum. When a ferromagnetic alloy contains many phases or many atomic configurations in one phase, its Mössbauer pattern consists of many components with varying amounts of Zeeman splitting. In the analyses of the spectra of ferromagnetic substances a large amount of work has been devoted to identifying the phases and determining the atomic and electronic configurations in the phases by finding the amount of Zeeman splitting in the corresponding spectral components.

Many investigations on iron solution alloys have revealed that the reduction of the internal field due to foreign neighbors is approximately additive, i.e. n nearest neighbor solute atoms produce n times the effect of one nearest neighbor solute atom. Another salient result is that, as far as the first neighbor interaction is concerned the internal field decrease due to a fixed number of foreign neighbors gradually changes with the solute concentration. As an example, the Fe–Be system [6.7] is shown in Fig. 6.2, where the lines for various occupation configurations in the first neighbor shell are parallel with the same separations and gradually change with the solute beryllium concentration. It appears that the additivity is obeyed for the short-range interaction between the probe

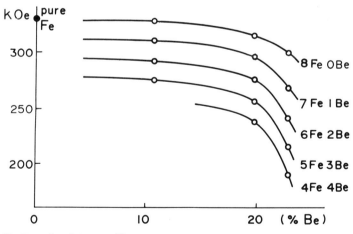

Fig. 6.2. Hyperfine field of Fe^{57} with various nearest neighbor configurations in Fe–Be alloys [6.7]

atom and its surroundings while the concentration dependence exhibits the non-localized long-range effect in alloys. The behavior, as shown in Fig. 6.2, is very useful in the pattern analysis. Nevertheless, when the same spectra are re-analyzed by taking farther neighbor shell configurations into account, the additivity still holds but the concentration dependence is drastically changed almost making the assumption of the non-localized interactions uncertain. The situation will not be improved by considering other Mössbauer parameters, because of the invariance of isomer shift and electric quadrupole splitting in these systems and therefore one has to be very careful in obtaining precise information on the atomic and electronic configurations in alloys.

Isomer Shift

As mentioned earlier in the first chapters, the observed isomer shift in Mössbauer spectroscopy is proportional to the *s* electron density at the nuclear site of the emitter and also to that of the absorber. In the case of metals and alloys the outermost *s* electrons or the conduction electrons predominantly affect the isomer shift, since among other *s* electrons only they contribute predominantly to the metallic bonding and, therefore, are largely modified by the environment. When a high valence metal is added as an alloying element to a low valence base metal, the number of electrons in the conduction band increases (and vice versa) and the isomer shift will be changed as an average effect. However, the behavior of conduction electrons is actually much more localized than expected from the simple band theory, and, accordingly, in a solid solution alloy such as the above, the probe atoms with different surrounding atomic configurations will exhibit different values of isomer shifts. Thus, variations of isomer shift in the alloy give rise to broadening and asymmetry of absorption lines.

A change in localized *d* electron configuration in the incomplete shell is reflected by the isomer shift through a comparatively strong interaction between the *d* electrons and conduction *s* electrons in transition metals and their alloys. Therefore, the information obtainable from isomer shift is not only on the conduction band but also on the *d* shell which also largely takes part in the metallic bonding.

Electric Quadrupole Splitting

When a crystal has a low symmetry or its high symmetry is broken locally, an electric field gradient, $eq = V_{zz}$, will result and interact with the electric quadrupole moment eQ of the probe isotope nucleus, causing a splitting ΔE_Q of the nuclear levels. For instance, in the case of Fe^{57} a double peak spectrum will appear when the crystal is paramagnetic, and an asymmetric positioning of the six absorption lines will be observed in the case of ferromagnetic ordering. Assuming the asymmetry parameter $\eta = 0$, the splitting ΔE_Q is given by

$$\Delta E_Q = \tfrac{1}{4} e Q V_{zz} \frac{3\cos^2\beta - 1}{2}, \qquad (6.1)$$

where β is the angle between the principal axis of the electric field gradient and the spin direction.

Although the usual solid solution alloys have high symmetries, mostly cubic symmetry, the electric quadrupole interaction can be observed sometimes because of foreign atoms which produces an asymmetric charge distribution around the probe atom. Due to the r^{-3} short range nature of the electric quadrupole interaction, the closer the asymmetric charge is to the nucleus the greater is the effect. Thus this effect will vary for the first, second, and further neighbor shell configurations, broadening the Mössbauer patterns like the internal field and isomer shift.

It is of some interest that the ferromagnetic patterns often exhibit a rather small asymmetry by the electric quadrupole interaction. The maximum principal axis of the electric field gradient produced by foreign neighbors and the spin orientations are usually along low index crystallographic orientations, and considering all possible directions the average value of ΔE_Q will be small; this means that the Mössbauer pattern has a rather symmetrical appearance. Some examples of symmetrical and asymmetrical cases are given in the following sections concerning the iron substitutional ferromagnetic alloys, martensite, amorphous alloys, etc.

Line Intensities

Irrespective of line broadening and splitting, in the thin absorber approximation the total absorption intensity of a Mössbauer spectrum is proportional to the amount of resonating isotopes and, therefore, to the corresponding element. When the substance under investigation is a multi-phase alloy, the total intensity of a spectral component corresponding to one phase should be proportional to the total amount of the element in it since no effect of isotope separation is expected in the process of formation of alloy phases. Similarly, in a complex spectrum of solid solution, the intensity of a resolved spectral component should represent the population of the corresponding atomic configuration around the central probe atoms in the solution. Here the assumption is made that the recoil-free fractions in the resonance processes are the same for the alloy phases and for the alloy lattice sites.

Another interesting problem is due to the angular dependence of the hyperfine pattern causing a relative line intensity distribution depending on the spin orientation and propagation direction of the γ-radiation. This polarization effect can be applied to the problem of magnetic domain orientation in thin films, directional atomic ordering in solid solution, etc. Some examples are introduced later.

In the ideal case each line component has the Lorentzian profile which can be written as

$$I = \frac{A_p}{1 + [(x - x_p)/\Gamma]^2} , \tag{6.2}$$

where A_p is the peak height in the spectrum, x_p represents the peak positions which can be expressed in energies, Doppler velocities, or channel number by using a multichannel analyzer, and 2Γ is the full width at half maximum. The assumption of a single value for 2Γ for all components in the analysis of a complex Mössbauer pattern is often not justified; for instance, velocity dependent machine error could be admixed to the natural width, some components could be broadened by the electric quadrupole interaction, and some ones could have inseparable substructures. Nevertheless, the values of 2Γ should not be taken arbitrarily but considerations mentioned above should be taken into account, especially in the computer analysis.

6.2.2. Statistical Calculations on the Atomic Arrangements in Alloys

Substitutional Solid Solutions

Let us first assume a random distribution of solute atoms in a closely packed substitutional solid solution, which is schematically shown in two dimensions in Fig. 6.3. Consider the near-neighbor configurations around the A-atoms denoted by numerals which are assumed to be the probe isotope atoms. Among six first neighbors of Atom 1, three are A-atoms and the other three are B-atoms. This configuration is denoted by $(3A, 3B)_{1st}$. Similarly, the second neighbor configuration for Atom 1 is $(1A, 5B)_{2nd}$, and for the third neighbor is $(1A, 5B)_{3rd}$. Since we know theoretically and empirically that the first neighbor interaction is predominant especially in the case of closely packed structures, we may take only the first neighbor configuration and neglect the further neighbors tentatively. $(3A, 3B)_{1st}$ is also found at Atom 2 and 3, but the relative positioning of the six atoms in the first neighbor shells is different for the three central atoms. Atom 3 will suffer the largest electric field gradient from the neighbors because of the most asymmetrical arrangement of

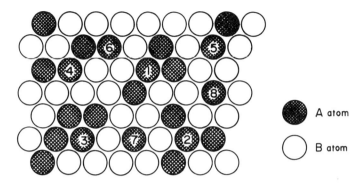

Fig. 6.3. Two-dimensional atomic arrangements concerning near-neighbor configurations

them while Atom 2 will suffer the smallest. Nevertheless, we may also neglect such differences since we know empirically, as previously mentioned, that the influence of the neighboring foreign atoms to the internal field and isomer shift is nearly additive and, therefore, is almost determined by the number of the foreign atoms. Similarly, we find that Atom 4 has the configuration (2A, 4B), Atoms 5 and 6 (1A, 5B), and Atoms 7 and 8 (0A, 6B).

When the concentration of A-atoms is c, the probability to find the configuration (3A, 3B) is

$$P(3A, 3B) = {}_6C_3 c^3 (1-c)^3, \tag{6.3}$$

C is a binominal coefficient. When $c = 0.5$, P is 0.125, and when $c = 0.05$, it is only 0.0021. These fractions can be regarded as the population of A-atoms with this configuration in the alloys of these concentrations.

If we employ the above concept and calculations to classify the neighboring configurations in the really closely packed substitutional solid solutions, either face centered cubic (f.c.c.) or close-packed hexagonal (h.c.p.), we find

$$P(0A, 12B) = {}_{12}C_0 c^0 (1-c)^{12}$$
$$P(1A, 11B) = {}_{12}C_1 c^1 (1-c)^{11}$$
$$\vdots$$
$$P(nA, mB) = {}_{12}C_n c^n (1-c)^m, \quad n+m = 12 \tag{6.4}$$
$$\vdots$$
$$P(12A, 0B) = {}_{12}C_{12} c^{12} (1-c)^0.$$

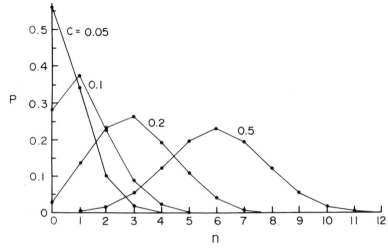

Fig. 6.4. Binomial distribution of the first neighbor configurations in the closely packed solid solution. P is the probability of finding n foreign atoms in the first neighbor shell

For example, the population distribution is calculated and shown for $c = 0.5 \sim 0.05$ in Fig. 6.4. It is clearly seen that among the thirteen configurations only four to six are predominant. Quantitative analyses of solid solution alloys are mostly based upon the above calculation.

By combining (6.2) and (6.4), a formula available for computer calculation of spectral intensity in channel x can be obtained as follows

$$I(x) = \sum_{n=0}^{12} \frac{\pi A_t}{\Gamma} \, {}_{12}C_n c^n (1-c)^{12-n} \frac{1}{1 + [(x - x_0 - \delta_\alpha n)\Gamma]^2}, \quad (6.5)$$

where A_t is the total absorption intensity, x_0 is the peak position of the component with no foreign neighbors, and δ_α measures the line shift due to one foreign neighbor. The additive law in the line shift may be assumed for either the isomer shift or internal field. In the computation to fit the whole spectrum with the synthetical curve of (6.5), the least mean-square deviation method is employed. In actual cases, only some of the thirteen terms of the equation will be used, as mentioned previously, but on the other hand, some important considerations such as the electric quadrupole interaction, or clustering of atoms, which upsets the random distribution of constituent atoms in solution, are necessary and the equation must be modified.

In order to analyze the iron-rich body centered cubic (b.c.c.) binary alloy systems, considerable improvement of the above equation is required, since interaction of the second neighbor is comparably as strong as that of the first neighbor. It was found by several investigators [6.8–10] that the reduction of the internal field due to the foreign second neighbors was again almost proportional to their occupation numbers. Therefore, for the internal field for a Fe^{57} atom with n foreign first and m foreign second neighbors in the alloy of concentration c, the simplest and probably most practical expression is

$$H(n, m) = H(1 - \delta_\alpha n - \delta_\beta m)(1 - K_c c),\qquad(6.6)$$

where H is the internal field in pure iron and the parameters δ_α and δ_β differ from one alloy system to another. It may be worthy of note that the parameter K_c is not a constant but rather increases with concentration, as shown in Fig. 6.2 and that in low concentration alloys, STEARNS [6.8] found that K_c is close to zero by taking account of the interactions from the first to the fifth neighbors. An improved expression available for the analysis of the six-line hyperfine spectra of iron-rich alloys will be

$$I(x) = \sum_{i=1}^{6} \sum_{n=0}^{8} \sum_{m=0}^{6} \frac{\pi A_{t,i}}{\Gamma} \,_8C_n\,_6C_m c^{n+m}(1-c)^{14-n-m}$$
$$\cdot \frac{1}{1 + [(x - x_i - \delta_{\alpha,i}n - \delta_{\beta,i}m)/\Gamma]^2} \cdot \qquad(6.7)$$

If the spins in the alloy are randomly oriented the values of $A_{t,i}$ can be taken as 3:2:1:1:2:3. Six sets of the other parameters, x_i, $\delta_{\alpha,i}$ and $\delta_{\beta,i}$ are determined by minimizing the mean square deviation between the computed and experimental points.

Interstitial Solid Solutions

As shown in Fig. 6.5, there are two kinds of atomic sites in the interstitial solid solution lattice, i.e. the normal lattice sites and their interstices. The former are fully occupied by the metal atoms and the latter are occupied by the interstitial metalloid atoms, such as of H, C, N, and O, with the probability, $c = c'/z(1 - c')$, where c' is the interstitial atomic concentration, and z is the ratio of the number of interstices and lattice points. Let the number of interstices in the jth near neighbor shell around an isotope probe atom be y_j. For the octahedral interstices in the b.c.c. lattice shown in Fig. 6.8a, z is 3 and y_j's are 6, 12, and 16 for the first, second, and third neighbor shells, respectively. This situation is shown two-dimensionally by the broken lines around the center atom

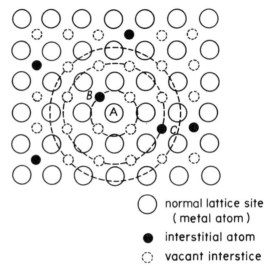

normal lattice site
(metal atom)

interstitial atom

vacant interstice

Fig. 6.5. Two-dimensional schematic representation of interstitial solid solution. Three large circles with broken lines are the 1st, 2nd, 3rd nearest interstitial shells, respectively

in Fig. 6.5. The probability of finding n_j interstitial atoms in the jth shell is

$$P_j(n_j) = {}_{y_j}C_{n_j}\, c^{n_j}(1-c)^{y_j-n_j}. \tag{6.8}$$

Then, the probability to have n_1 interstitials in the first shell, n_2 in the second shell, and so on is

$$P(n_1, n_2, \ldots, n_k) = P_1(n_1)\, P_2(n_2), \ldots, P_k(n_k). \tag{6.9}$$

If the interstitial concentration c' is low, we simply find that the concentration of the metal atoms having as first neighbor an interstitial is $2c'$, as second neighbor $4c'$, etc.

If c' is high, however, an overlapping effect occurs; for instance, the A-atom in Fig. 6.5 is a first neighbor to the interstitial B and a second neighbor to the interstitial C at the same time. This makes simple estimations rather difficult, and it is recommended that the above formula should be used in which the overlapping is automatically taken into consideration. The configuration in which the interstitial atoms exist in the ith and jth shell at the same time may be classified into the group of the ith neighbor configuration provided $i < j$, because the nearest interstitial atom will interact predominantly with the probe metal atom. Thus, classifying the P's of (6.9) and combining them with (6.2) the formula

for the quantitative analysis of interstitial solutions with random distribution [6.11] is obtained.

6.3. Interstitial Alloys (Carbon Steel)

Interstitial alloys are found in combinations of transition metal elements
and some light elements, such as Fe–C, Fe–N, Ti–O, Pd–H, etc. Among
other combinations, the iron-carbon system occupies the most important
position in metallurgy, since iron and steel are the largest in terms of
productions and the most useful in our technological world. In this
chapter we will describe how one can obtain information concerning the
behavior of carbon in steel through the Mössbauer effect of Fe^{57} atoms,
which are affected by nearby carbon atoms in the iron lattice or various
compounds. More specifically concerning the iron-carbon system, the
carbon interstitial positions in the martensite structure will be discussed
in relation to the mechanism of martensite transformation.

Other important problems in interstitial alloys are, for instance, the
hydrogen absorption and permeation, hydrogen embrittlement and
delayed fracture, internal friction and diffusion of interstitial atoms in
b.c.c. metals, and occlusion, ordering, and nonstoichiometric compound
formation of oxygen in transition metals. However, most of these
problems are not suitable for investigation by Mössbauer spectroscopy
because of either the average location of the resonance probe is not
specific enough or the amount of solute atoms is insufficient and therefore
difficult to detect. Accordingly, in this chapter no studies on these topics
will be mentioned although some preliminary results have been obtained.

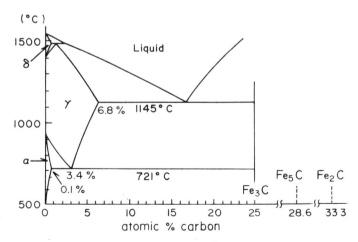

Fig. 6.6. Phase diagram of the Fe–C system

6.3.1. Quenching and Tempering of Plain Carbon Steel

As the phase diagram in Fig. 6.6 shows, α-iron dissolves carbon interstitially by only 0.1 at.-% at the eutectoid temperature, 721° C, and less than 0.04 at.-% at room temperature. Because of this small solubility in equilibrium, the interstitial solute carbon in α-iron cannot be examined by Mössbauer spectroscopy. However, when a steel specimen containing several percent of carbon is quenched from the α-phase region, martensitic transformation takes place and a supersaturated solid solution with a body centered tetragonal structure, the martensite (α_m) phase, is obtained together with the retained austenite (γ) phase which is the f.c.c. interstitial solution. Both phases have been the main object of many Mössbauer studies [6.11–13].

In this section only the qualitative phase analysis of plain carbon steel, quenched and tempered at various temperatures, is explained in conjunction with the above two phases and their decomposition products.

Figure 6.7 shows a room temperature Mössbauer spectrum of plain carbon steel containing 4.2 at.-% carbon which was quenched from 850° C with brine water [6.14]. The central paramagnetic absorption line arises from the retained austenite, the amount of which is estimated from its total intensity to be about 8%. This already shows how Mössbauer spectroscopy can be utilized for the phase analysis of steel for the metallurgical purposes as well as the X-ray diffraction method [6.15]. The isomer shift of the austenite phase is −0.1 mm/sec relative to pure

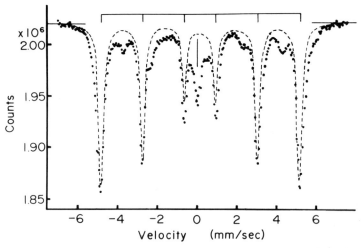

Fig. 6.7. Mössbauer spectrum of a water quenched 4.2 at.-% carbon steel. The broken line represents a pure iron spectrum [6.14]

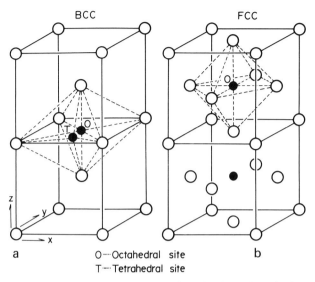

Fig. 6.8a and b. The octahedral and tetrahedral interstice in the b.c.c. lattice (a), and the octahedral interstice in the f.c.c. lattice (b)

α-iron. When the carbon content is increased and the amount of the retained austenite is thereby increased, the central peak becomes accompanied by two shoulders, as shown in Fig. 6.11. Deconvolution of the peak shows that they are a double peak component with a quadrupole splitting of 0.6 mm/sec and an intensity corresponding to six times the carbon concentration. This indicates that the double peak arises from the Fe^{57} atoms in the first neighbor octahedral shell enclosing the interstitial carbon atom, as shown in Fig. 6.8b. The large electric field gradient is produced by the asymmetrical extra charge near or in the Fe^{57} atom due to a strong interaction with the neighboring carbon atom. Second and farther neighbor interactions exist but a detailed analysis of the paramagnetic peak is not available at present.

The influence of interstitial carbon atoms in the α_m-phase can be seen in the six line spectral component in Fig. 6.7. For instance, the fact that the intensity of the satellite peaks between the two outer main peaks on each side of the six line spectrum is twice as large as the carbon content suggests that it arises from the two first neighboring iron atoms of the central carbon atom at the octahedral site, which are shown in Fig. 6.8a. Note that the octahedral site in b.c.c. is squashed; two neighbors are closer to the center than the remaining four forming a ring. Precise quantitative analyses have been done successfully on the steel with various carbon concentrations taking account of near neighbor configura-

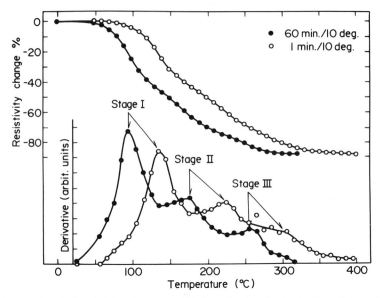

Fig. 6.9. Electrical resistivity changes and their derivatives in the isochronal annealing of water quenched 5 at.-% carbon steel [6.16]

tions around the interstitial carbon atom. Since the results have already been given by GONSER [6.6] a detailed explanation of the analysis will not be attempted here. It may be noteworthy that this analysis could also be applied successfully to plain nitrogen steel [6.18].

When the quenched carbon steel is subjected to tempering, which is necessary to improve the stability and toughness of steels, the supersaturated carbon atoms begin to migrate and precipitate in martensite and austenite, leading to phase separation. This carbon movement naturally gives rise to the changes in the Fe^{57} Mössbauer pattern. As the electrical resistivity changes, as shown in Fig. 6.9, the tempering process of carbon steel takes place stepwise. The first stage at around $120°$ C corresponds to the formation of the ε (Fe_2C) phase, the second to the decomposition of the retained austenite, and the third to the precipitation of the cementite (Fe_3C) phase. In conjunction with the resistivity change, the octahedral first neighbor peaks in the Mössbauer pattern broaden and sink into the background in the first stage, as shown in Fig. 6.10b, the central paramagnetic peak disappears in the second stage, as shown in Fig. 6.10c, and finally in the third stage a new satellite component from cementite (Fe_3C) appears, as seen in Fig. 6.10d. During this tempering treatment the main six line pattern becomes narrower and finally coincide with the pure α-Fe spectrum which is indicated by

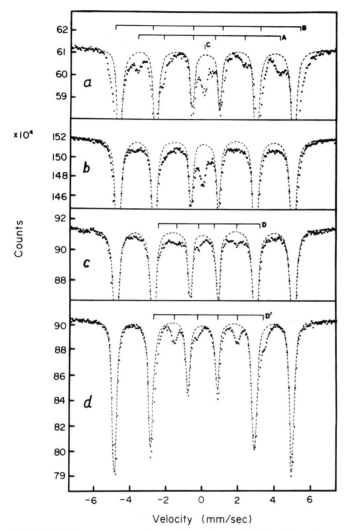

Fig. 6.10a–d. Mössbauer spectra of quenched and annealed 5 at.-% carbon steel; (a) as quenched, (b) 140° C, 1 hr annealed, (c) 220° C, 1 hr annealed, and (d) 340° C, 1 hr annealed. The graphs A, B, C, D, and D' show the peak positions of the 1st and 2nd iron neighbors of the octahedral interstitial carbon atoms in martensite, austenite (γ), $Fe_5C_2(\chi)$, and $Fe_3C(\theta)$, respectively [6.16]

the broken line in the figures. It has also been realized that the χ-phase (Fe_5C_2) appeared at an early stage of the cementite precipitations. As shown in Fig. 6.10c, some peaks appear already at 220° C, but its internal field does not coincide with that of the normal cementite structure but with that of the χ-phase which can be synthesized by the powder-gas reaction. An analysis shows that tempering leads first to the χ-phase which changes gradually in its internal structure to cementite (Fe_3C) [6.16].

Quantitative analysis can be done by measuring the fractional intensities of the phases concerned. The above observation is a simple example of the application of Mössbauer spectroscopy to steel problems. The same technique is applicable to more complex heat treatment problems of steels, such as the instability and embrittlement of some alloy steels by heating [6.17].

6.3.2. Low Temperature Martensite Phase and Martensitic Transformation

A new aspect of the martensite structure of steel concerning its transformation mechanism was found recently by Mössbauer spectroscopy. When plain high carbon steel, 6% Ni carbon steel, and 3% Mn carbon steel were quenched from the γ-phase region to liquid nitrogen temperature, a new orthorhombic martensite structure with the axial ratio c/a smaller, and the volume $a \times b \times c$ larger, than those of the normal martensite structure was obtained [6.18]. This low temperature phase began to change to the normal one at around $0°$ C where the supersaturated carbon atoms were allowed to move in the martensite lattice [6.19]. A characteristic feature of the low temperature phase clarified by Mössbauer spectroscopy was that in addition to the octahedral first neighbor iron peaks, denoted by O_1, a new satellite component T_1 appeared, as shown in Fig. 6.11. The T_1 peaks decreased by aging between $-50°$ C and $+50°$ C while the O_1 peaks increased at the same time. One-half of the O_1 peak intensity plus a quarter of the T_1 peak intensity just correspond to the carbon content at any stage of aging. The value of the internal field of T_1 lies exactly on the experimental curve relating the internal field of various near neighbor iron atoms to the neighboring distance from the interstitial carbon atom. T_1 was taken as the distance between the tetrahedral interstice and its four first neighbor iron sites in the martensite lattice, as shown in Fig. 6.12. From these facts it was concluded that the T_1 component arises from the four first iron neighbors surrounding the terahedral interstitial carbon atoms, which is shown in Fig. 6.8a and precise quantitative analyses were successfully carried out on the Mössbauer spectra taken from the three kinds of martensite steel described above, immediately after quenching and after various aging treatments. Up to 1973 it was believed that the octahedral interstice was the stable site and the tetrahedral interstice was the unstable saddle point along the diffusion path for interstitial carbon and nitrogen in the martensite lattice. Now the Mössbauer effect has revealed that the

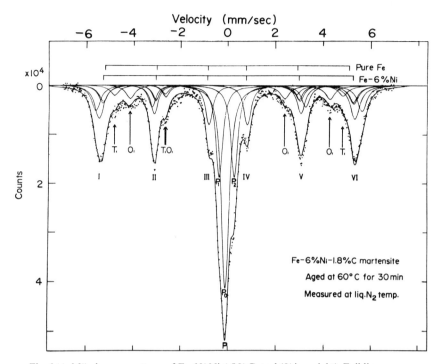

Fig. 6.11. Mössbauer spectrum of Fe-6 % Ni-1.8 % C steel (% in weight). Full line curves are calculated ones. P's are the components of paramagnetic austenite

tetrahedral interstices are occupied to a large extent by the carbon atoms at low temperatures. Moreover, it was found that when the carbon content exceeds about 5 at.-% the T_1 peaks do not fully decrease but remain in measurable amounts even after a long period of aging at room temperature. If the starting temperature of martensite transformation M_s is low enough, e.g. below 0° C the intensity ratio of O_1 and T_1 immediately after quenching becomes 1:2, i.e. by taking into account the occurence of the sites the ratio of the octahedral and tetrahedral occupancy is exactly 1:1. This situation cannot be explained by the assumption that carbon originally carried from the octahedral interstices in austenite to the octahedral interstices in martensite are squeezed out or flipped into the tetrahedral interstices by the stresses produced by dislocations, twins or coherence boundary associating the martensitic transformation but rather by the concept that the 1:1 occupancy is inherited from the transformation mechanism itself. The direct transformation mechanism by simple lattice shears and axial contractions and dilatations proposed by KURDJUMOV and SACHS [6.20], NISHIYAMA [6.21], and others leads

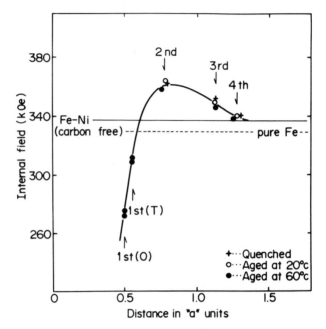

Fig. 6.12. Variation of internal field of Fe atoms at different sites in the martensite structure of Fe-6 wt.-% Ni-1.8 wt.-% C alloy with the distance from an interstitial C atom. "a" is the lattice constant

only to the octahedral occupancy. There are two other possible mechanisms which give rise to the 1:1 occupancy; one is a path through the h.c.p. structure suggested and observed by VENABLES [6.22] and others [6.23], and the other is through a newly proposed six-layer structure [6.24]. For more precise discussions reading of the original papers [6.24, 25] is recommended. No methods other than Mössbauer spectroscopy are capable of detecting the positions of interstitial carbon atoms in the martensite of steel quantitatively and therefore cannot be used to solve an old problem such as mentioned above. Not only the values of the internal field but also the isomer shift and electric quadrupole effect have been measured and analyzed for various near neighbor configurations of iron atoms and electronic configurations around the interstitial atoms in martensite, particularly with respect to the covalent bonding between the interstitial carbon atoms and surrounding iron atoms [6.11, 14, 26]. GENIN and FLINN [6.27] observed the variation of the O_1 and T_1 peak heights by aging. They assigned the T_1 peaks to the component arising from the iron first neighbors of single carbon atoms at the octahedral interstices and the O_1 peaks to the component due to the iron atoms neighboring with the carbon clusters. However, their analysis is not conclusive in explaining the low temperature phase of martensite, the quantitative intensity relationship, and the electronic structures elucidated with regard to the O_1 and T_1 components. Clustering of carbon atoms in martensite by room temperature aging has been known and studied by many investigators [6.28]. The driving force for clustering is undoubtedly the strain field interaction, which would not cause such a large change in the electronic states to be observed in Mössbauer parameters because the interaction of the iron atoms near the carbon clusters is similar to that of the iron neighbors of the single interstitials.

6.4. Substitutional Alloys (Magnetic Perturbation)

The technique of resolving Mössbauer spectra of solid solution alloys, outlined in the previous sections, has been extensively developed and applied to atomic distributions and magnetic perturbations around impurities in ferromagnetic alloys. This important subject in physical metallurgy has been worked on by many investigators.

STEARNS [6.8] was the first to measure the magnetic disturbance around Al, Si, Mn, V, and Cr solute atoms in ferromagnetic iron-rich alloys analyzing up to the fifth neighbor shells around them. The extremely good agreement between the experimental points obtained and the synthetic curve calculated by computer is shown in Fig. 6.13. On analysis, it was found that the line shifts of either isomer or magnetic hyperfine origin induced by the impurity atoms in any neighbor shell were always additive, as mentioned previously, and that the disturbance around the impurity atoms oscillated spacewise, as predicted by recent theories on the exchange polarization of the 4s conduction electrons around

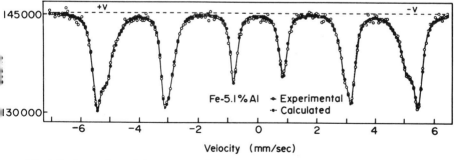

Fig. 6.13. Comparison of the spectrum of the Fe-5.1 at.-% Al alloy (white circles) with the computer calculated spectrum (black circles)

impurity atoms. No appreciable quadrupole interaction was observed in this experiment: The magnetization axis (easy axis) was along $\langle 100 \rangle$ and all foreign first neighbors were distributed symmetrically in $\langle 111 \rangle$ directions so that the function $\cos \beta$ in 6.1 was $1/\sqrt{3}$ (see Subsection 6.2.1).

LONGWORTH and WINDOW [6.29, 30] measured the Mössbauer spectra for 1% iron in Ni, Pd, and PtX alloys where X is approximately 10% of a transition or noble metal, in both the ferromagnetic and paramagnetic state. They determined the values of mean and most probable hyperfine fields, the electric field gradient, and the isomer shift changes for X neighbors. Variation of the former two in Ni $3d$ alloys as a function of the number of outer electrons of the alloying element X was compared with the change of the average magnetization with concentration in the same alloys. Strong correlation between the average internal field and average magnetization also exists in other series and was explained in terms of the screening charge interactions first put forward by FRIEDEL.

VINCZE and CAMPBELL [6.31] measured the hyperfine field and isomer shift changes due to Cr, Mo, V, and Pt solute atoms in near neighbor shells in dilute Fe-based alloys, and obtained results similar to the above.

Recently CRANSHAW [6.32] developed an ingenious method for estimating the electric field gradient in the ferromagnetic state by using single crystal Fe specimens containing Cr impurity. The principle of his measurement is as follows: Consider a b.c.c. lattice of a dilute alloy. The single solute atoms are mostly in a position of cubic symmetry, but the host atoms are not always because of nearby foreign neighbors. However, all the atoms in a given neighbor shell are in equivalent positions. If we add a magnetization axis, this degeneracy may be lifted. For example, when the magnetization axis lies along $\langle 111 \rangle$, there are two sets of first neighbors consisting of two atoms on the axis and six atoms off the axis. On the other hand, the six atoms in the second neighbor shell are all in equivalent positions. When the magnetization axis lies along $\langle 100 \rangle$ the situation is reversed; all the eight first neighbors are in equivalent positions but there are two sets of second neighbors consisting of two atoms on the axis and four off the axis.

Mössbauer spectra of an alloy containing 4.8% Cr were taken with the magnetization along the $\langle 100 \rangle$ axis and the $\langle 111 \rangle$ axis. A difference spectrum was evaluated which is a sensitive indicator of the components being split and shifted by anisotropic interactions. From this difference and the spectra fitting the spin density disturbance around a Cr impurity was precisely figured out.

Another interesting observation on dilute substitutional alloys was made by RIDOUT [6.33]. He analyzed the Mössbauer spectra of Fe^{57} in Au–Fe alloys for the concentration range $0.5 \sim 12.8\%$ at room temperature and for the 12.5% alloy from room temperature down to 0.4 K, and obtained significantly different spectral components for iron atoms with 0, 1, 2, … iron nearest neighbors. As the temperature decreased, measurable hyperfine fields appeared first at the iron site with the largest number of iron nearest neighbors and then at lower temperature at sites with fewer iron neighbors. The result was explained in terms of the long-range and short-range magnetic interactions among the near neighbor iron atoms.

6.5. Solid Solubility Limit

Mössbauer spectroscopy can be applied to determine the phase boundary in alloy systems according to the different electronic and magnetic properties of the phases concerned. The miscibility gap in the Au–Ni system was determined by HOWARD et al. [6.34] using Fe^{57} as a probe. They measured the isomer shift value from the solid solutions containing from 25 to 96% Ni as well as pure nickel, and used these values as calibration factors for the phase composition of the paramagnetic component in the two phase Mössbauer spectra. The ferromagnetic Curie temperatures were obtained by the thermal scanning technique, i.e. the measurement at a constant velocity, for instance at zero velocity of the γ-ray count rate by changing the temperature of the specimen [6.35]. From these isomer shift values and Curie temperatures, they determined the miscibility gap in this alloy system and the results obtained agreed well with the results from X-ray diffraction measurements. The scanning technique was also applied to estimate the amount of the retained austenite in steel [6.15].

A very accurate determination of the solubility of iron in aluminum was done by NISHIO et al. [6.36] by analyzing the Fe^{57} spectra of Al–Fe alloys containing Fe less than 0.04 at.-% Fe. Since in the second phase, Al_3Fe has a large quadrupole splitting and a negative isomer shift relative to the α solid solution phase, exact deconvolution was possible and the solubility of iron as small as 0.025 at.-% Fe at 640° C and 0.0025 at.-% Fe at 450° C was obtained. Even though the iron was not enriched on Fe^{57}, the result seems to be much more accurate than that obtained by measurement of electrical resistivity.

Recently SWARTZENDRUBER and BENNETT [6.37] detected a very thin layer of austenite on the surface of a lightly ground Fe–C alloy of eutectoid composition by Mössbauer scattering experiments using conversion electrons. This non-destructive technique may become an unique and excellent one for estimating the phase condition in the vicinity of alloy surfaces.

6.6. Order-Disorder Alloys

The Mössbauer studies introduced in the preceding chapters are concerned with the solid solutions with random distribution of constituent atoms, which allows us to use the binomial formulae such as (6.4) and (6.7) in a quantitative analysis. If the randomness of the atomic distribution is disturbed by some metallurgical internal process such as ordering in the atomic arrangement, clustering, precipitation, or spinodal decomposition, the binomial formulae become invalid and other special assumptions or parameters will be required in the analysis. For instance, for an alloy in the process of ordering we have to find the short-range order parameter either from another experiment or by the spectral analysis. Ordered Fe–Al and Fe–Si alloys were studied by STEARNS [6.8] but the ordering process itself was not examined. Two types of superlattices appear in the Fe–Al alloy system in the range of $22 \sim 35$ at.-% Al, i.e. Fe_3Al (DO_3) and FeAl ($B2$) below and above $550°$ C, respectively. Consider the stoichiometric composition Fe_3Al, in the disordered state, the nearest neighbor configurations are widely distributed from $(8\,Fe, 0\,Al)$, to $(0\,Fe, 8\,Al)$, the center of gravity being around $(6\,Fe, 2\,Al)$. Therefore, a broad Mössbauer pattern is expected which can be analyzed with the aid of binomial equations. If it is perfectly ordered in DO_3 type, the configurations are only $(8\,Fe, 0\,Al)$ and $(4\,Fe, 4\,Al)$ and the population

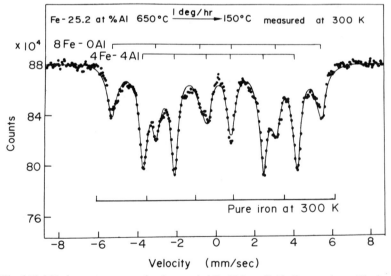

Fig. 6.14. Mössbauer spectrum of a slow cooled Fe 25.2 at.-% Al alloy specimen. The least square fitting by computer technique is shown by the solid line [6.46]

ratio is 1:2. Then the spectrum will consist of two components, as shown in Fig. 6.14. Above 550° C the $B2$ type superlattice appears, in which one sublattice is disordered while the other maintains its order and configurations other than (8 Fe, 0 Al) and (4 Fe, 4 Al) will be present. Thus, the lines in the spectrum will be broader in comparison to the lines of DO_3 but not quite as much as for the disordered state. The configurations of the above three cases can be calculated, as shown by the solid line in Fig. 6.14, for example. However, if the alloy composition deviates from stoichiometry or it is in the state of neither perfect order nor perfect disorder, the quantitative analysis will become complicated and it will be necessary to find a short-range order parameter.

From electron-microscopic observations some investigators concluded that the disordered and DO_3 type ordered phase coexist in the range of $19 \sim 24.8$ at.-% at room temperature. However, our Mössbauer effect study [6.38] revealed that a two-phase region did not exist at room temperature but at considerably higher temperatures and re-examination by electron microscopy showed that the dark areas in the bright field image which had been associated with the disordered regions, actually consisted of aggregates of small bubble-like ordered domains bounded by the antiphase domain boundaries which exhibited the dark contrast.

6.7. Precipitation

The early state of the processes leading to precipiation is characterized by a deviation from random distribution of a supersaturated solid solution. The formation of aggregates or regions which are different from the average composition of the solid solution may be the result of aging, temperature anneal, induced lattice defects by bombardment, cold work, quenching, etc. Considerable experimental work has been done and ideas brought forward on the problem of nucleation of precipitation which, in general, can occur in a heterogeneous and homogeneous fashion, i.e. by nucleation and growth of a new phase or by spinodal decomposition.

Al-rich Al–Fe alloys which have been investigated extensively by various methods can serve as examples of how the Mössbauer effect is able to obtain the information concerning precipitation [6.39, 40]. The following phases have been identified: Fe in solution, Fe associations and precipitation of Al_6Fe and $Al_{13}Fe_4$ phases [6.41]. The splat-quenching gun technique allows highly supersaturated alloys to be produced. A Mössbauer spectrum at room temperature of a splat-quenched Al-1 at.-% Fe sample is shown in Fig. 6.15a. This spectrum can be understood as a superposition of a single line due to Fe in solution

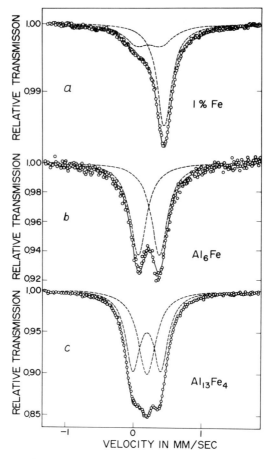

Fig. 6.15a–c. (a) Mössbauer spectrum at room temperature obtained from a splat-quenchet Al-1 at.-% Fe specimen. The single line represents the component from the Fe in solution, and the doublet represent the component from the Fe clusters. (b) Mössbauer spectrum at room temperature from an Al-0.5 at.-% Fe shill-cast alloy. The spectrum is typical of Al_6Fe precipitates. (c) Mössbauer spectrum obtained from $Al_{13}Fe_4$ precipitates at room temperature [6.41]

and a quadrupole split component which indicates formation of nearest neighbor configurations of Fe atoms, mainly dimer and trimer. The occurence of the associations in the Al matrix is approximately reflected in the integrated intensity of the lines. Similar results have been obtained for Fe in Cu and Au [6.42–44]. Another type of association in Al doped with Co^{57} was observed in a source experiment after neutron irradiation where the trapping and the release of Al interstitial atoms at the impurity

Co^{57} site — probably in an dumbbell configuration — can be followed by the appearance and disappearance of an extra line [6.45].

By chill-cast of an Al-0.5 at.-% Fe alloy one obtains the phase Al_6Fe which only appears to exist as metastable precipitates in an Al matrix. The structure is orthorhombic isomorphous with Al_6Mn. The spectrum of this phase is shown in Fig. 6.15b. The phase $Al_{13}Fe_4$ precipitates in an Al-20 at.-% Fe alloy which is slowly cooled from the melt. The $Al_{13}Fe_4$ phase can be identified by X-ray analysis. The Mössbauer spectrum of a sample with $Al_{13}Fe_4$ precipitates is shown in Fig. 6.15c. Fe in various lattice sites in this phase produces a single line superimposed on quadrupole components. By annealing treatments the transformation from the Al_6Fe phase to the $Al_{13}Fe_4$ phase can be observed by the change in the resonance spectrum.

The process of spinodal decomposition has been studied by the Mössbauer effect. Differing from the nucleation and growth process, it is characterized by unstable concentration fluctuations which are presumably started by thermal fluctuations and gradual growth of a regular periodic structure with a continuously changing amplitude and wavelength in concentration distribution. Therefore, the spinodal decomposition is observed by the continuous changes of Mössbauer parameters which appear, for instance, as the gradual line shift and broadening. This is in contrast to the normal precipitation process which is observed as the appearance of a new component in the Mössbauer pattern arising from the precipitate phase.

SAITO et al. [6.46] verified that the process of phase separation in Fe–Ni–Al alloys quenched from the melt was by spinodal decomposition; gradual changes of the hyperfine field and isomer shift of Fe^{57} and spreading of the width of absorption peaks indicated that the separating phases did not have any definite compositions but wide and continuous changes in concentration in time and space.

SUMITOMO [6.7] studied decomposition of supersaturated Fe–Be alloys by using the Mössbauer effect, electron microscopy, and electron and X-ray diffraction, and he was able to follow the spinodal decomposition process. In the early stage of aging, the $L2_0$ type ordered structure was seen to coexist with the concentration modulated structure.

6.8. Invar

The magnetic hyperfine interaction became an important tool in the study of magnetic properties of magnetic materials in the metallic and non-metallic states. In particular, the use of Fe^{57}, Sn^{119}, and various rare-earth isotopes produced significant information on their respective hyperfine spectra. For instance, in favored cases the Mössbauer effect allows the population and behavior of various lattice sites to be investigated individually. The application to the invar problem should serve as a demonstration of the successes and also the limitations of the effect.

At the end of the last century GUILLAUME discovered that the thermal expansion coefficient of the àlloy $Fe_{1-x}Ni_x$ has its minimum at about $x = 0.35$ [6.47]. This invariance, that was found in later years in many alloys, was given the name "Invar". It was also recognized that these alloys have a number of concurrent properties and anomalies like deviation of the saturation magnetization and lattice parameters, low Curie temperature, large electric resistance, sensitive behavior in regard to mechanical and thermal treatment, and many others. Naturally, these anomalies demanded an explanation and attracted many scientists to study these properties from a technological as well as fundamental point of view. In the course of this work a number of models were suggested to decribe the invar behaviors in a unified way. However, none of these ideas have been conclusive up to the present time; see, for instance, [6.48–53]. Most models are based on two competing magnetic interactions with ferromagnetic and antiferromagnetic tendencies which can be associated to specific atomic environments or inhomogenities in the lattice. It was thought that the Mössbauer effect could be used to distinguish between different interactions because it was found that the Fe^{57} in ferromagnetic f.c.c. Ni exhibits a large internal

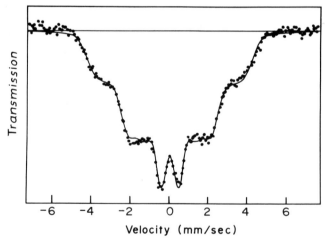

Fig. 6.16. Typical Mössbauer spectrum obtained from an $Fe_{0.69}Ni_{0.28}Co_{0.03}$ invar alloy at room temperature

field ($H_{int} = 280$ kOe [6.54]) and in the antiferromagnetic γ-Fe a small internal field ($H_{int} = 24$ kOe) [6.35, 55].

A typical invar spectrum is shown in Fig. 6.16. Although the lines are not well resolved as normally found in hyperfine spectra, values such as the distribution of the hyperfine field can be obtained. The probability of finding a certain field at an Fe^{57} nucleus, $P(H_{int})$, can be written as a linear combination of N distribution functions $F_n(H_{int})$

$$P(H_{int}) = \sum_{n=1}^{N} a_n F_n(H_{int}).$$ (6.10)

In evaluating this equation by a computer program one has to consider the magnetic ordering and the angular dependence of the hyperfine interactions influencing the relative line intensities, particularly when an external magnetic field is applied to the sample.

The Mössbauer spectra in Fig. 6.17 were obtained at 22 K from an $Fe_{0.69}Ni_{0.28}Co_{0.03}$ alloy with and without an external magnetic field ($H_{ext} = 50$ kOe). In Fig. 6.18 the distribution functions $P(H_{int})$ from these spectra are shown. The best fit to the data was obtained by assuming that the Fe atoms exhibiting large internal fields (H_{int}) are ferromagnetically coupled and a colinear alignment of the spins to the external magnetic field exists while the Fe atoms exhibiting a small (or no) internal magnetic field tend to couple antiferromagnetically with perpendicular alignment of the spins to the external magnetic field.

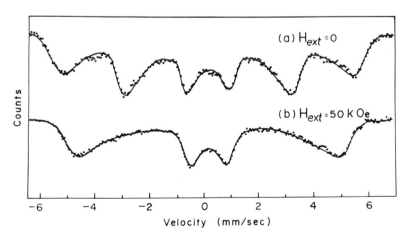

Fig. 6.17a and b. Mössbauer spectra obtained at 22 K with an $Fe_{0.69}Ni_{0.28}Co_{0.03}$ invar alloy with and without external magnetic field ($H_{ext} = 50$ kOe)

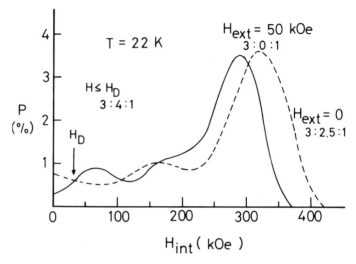

Fig. 6.18. Hyperfine field distribution obtained from the spectra in Fig. 6.17

By observing the variation in the spectra produced by changing various parameters like concentration, temperature, order state, and external fields, etc. eventually it may be possible to produce a model which describes the complex nature of invar correctly.

6.9. Texture

Orientation effects are reflected in the angular dependence of the hyperfine interaction. Disregarding relaxation and saturation effects the relative line intensities in a hyperfine pattern of a polycrystalline sample are influenced by lattice vibrational anisotropy (Goldanskii-Karyagin effect) and by preferred orientation (texture) of the spins or the axes of the electric field gradient in the sample [6.56]. In polycrystalline materials it is often difficult to differentiate between the two effects. However, most metals or alloys have cubic or almost cubic crystallographic structures, thus, the recoil-free γ-ray resonance can be regarded as isotropic and the Goldanskii-Karyagin effect can be neglected. On the other hand, texture or preferred orientations of the crystallites in certain directions might be very pronounced. In two ways the Mössbauer effect offers some interesting applications: 1) The texture measured by X-rays and the relative line intensities obtained by the Mössbauer effect can be correlated in determining the orientation of the spin in a magnetic material or the principal axes of the EFG. This technique was used in an investigation regarding the spin orientation of cementite Fe_3C [6.57]. 2) The reverse application is also possible, i.e. from the relative line intensities at various angles and the known orientations of the spins or the principal axes of the EFG, respectively, the texture of a polycrystalline material is determined. Of course, the X-ray technique will remain superior for texture determinations in all ordinary cases, but there might be some special applications, e.g. the preferred orientation of very fine particles which are too small to be detected by X-ray technique.

6.10. Amorphous Alloys

Metal atoms sometimes coagulate not in the crystalline state but in an extraordinarily disordered state, i.e. the amorphous state, especially when associated with metalloid atoms. The amorphous state of metals and alloys has been achieved by rapid quenching techniques, such as vapor deposition and splat cooling, and investigated mainly by diffraction techniques, e.g. X-ray and electron diffraction. By analyzing the diffuse halo diffraction patterns from various amorphous alloys the random distribution functions which are more or less similar to each other but clearly different from that of liquid have been obtained, but the proposed models for the amorphous structure are quite different. Some amorphous alloys have interesting properties and therefore the study of their real structure became a center of interest with respect to, e.g. their mechanical strength, phase stability, resistance to chemical reactions, magnetic behavior etc.

TSUEI et al. [6.58] analyzed a Mössbauer spectrum of $Fe_{80}P_{12.5}C_{7.5}$ ferromagnetic amorphous alloy by assuming that the iron atoms in the structure have seven nearest neighbors; a result which was confirmed by X-ray diffraction analysis. The binomial expansion to determine the near neighbor configurations was not employed but the weighting factors for five prominent internal field components were determined so as to have the best fit between the experimental and synthetic curve. However, the seven nearest neighbor configuration is not always characteristic of the amorphous state of this alloy, since an amorphous alloy with nearly the same composition was reexamined by X-ray diffraction, and it was found that its structure could be described by a randomized b.c.c. iron lattice with 13.6 nearest neighbors [6.59].

Actually, the above alloy and $Fe_{80}P_{13}C_7$ and $Fe_{80}P_{17}C_3$ amorphous alloy exhibited exactly the same Mössbauer patterns, which are shown in Fig. 6.19, and it was possible to analyze them by assuming that the structure is a nearly perfect b.c.c. consisting of very small crystallites [6.60]. Eight first neighbors and six second neighbors were assumed to have the normal b.c.c. structure, and metalloid atoms were regarded as occupying, substitutionally, the normal lattice points reducing the hyperfine field proportional to their numbers. Thus, the hyperfine field for an Fe^{57} atom with n first neighbor and m second neighbor metalloid atoms in the alloy of concentration c was expressed by (6.6). Further necessary assumptions were that the line shape of all components of the spectra was Lorentzian with a line width a few ten percent broader than that of pure iron and the near neighbor configurations exactly followed the binomial distribution. The former took into account the effect of the different relative locations of metalloid neighbors of the same numbers, n and m, and at the same time the effect of disorder in the lattice or crystalline structure of the amorphous alloys, while the latter represented perfect randomness in the atomic distribution in them. The agreement between the experimental points and calculated curve shown in Fig. 6.19 is as good as those found in the cases of ordinary b.c.c. iron alloys. This means that it is not always necessary to assume some special lattice structure for the amorphous state but the structure can be regarded as the aggregates of the very smallest crystals with the regular lattice form.

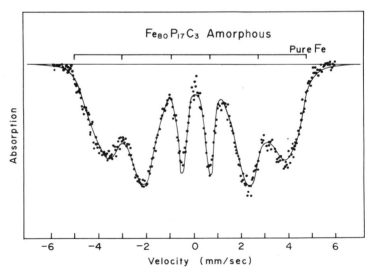

Fig. 6.19. Mössbauer spectrum of the amorphous $Fe_{80}P_{17}C_3$ alloy obtained after splat-quenching and the calculated computer spectrum. To reduce the effect of the magnetic anisotropy in the foil specimen, the incident γ-rays are inclined by 40° to the normal of the specimen surface

6.11. Oxidation

The Mössbauer effect is an excellent analytical method for the study of oxidation and corrosion phenomena on surfaces, the initial states of internally oxidized atoms, and the internally oxidized phases. The internal oxide phases in the Cu-rich alloys containing Fe were carefully examined by GONSER et al. [6.61], and HUFFMAN and PODGURSKI studied the ionization state and electronic configuration of internally oxidized Ag–Sn alloys [6.62]. The isomer shift of internally oxidized Sn atoms of an Ag–Sn alloy indicated that the ionization state is close to $+4$ and that most of the oxidized Sn has been precipitated as SnO_2 particles. For dilute alloys, they proposed an interesting model for a Sn–O–Ag complex. Mössbauer spectroscopy is very suitable to study oxidation processes on surfaces and corrosion phenomena, thus it represents an important addition to the other surface spectroscopy tools like LEED (low energy electron diffraction), ESCA (electron spectroscopy by chemical analysis), and Auger electron spectroscopy.

6.12. Diffusion

The shape of the Mössbauer line has been discussed in Chapter 1 by GONSER where it was pointed that the full width at half maximum of the spectrum depends on the mean lifetime of the excited state. However, at elevated temperatures the relaxation time for diffuse jumps of the resonance atoms is in the same order of magnitude as the mean lifetime of the excited state. Broadening was predicted by SINGWI and SJOLANDER [6.63] and given for random jumps of a diffusing Mössbauer atom

$$\Delta\Gamma_{\text{exp}} = \frac{2\hbar}{\tau_0}(1 - \alpha_{\text{g}}), \tag{6.11}$$

where τ_0 is the mean stay time of an atom at a lattice site ($1/\tau_0$ is the jump frequency), α_{g} is a geometric factor, and $\Delta\Gamma_{\text{exp}}$ is the line broadening. The diffusion coefficient is given by

$$D_{\text{d}} = \frac{1}{6\tau_0} r_0^2 f_{\text{c}}, \tag{6.12}$$

where r_0 is the jump distance and f_{c} is a factor which describes the correlation in direction between successive jumps of one and the same atom. Combining the above two equations yields

$$\Delta \Gamma_{\text{exp}} = \frac{12\hbar}{r_0^2 f_c} D_d (1 - \alpha_g) . \tag{6.13}$$

From this expression it should be possible to determine not only the diffusion coefficient (and jump frequency) but also the jump direction. This unique feature of the Mössbauer effect has not yet been exploited but it could be very useful in a study of diffusion mechanism; especially, for the anisotropic diffusion including surface diffusion.

LEWIS and FLINN [6.64] used this technique to study the diffusion phenomena of Fe in β-Ti. Tracer measurements for the diffusion in β-Ti indicates an anomaly in the $\log D$ versus $1/T$ plot. The observed diffusional broadening could be analyzed in terms of an appropriate diffusion mechanism for this alloy system.

6.13. Dislocation and Point Defect

The Mössbauer effect may be a useful technique for the study of the electronic and vibrational states perturbed by lattice defects (dislocations and lattice vacancies). Detailed investigations on this problem in metals and alloys have been reported in only a few cases. SAUER [6.65] used Ta^{181} and showed that the spectra were broadened and sharpened by plastic deformation and successive annealing treatment. DEKHTYAR et al. [6.66] measured the effect of the quenched in vacancy clusters in Pd on the Fe^{57} recoil-free fraction. JANOT and GIBERT [6.67] recently interpreted an additional broadening of the Fe resonance line in Al by the interaction between Fe atoms and dislocation.

The Mössbauer effect technique has proved to be a very powerful tool in physical metallurgy and other fields. Light may be thrown on certain problems, which cannot be studied by other means. Most valuable, however, is the information from Mössbauer effect measurements discussed in connection with results of other spectroscopic methods.

Acknowledgement

The author wishes to express his hearty thanks to Prof. Dr. U. GONSER, Universität des Saarlandes, F. R. Germany, for his kind suggestion to write this article and many useful discussions and advice on the manuscript. Thanks are also due to Dr. S. NASU, University of Osaka, Japan, for his great help in the preparation of the manuscript.

References

6.1.   The original papers recollected in: Naturwissenschaften **16**, 361 (1952).

6.2.   C. H. JOHANSSON, J. O. LINDE: Ann. Physik **78**, 439 (1925).

6.3.   G. KURDJUMOV, G. SACHS: Z. Physik **64**, 325 (1930).

6.4.   W. BOLLMANN: Phys. Rev. **103**, 1588 (1956).

6.5.   M. J. WHELAN, P. B. HIRSCH, R. W. HORNE, W. BOLLMANN: Proc. Roy. Soc. A **240**, 524 (1957).

6.6.   U. GONSER: In *An Introduction of Mössbauer Spectroscopy*, ed. by L. MAY (Plenum Press, New York, 1971), p. 155.

6.7.   Y. SUMITOMO: The Phase Seperation in FeBe Alloys, Ph. D. Thesis, Osaka University (1972).

6.8.   M. B. STEARNS: Phys. Rev. **129**, 1136 (1963); **149**, 439 (1966); J. Appl. Phys. **25**, 1095 (1964); **36**, 913 (1965).

6.9.   G. K. WERTHEIM, V. JACCARINO, J. H. WERNICK, D. N. E. BUCHANAN: Phys. Rev. Letters **12**, 24 (1964).

6.10. C. E. JOHNSON, M. S. RIDOUT, T. E. CRANSHAW: Proc. Phys. Soc. (London) **81**, 1079 (1963).

6.11. C. SHIGA, F. E. FUJITA, M. KIMURA: Nippon-Kinzoku-Gakkai-Shi. **38**, 1037 (1974).

6.12. M. RON, H. SHECHTER, A. KIDRON, S. NIEDZWIEDZ: J. Appl. Phys. **38**, 590 (1967).

6.13. P. M. GIELEN, R. KAPLOW: Acta Met. **15**, 49 (1967).

6.14. T. MORIYA, H. INO, F. E. FUJITA, Y. MAEDA: J. Phys. Soc. Japan **24**, 60 (1968).

6.15. B. W. CHRIST, P. M. GILES: Trans. AIME **242**, 1915 (1968).

6.16. H. INO, T. MORIYA, F. E. FUJITA, Y. ONO, Y. INOKUTI: J. Phys. Soc. Japan **25**, 83 (1968).

6.17. R. B. ROY, B. SOLLY: Scandinavian J. Met. **2**, 243 (1973).

6.18. L. I. LYSAK, Y. N. VOVK: Fiz. Metal. i Metalloved. **20**, 540 (1965); L. I. LYSAK, B. I. NIKOLIN: Fiz. Metal. i Metalloved. **20**, 547 (1965); **22**, 730 (1966); **23**, 93 (1967); L. I. LYSAK, L. O. ANDRUSHCHIK, Y. M. POLISHCHUK: Fiz. Metal. i Metalloved. **27**, 827 (1969).

6.19. F. E. FUJITA, T. MORIYA, H. INO: Proc. ICSTIS, Suppl. Trans. ISIJ **11**, 1273 (1971).

6.20. G. KURDJUMOV, G. SACHS: Z. Physik **64**, 325 (1930).

6.21. Z. NISHIYAMA: Sci. Rep. Tohoku Univ. **23**, 637 (1934, 1935); **25**, 79 (1936).

6.22. J. A. VENABLES: Phil. Mag. **7**, 35 (1961).

6.23. B. CINA: J. Iron St. Inst. **177**, 406 (1954); Acta Met. **6**, 748 (1958); H. M. OTTE: Acta Met. **2**, 349 (1954); **5**, 614 (1947).

6.24. F. E. FUJITA, C. SHIGA, M. KIMURA: Nippon-Kinzoku-Gakkai-Shi. **38**, 1030 (1974).

6.25. F. E. FUJITA: Nippon-Kinzoku-Gakkai-ho. **13**, 713 (1974).

6.26. T. MORIYA, Y. SUMITOMO, H. INO, F. E. FUJITA, Y. MAEDA: J. Phys. Soc. Japan **35**, 1378 (1973).

6.27. J. M. GENIN, P. A. FLINN: Trans. AIME **242**, 1419 (1968).

6.28. V. I. IZOTOV, L. M. UTEVSKIY: Fiz. Metal. i Metalloved. **25**, 98 (1968); L. I. LYSAK, A. G. DRACHINSKAYA: Fiz. Metal. i Metalloved. **25**, 341 (1968); P. G. WINCHELL, M. COHEN: Trans. Ann. Sic. Metals **45**, 576 (1963).

6.29. G. LONGWORTH, B. WINDOW: J. Phys. F (Metal Phys.) **3**, 832 (1973).

6.30. B. WINDOW, G. LONGWORTH: J. Phys. F (Metal Phys.) **1**, 718 (1971).

6.31. I. VINCZE, I. A. CAMPBELL: J. Phys. F (Metal Phys.) **3**, 647 (1973).

6.32. T. E. CRANSHAW: J. Phys. F (Metal Phys.) **2**, 615 (1972).

6.33. M. S. RIDOUT: J. Phys. C **2**, 1258 (1969).

6.34. E. M. HOWARD, C. E. VIOLET, R. J. BORG: Trans. AIME **242**, 1503 (1968).

6.35. U. Gonser, C. J. Meechan, A. H. Muir, H. Wiedersich: J. Appl. Phys. **34**, 2373 (1963).
6.36. M. Nishio, S. Nasu, Y. Murakami: Nippon-Kinzoku-Gakkai-shi **34**, 1173 (1970).
6.37. L. J. Swartzendruber, L. H. Bennett: Scripta Met. **6**, 737 (1972).
6.38. K. Yamanaka, H. Ino, R. Oshima, F. E. Fujita: Nippon-Kinzoku-Gakkai-shi **35**, 566 (1971).
6.39. R. S. Preston, R. Gerlach: Phys. Rev. B**3**, 1519 (1971).
6.40. C. Janot, G. Lelay: Compt. Rend. Acad. Sci. (Paris) **269**, 823 (1969).
6.41. S. Nasu, U. Gonser, P. H. Shingu, Y. Murakami: J. Phys. F (Metal Phys.) **4**, L 24 (1974).
6.42. C. E. Violet, R. I. Borg: Phys. Rev. **162**, 608 (1967).
6.43. B. Window: J. Phys. C (Metal Phys.) Suppl. No. 3, 323 (1970).
6.44. S. J. Cambell, P. E. Clark, P. B. Liddell: J. Phys. F (Metal Phys.) **2**, L 114 (1972).
6.45. W. Mansel, G. Vogl, W. Koch: Phys. Rev. Letters **31**, 359 (1973); The 5th Int. Conf. Mössbauer Spectroscopy, Bratislava 1973.
6.46. M. Saito, H. Ino, Y. Sumitomo: Nippon-Kinzoku-Gakkai-shi **37**, 540 (1973).
6.47. C. E. Guillaume: Compt. Rend. Acad. Sci. (Paris) **124**, 176 (1897).
6.48. E. I. Kondorsky, V. L. Sedov: J. Appl. Phys. **31**, 331 (1960).
6.49. R. J. Weiss: Proc. Phys. Soc. London **82**, 281 (1963).
6.50. S. Chikazumi, T. Mizoguchi, N. Yamaguchi, P. Beckwith: J. Appl. Phys. **39**, 939 (1968).
6.51. Y. Nakamura, M. Shiga, Y. Takeda: J. Phys. Soc. Japan **27**, 1470 (1969).
6.52. W. F. Schlosser: J. Phys. Chem. Solids **32**, 939 (1971).
6.53. B. Window: J. Appl. Phys. **44**, 2853 (1973).
6.54. J. G. Dash, B. B. Dunlap, D. G. Howard: Phys. Rev. **141**, 376 (1966).
6.55. D. L. Williamson, W. Keune, U. Gonser: In Proc. Int. Conf. Magn. ICM-73 (Publishing House "Nauka", Moscow 1974).
6.56. H.-D. Pfannes, U. Gonser: Appl. Phys. **1**, 93 (1973).
6.57. U. Gonser, M. Ron, H. Ruppersberg, W̌. Keune, A. Trautwein: Phys. Status Solidi (a) **10**, 493 (1972).
6.58. C. C. Tsuei, G. Longworth, S. C. H. Lin: Phys. Rev. **170**, 603 (1968).
6.59. S. C. H. Lin, P. Duwez: Phys. Status Solidi **34**, 469 (1969).
6.60. M. Ura: The Structure and Stability of Amorphous Fe–P–C Alloys, Ph. D. Thesis, Osaka University (1974).
6.61. U. Gonser, R. W. Grant, A. H. Muir, Jr., H. Wiedersich: Acta Met. **14**, 259 (1966).
6.62. G. P. Huffman, H. H. Podgurski: Acta Met. **21**, 449 (1973).
6.63. K. S. Singwi, A. Sjolander: Phys. Rev. **120**, 1093 (1960).
6.64. S. J. Lewis, P. A. Flinn: Phil. Mag. **26**, 977 (1972).
6.65. C. Sauer: Z. Physik **222**, 439 (1969).
6.66. I. Y. Dekthyar, P. S. Nizin, R. G. Fedchenko: Phys. Metals Metallogr. **27**, 431 (1969).
6.67. C. Janot, H. Gibert: Phil. Mag. **27**, 545 (1973).

Subject Index

A *monthly journal*

Applied Physics

Board of Editors	**A. Benninghoven,** Münster · **R. Gomer,** Chicago, Ill. **F. Kneubühl,** Zürich · **H. K. V. Lotsch,** Heidelberg **H. J. Queisser,** Stuttgart · **F. P. Schäfer,** Göttingen **A. Seeger,** Stuttgart · **K. Shimoda,** Tokyo **T. Tamir,** Brooklyn, N.Y. · **H. P. J. Wijn,** Eindhoven **H. Wolter,** Marburg

Coverage — application-oriented experimental and theoretical physics:

Solid-State Physics   *Quantum Electronics*
Surface Physics   *Coherent Optics*
Infrared Physics   *Integrated Optics*
Microwave Acoustics   *Electrophysics*

Special Features — **rapid** publication (3-4 months)
no page charges for **concise** reports

Languages — Mostly English; with some German

Articles — review and/or tutorial papers
original reports, and short communications
abstracts of forthcoming papers

Manuscripts — to Springer-Verlag (Attn. H. Lotsch), P.O. Box 105 280
D-69 Heidelberg 1, F.R. Germany

Distributor for North-America:
Springer-Verlag New York Inc., 175 Fifth Avenue, New York. N.Y. 100 10, USA

Springer-Verlag
Berlin Heidelberg New York

SPRINGER TRACTS IN MODERN PHYSICS

Ergebnisse der exakten Naturwissenschaften

Editor: G. Höhler

Associate Editor:
E. A. Niekisch

Editorial Board:
S. Flügge, J. Hamilton,
F. Hund, H. Lehmann,
G. Leibfried, W. Paul

Springer-Verlag
Berlin
Heidelberg
New York

Volume 66
30 figures. III, 173 pages. 1973
ISBN 3-540-06189-4 Cloth DM 78,–
ISBN 0-387-06189-4
(North America) Cloth $33.60

Quantum Statistics

in Optics and Solid-State Physics

R. Graham: Statistical Theory of Instabilities
in Stationary Nonequilibrium Systems with
Applications to Lasers and Nonlinear Optics.
F. Haake: Statistical Treatment of Open
Systems by Generalized Master Equations.

Volume 67
III, 69 pages. 1973
ISBN 3-540-06216-5 Cloth DM 38,–
ISBN 0-387-06216-5
(North America) Cloth $16.40

S. Ferrara, R. Gatto, A. F. Grillo:

Conformal Algebra in Space-Time

and Operator Product Expansion

Introduction to the Conformal Group in
Space-Time. Broken Conformal Symmetry.
Restrictions from Conformal Covariance on
Equal-Time Commutators. Manifestly
Conformal Covariant Structure of
Space-Time. Conformal Invariant Vacuum
Expectation Values. Operator Products and
Conformal Invariance on the Light-Cone.
Consequences of Exact Conformal
Symmetry on Operator Product Expansions.
Conclusions and Outlook.

Volume 68
77 figures. 48 tables. III, 205 pages. 1973
ISBN 3-540-06341-2 Cloth DM 88,–
ISBN 0-387-06341-2
(North America) Cloth $37.90

Solid-State Physics

D. Schmid: Nuclear Magnetic Double
Resonance — Principles and Applications
in Solid-State Physics.
D. Bäuerle: Vibrational Spectra of Electron
and Hydrogen Centers in Ionic Crystals.
J. Behringer: Factor Group Analysis
Revisited and Unified.

Volume 69
13 figures. III, 121 pages. 1973
ISBN 3-540-06376-5 Cloth DM 78,–
ISBN 0-387-06376-5
(North America) Cloth $33.60

Astrophysics

G. Börner: On the Properties of Matter in
Neutron Stars.
J. Stewart, M. Walker: Black Holes:
the Outside Story.

Prices are subject to change
without notice
■ Prospectus with Classified Index
of Authors and Titles
Volumes 36–74 on request

Volume 70
II, 135 pages. 1974
ISBN 3-540-06630-6 Cloth DM 77,–
ISBN 0-387-06630-6
(North America) Cloth $33.20

Quantum Optics

G. S. Agarwal: Quantum Statistical Theories
of Spontaneous Emission and their Relation
to Other Approaches.

Volume 71
116 figures. III, 245 pages. 1974
ISBN 3-540-06641-1 Cloth DM 98,–
ISBN 0-387-06641-1
(North America) Cloth $42.20

Nuclear Physics

H. Überall: Study of Nuclear Structure by
Muon Capture.
P. Singer: Emission of Particles Following
Muon Capture in Intermediate and Heavy
Nuclei.
J. S. Levinger: The Two and Three Body
Problem.

Volume 72
32 figures. II, 145 pages. 1974
ISBN 3-540-06742-6 Cloth DM 78,–
ISBN 0-387-06742-6
(North America) Cloth $33.60

D. Langbein:

Theory of Van der Waals Attraction

Introduction. Pair Interactions. Multiplet Inter-
actions. Macroscopic Particles. Retardation.
Retarded Dispersion Energy. Schrödinger
Formalism. Electrons and Photons.

Volume 73
110 figures. VI, 303 pages. 1975
ISBN 3-540-06943-7 Cloth DM 97,–
ISBN 0-387-06943-7
(North America) Cloth $41.80

Excitons at High Density

Editors: H. Haken, S. Nikitine
Biexcitons. Electron-Hole Droplets.
Biexcitons and Droplets. Special Optical
Properties of Excitons at High Density.
Laser Action of Excitons. Excitonic
Polaritons at Higher Densities.

Volume 74
75 figures. III, 153 pages. 1974
ISBN 3-540-06946-1 Cloth DM 78,–
ISBN 0-387-06946-1
(North America) Cloth $33.60

Solid-State Physics

G. Bauer: Determination of Electron
Temperatures and of Hot Electron Distri-
bution Functions in Semiconductors.
G. Borstel, H. J. Falge, A. Otto: Surface
and Bulk Phonon-Polaritons Observed by
Attenuated Total Reflection.